Teacher Edition

Eureka Math® Grade 2 Module 8

TEKS EDITION

Special thanks go to the Gordon A. Cain Center and to the Department of Mathematics at Louisiana State University for their support in the development of *Eureka Math*.

Great Minds® is the creator of *Eureka Math*®, *Wit & Wisdom*®, *Alexandria Plan*™, and *PhD Science*®.

Published by Great Minds PBC.
greatminds.org

Copyright © 2021 Great Minds PBC. Except where otherwise noted, this content is published under a limited public license with the Texas Education Agency. Use limited to Non-Commercial educational purposes. Where indicated, teachers may copy pages for use by students in their classrooms. For more information, visit https://gm.greatminds.org/texas.

Printed in the USA

1 2 3 4 5 6 7 8 9 10 CCD 25 24 23 22 21

ISBN 978-1-64929-655-9

Eureka Math: A Story of Units® **Contributors**

Katrina Abdussalaam, Curriculum Writer
Tiah Alphonso, Program Manager—Curriculum Production
Kelly Alsup, Lead Writer / Editor, Grade 4
Catriona Anderson, Program Manager—Implementation Support
Debbie Andorka-Aceves, Curriculum Writer
Eric Angel, Curriculum Writer
Leslie Arceneaux, Lead Writer / Editor, Grade 5
Kate McGill Austin, Lead Writer / Editor, Grades PreK–K
Adam Baker, Lead Writer / Editor, Grade 5
Scott Baldridge, Lead Mathematician and Lead Curriculum Writer
Beth Barnes, Curriculum Writer
Bonnie Bergstresser, Math Auditor
Bill Davidson, Fluency Specialist
Jill Diniz, Program Director
Nancy Diorio, Curriculum Writer
Nancy Doorey, Assessment Advisor
Lacy Endo-Peery, Lead Writer / Editor, Grades PreK–K
Ana Estela, Curriculum Writer
Lessa Faltermann, Math Auditor
Janice Fan, Curriculum Writer
Ellen Fort, Math Auditor
Peggy Golden, Curriculum Writer
Maria Gomes, Pre-Kindergarten Practitioner
Pam Goodner, Curriculum Writer
Greg Gorman, Curriculum Writer
Melanie Gutierrez, Curriculum Writer
Bob Hollister, Math Auditor
Kelley Isinger, Curriculum Writer
Nuhad Jamal, Curriculum Writer
Mary Jones, Lead Writer / Editor, Grade 4
Halle Kananak, Curriculum Writer
Susan Lee, Lead Writer / Editor, Grade 3
Jennifer Loftin, Program Manager—Professional Development
Soo Jin Lu, Curriculum Writer
Nell McAnelly, Project Director

Ben McCarty, Lead Mathematician / Editor, PreK–5
Stacie McClintock, Document Production Manager
Cristina Metcalf, Lead Writer / Editor, Grade 3
Susan Midlarsky, Curriculum Writer
Pat Mohr, Curriculum Writer
Sarah Oyler, Document Coordinator
Victoria Peacock, Curriculum Writer
Jenny Petrosino, Curriculum Writer
Terrie Poehl, Math Auditor
Robin Ramos, Lead Curriculum Writer / Editor, PreK–5
Kristen Riedel, Math Audit Team Lead
Cecilia Rudzitis, Curriculum Writer
Tricia Salerno, Curriculum Writer
Chris Sarlo, Curriculum Writer
Ann Rose Sentoro, Curriculum Writer
Colleen Sheeron, Lead Writer / Editor, Grade 2
Gail Smith, Curriculum Writer
Shelley Snow, Curriculum Writer
Robyn Sorenson, Math Auditor
Kelly Spinks, Curriculum Writer
Marianne Strayton, Lead Writer / Editor, Grade 1
Theresa Streeter, Math Auditor
Lily Talcott, Curriculum Writer
Kevin Tougher, Curriculum Writer
Saffron VanGalder, Lead Writer / Editor, Grade 3
Lisa Watts-Lawton, Lead Writer / Editor, Grade 2
Erin Wheeler, Curriculum Writer
MaryJo Wieland, Curriculum Writer
Allison Witcraft, Math Auditor
Jessa Woods, Curriculum Writer
Hae Jung Yang, Lead Writer / Editor, Grade 1

Board of Trustees

Lynne Munson, President and Executive Director of Great Minds
Nell McAnelly, Chairman, Co-Director Emeritus of the Gordon A. Cain Center for STEM Literacy at Louisiana State University
William Kelly, Treasurer, Co-Founder and CEO at ReelDx
Jason Griffiths, Secretary, Director of Programs at the National Academy of Advanced Teacher Education
Pascal Forgione, Former Executive Director of the Center on K-12 Assessment and Performance Management at ETS
Lorraine Griffith, Title I Reading Specialist at West Buncombe Elementary School in Asheville, North Carolina
Bill Honig, President of the Consortium on Reading Excellence (CORE)
Richard Kessler, Executive Dean of Mannes College the New School for Music
Chi Kim, Former Superintendent, Ross School District
Karen LeFever, Executive Vice President and Chief Development Officer at ChanceLight Behavioral Health and Education
Maria Neira, Former Vice President, New York State United Teachers

A STORY OF UNITS — TEKS EDITION

GRADE 2

Mathematics Curriculum

GRADE 2 • MODULE 8

Table of Contents
GRADE 2 • MODULE 8
Time, Shapes, and Fractions as Equal Parts of Shapes

Module Overview 2

Topic A: Attributes of Geometric Shapes 9

Topic B: Composite Shapes and Fraction Concepts 86

Mid-Module Assessment and Rubric 121

Topic C: Fractions of Circles and Rectangles 127

Topic D: Application of Fractions to Tell Time 171

End-of-Module Assessment and Rubric 243

Answer Key 257

Module 8: Time, Shapes, and Fractions as Equal Parts of Shapes

© Great Minds PBC
TEKS Edition | greatminds.org/texas

A STORY OF UNITS – TEKS EDITION   Module Overview   2•8

Grade 2 • Module 8
Time, Shapes, and Fractions as Equal Parts of Shapes

OVERVIEW

In Module 8, the final module of the year, students extend their understanding of part–whole relationships through the lens of geometry. As students compose and decompose shapes, they begin to develop an understanding of unit fractions as equal parts of a whole.

In Topic A, students build on their prior knowledge of a shape's defining attributes (**1.6A, 1.6B, 1.6D**) to recognize and draw categories of polygons with specified attributes: the number of sides, vertices, and angles (**2.8A, 2.8C**). For example, students see that a rectangle has four straight sides, four right angles, and opposite sides with equal length. Students then relate two-dimensional shapes to three-dimensional shapes. They describe three-dimensional shapes in terms of their attributes, counting the number of edges, faces, and vertices (**2.8B**). Once students are able to describe and analyze polygons and solids according to their attributes in Topic A, they are ready to combine shapes and build composite shapes in Topic B.

Topic B opens with students using a tangram, a set of seven shapes that compose a square, to create a new shape. Students see that they can arrange two-dimensional shapes to create a new whole, or composite, shape, which can become part of an even larger whole. As students progress through the topic, they build and partition shapes by combining two or more smaller shapes and relating the parts to the whole. For example, they use different pattern blocks to show that a regular hexagon might be composed of two trapezoids or three rhombuses. One might say, "This hexagon is made from two identical trapezoids, or two equal parts." This allows for interpreting equal shares of a whole as a fraction as students name the equal parts *halves*, *thirds*, or *fourths* (**2.8E**). Although thirds and sixths are explored, these fractional units are not assessed.

Next, in Topic C, students decompose circles and rectangles into equal parts and describe them as halves (a half of), fourths (a fourth of) or quarters, and eighths (an eighth of) (**2.3A, 2.8E**). For example, students see that a circle can be partitioned into four quarter-circles, or parts, which can be described as fourths. They learn to describe the whole by the number of equal parts. For example, one whole circle is composed of 4 fourths. In this topic, students count beyond 1 in fractional units. For example, they count 1 half, 2 halves, 3 halves. This is to show that the counting sequence does not change. What can change is *what* we count: the unit. Finally, students decompose a rectangle into four parts that have equal areas but different shapes (**2.3A, 2.3C, 2.3D, 2.8E**).

The module closes with Topic D, where students apply their understanding of partitioning the whole into halves and fourths to tell time to the nearest five minutes and then the nearest minute (**2.9G**) using both analog and digital clocks. They construct simple clocks and see the relationship to partitioning a circle into quarters and halves, thereby decomposing 60 minutes. For example, 3 fourths of the circle can be interpreted as 3 intervals of 15 minutes; that is, 15 + 15 + 15 = 45 (**2.4B**), or 45 minutes. They also use their understanding of skip-counting by fives and tens to tell time on an analog clock (**2.9G**).

The Mid-Module Assessment follows Topic B. The End-of-Module Assessment follows Topic D.

Module 8:   Time, Shapes, and Fractions as Equal Parts of Shapes

Notes on Pacing for Differentiation

If pacing is a challenge, consider consolidating Lessons 9 and 10.

Focus Grade Level Standards

Number and Operations

The student applies mathematical process standards to recognize and represent fractional units and communicates how they are used to name parts of a whole. The student is expected to:

- **2.3A**   partition objects into equal parts and name the parts, including halves, fourths, and eighths, using words;

- **2.3C**   use concrete models to count fractional parts beyond one whole using words and recognize how many parts it takes to equal one whole;

- **2.3D**   identify examples and non-examples of halves, fourths, and eighths.

Geometry and Measurement

The student applies mathematical process standards to analyze attributes of two-dimensional shapes and three-dimensional solids to develop generalizations about their properties. The student is expected to:

- **2.8A**   create two-dimensional shapes based on given attributes, including number of sides and vertices;

- **2.8B**   Classify and sort three-dimensional solids including spheres, cones, cylinders, rectangular prisms (including cubes as special rectangular prisms) and triangular prisms, based on attributes using formal geometric language;

- **2.8C**   classify and sort polygons with 12 or fewer sides according to attributes, including identifying the number of sides and number of vertices;

- **2.8D**   compose two-dimensional shapes and three-dimensional solids with given properties or attributes;

- **2.8E**   decompose two-dimensional shapes such as cutting out a square from a rectangle, dividing a shape in half, or partitioning a rectangle into identical triangles and identify the resulting geometric parts.

Geometry and Measurement

The student applies mathematical process standards to select and use units to describe length, area, and time. The student is expected to:

- **2.9G**   read and write time to the nearest one-minute increment using analog and digital clocks and distinguish between a.m. and p.m.

Module 8:   Time, Shapes, and Fractions as Equal Parts of Shapes

Foundational Standards

The student is expected to:

1.6A	classify and sort regular and irregular two-dimensional shapes based on attributes using informal geometric language;
1.6B	distinguish between attributes that define a two-dimensional or three-dimensional figure and attributes that do not define the shape;
1.6C	create two-dimensional figures, including circles, triangles, rectangles, and squares, as special rectangles, rhombuses, and hexagons;
1.6D	identify two-dimensional shapes, including circles, triangles, rectangles, and squares, as special rectangles, rhombuses, and hexagons and describe their attributes using formal geometric language;
1.6E	identify three-dimensional solids, including spheres, cones, cylinders, rectangular prisms (including cubes), and triangular prisms, and describe their attributes using formal geometric language;
1.6F	compose two-dimensional shapes by joining two, three, or four figures to produce a target shape in more than one way if possible;
1.6G	partition two-dimensional figures into two and four fair shares or equal parts and describe the parts using words;
1.6H	identify examples and non-examples of halves and fourths;
1.7E	tell time to the hour and half hour using analog and digital clocks;
2.2C	generate a number that is greater than or less than a given whole number up to 1,200;
2.4A	recall basic facts to add and subtract within 20 with automaticity;
2.4B	add up to four two-digit numbers and subtract two-digit numbers using mental strategies and algorithms based on knowledge of place value and properties of operations;
2.9A	find the length of objects using concrete models for standard units of length;
2.9D	determine the length of an object to the nearest marked unit using rulers, yardsticks, meter sticks, or measuring tapes.

Focus Mathematical Process Standards

The student uses mathematical processes to acquire and demonstrate mathematical understanding. The student is expected to:

MPS(A)	apply mathematics to problems arising in everyday life, society, and the workplace;
MPS(B)	use a problem-solving model that incorporates analyzing given information, formulating a plan or strategy, determining a solution, justifying the solution, and evaluating the problem-solving process and the reasonableness of the solution;
MPS(E)	create and use representations to organize, record, and communicate mathematical ideas;
MPS(G)	display, explain, and justify mathematical ideas and arguments using precise mathematical language in written or oral communication.

Overview of Module Topics and Lesson Objectives

TEKS	ELPS		Topics and Objectives		Days
2.8A 2.8B 2.8C	1.A 1.C 1.E 2.C 2.E 3.E 3.J 4.F 5.G	A	**Attributes of Geometric Shapes**		5
			Lesson 1:	Describe two-dimensional shapes based on attributes.	
			Lesson 2:	Build, identify, and analyze two-dimensional shapes with specified attributes.	
			Lesson 3:	Use attributes to draw different polygons including triangles, quadrilaterals, pentagons, and hexagons.	
			Lesson 4:	Use attributes to identify and draw different quadrilaterals including rectangles, rhombuses, parallelograms, and trapezoids.	
			Lesson 5:	Classify and sort three-dimensional shapes by their attributes.	
2.3A 2.8D 2.8E 2.3C 2.3D 2.8A 2.8C	2.E 3.C 3.E 3.J 4.B	B	**Composite Shapes and Fraction Concepts**		3
			Lesson 6:	Combine shapes to create a composite shape; create a new shape from composite shapes.	
			Lessons 7–8:	Interpret equal shares in composite shapes as halves, thirds, and fourths.	
			Mid-Module Assessment: Topics A–B (assessment ½ day, return ½ day, remediation or further applications 1 day)		2
2.3A 2.3B 2.3C 2.3D 2.8E 2.8A 2.8C	1.A 1.F 2.C 2.E 2.I 3.E 4.F	C	**Fractions of Circles and Rectangles**		3
			Lessons 9:	Partition circles and rectangles into equal parts, and describe those parts as halves, thirds, or fourths.	
			Lesson 10:	Partition circles and rectangles into equal parts, and describe those parts as halves, fourths, and eighths.	
			Lesson 11:	Use concrete models to count fractional parts beyond one whole.	
2.3A 2.8E 2.9G 2.2C 2.4A 2.4B	1.C 1.H 2.I 3.C 3.E 3.H 3.J	D	**Application of Fractions to Tell Time**		5
			Lesson 12:	Construct a paper clock by partitioning a circle into halves and quarters, and tell time to the half hour or quarter hour.	
			Lesson 13:	Tell time to the nearest five minutes.	
			Lesson 14:	Tell time to the nearest five minutes; relate *a.m.* and *p.m.* to time of day.	

Module 8: Time, Shapes, and Fractions as Equal Parts of Shapes

TEKS	ELPS	Topics and Objectives		Days
	4.F 4.G	Lesson 15:	Relate skip counting by fives on the clock and telling time to a continuous measurement model, the number line.	
		Lesson 16:	Count by fives and ones on the number line as a strategy to tell time to the nearest minute on the clock.	
		End-of-Module Assessment: Topics A–D (assessment ½ day, return ½ day, remediation or further applications 1 day)		2
Total Number of Instructional Days				**20**

Terminology

New or Recently Introduced Terms

- a.m./p.m.
- Analog clock
- Angle (e.g., a figure formed by the corner of a polygon)
- Base (the surface a solid object stands on)
- Congruent (exactly the same)
- Decagon (a polygon with ten sides and ten vertices)
- Heptagon (a polygon with seven sides and seven vertices)
- Nonagon (a polygon with nine sides and nine vertices)
- Octagon (a polygon with eight sides and eight vertices)
- Parallel (used to describe opposite sides of a parallelogram, e.g., "These sides are parallel because if they kept on going, they'd never intersect!")
- Parallelogram (a quadrilateral with both pairs of opposite sides parallel)
- Partition (used in reference to partitioning rectangles, e.g. "Let's partition this rectangle to make an array" or "Let's partition this tape to show the money that was spent and the money that was left. Which part will be longer?")
- Pentagon (a two-dimensional figure enclosed by five straight sides and five angles)
- Polygon (a closed figure with three or more straight sides, e.g., triangle, quadrilateral, pentagon, hexagon)
- Quadrilateral (a four-sided polygon, e.g., square, rhombus, rectangle, parallelogram, trapezoid)
- Quarter past, quarter to
- Right angle (e.g., a square corner)
- Third of (shapes), thirds (three equal shares)
- Whole (used in reference to fractions, e.g., 2 halves make 1 whole, and 3 thirds make 1 whole)

Familiar Terms and Symbols[1]

- Attributes (the characteristics of an object such as number of sides, angles, or faces)
- Cone (a three-dimensional solid with a circular base and a curved surface that tapers to a point)
- Cube (a three-dimensional shape composed of six squares)
- Cylinder (a three-dimensional solid with a curved surface and 2 congruent circular bases)
- Digital clock
- Edge (a line segment where two faces meet)
- Face (a two-dimensional side of a three-dimensional shape)
- Fourth of (shapes), fourths (four equal shares)
- Half hour (an interval of time lasting 30 minutes)
- Half of (shapes), halves (two equal shares)
- Half past (an expression for 30 minutes past a given hour)
- Hour (a unit for measuring time, equivalent to 60 minutes or 1/24 of a day)
- Minute (a unit for measuring time, equivalent to 60 seconds or 1/60 of an hour)
- O'clock (used to indicate time to a precise hour with no additional minutes)
- Quarter of (shapes), quarters (four equal shares)
- Rectangular prism (a prism with 2 identical rectangular bases)
- Solid (a three-dimensional object)
- Sphere (a three-dimensional object shaped like a ball)
- Tangram (a special set of puzzle pieces with five triangles and two quadrilaterals that compose a square)
- Triangular prism (a prism with 2 identical triangular bases)
- Two-dimensional shapes (familiar prior to Grade 2):
    - Circle
    - Half-circle
    - Hexagon (a two-dimensional figure enclosed by six straight sides and six angles)
    - Quarter-circle
    - Rectangle (a two-dimensional figure enclosed by four straight sides and four right angles)
    - Rhombus (a two-dimensional figure enclosed by four straight sides of the same length)
    - Square (a rectangle with four sides of the same length)
    - Trapezoid (a two-dimensional figure enclosed by four straight sides with exactly one pair of parallel sides)
    - Triangle (a two-dimensional figure enclosed by three straight sides and three angles)
- Vertex/Vertices (a point where two or more line segments meet; a corner)

Cube

---

[1]These are terms and symbols students have seen previously.

Module 8: Time, Shapes, and Fractions as Equal Parts of Shapes

Suggested Tools and Representations

- Cube: a three-dimensional shape (real-world examples such as a die, alphabet blocks, or a box)
- Geoboards
- Large instructional geared clock
- Pattern blocks
- Personal white boards
- Rulers or straightedges
- Spaghetti
- Student clocks, preferably those with gears that can provide the appropriate hour-hand alignment
- Tangrams
- Toothpicks

Scaffolds

The scaffolds integrated into *A Story of Units*® give alternatives for how students access information as well as express and demonstrate their learning. Strategically placed margin notes are provided within each lesson elaborating on the use of specific scaffolds at applicable times. They address many needs presented by English language learners, students with disabilities, students performing above grade level, and students performing below grade level. Many of the suggestions are organized by Universal Design for Learning (UDL) principles and are applicable to more than one population.

Assessment Summary

Type	Administered	Format	Standards Addressed
Mid-Module Assessment Task	After Topic B	Constructed response with rubric	2.3A 2.3C 2.3D 2.8A 2.8B 2.8C 2.8E
End-of-Module Assessment Task	After Topic D	Constructed response with rubric	2.3A 2.3C 2.3D 2.8B 2.8C 2.8E 2.9G

A STORY OF UNITS TEKS EDITION

Mathematics Curriculum

GRADE 2 • MODULE 8

Topic A
Attributes of Geometric Shapes

2.8A, 28B, 2.8C

Focus Standards:	2.8A	Create two-dimensional shapes based on given attributes, including number of sides and vertices.
	2.8B	Classify and sort three-dimensional solids including spheres, cones, cylinders, rectangular prisms (including cubes as special rectangular prisms) and triangular prisms, based on attributes using formal geometric language.
	2.8C	Classify and sort polygons with 12 or fewer sides according to attributes, including identifying the number of sides and number of vertices.
Instructional Days:	5	
Coherence -Links from:	G1-M5	Identifying, Composing, and Partitioning Shapes
-Links to:	G3-M7	Geometry and Measurement Word Problems

In Module 8, students continue to develop their geometric thinking from Grade 1, progressing from a descriptive to an analytic level of thinking where they can recognize and characterize shapes by their attributes and properties.

In Lesson 1 of Topic A, students describe various two-dimensional shapes according to specified attributes, such as the number of sides or angles (**2.8C**). The names of the shapes are intentionally omitted in this lesson in order to encourage students to use precise language in their descriptions. Students must attend to a shape's defining attributes in order to describe the difference between shapes. For example, rather than describing a shape as a quadrilateral, students describe it as a shape having four sides and four angles. In this lesson, students come to see the corner of a polygon as an angle and the point where the sides of the angle meets the vertex. In Lesson 4, the right angle is introduced as a square angle. After students name the attributes of shapes, they use geoboards to create a shape given its attributes.

In Lesson 2, students build various polygons as they name them based on attributes. Using uncooked spaghetti of various lengths, they build a triangle, quadrilateral, pentagon, hexagon, heptagon, octagon, nonagon, and decagon (**2.8A**), adding another piece of spaghetti for each construction. They then identify a collection of various polygons, both exemplars and variants of shapes (as shown below), including those with sides of unequal length. As they analyze shapes, the students expand their bank of mental images associated with names of shapes. Hence, this task serves to broaden, rather than limit, their understanding and to clarify common misconceptions about shapes.

Topic A: Attributes of Geometric Shapes

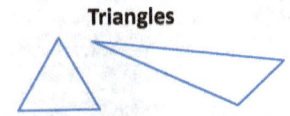

Now that they have created, manipulated, and named shapes, students are ready to draw their own in Lesson 3. This lesson focuses on the four categories of polygons that students built in Lesson 2: triangles, quadrilaterals, pentagons, and hexagons. After the teacher-guided portion of the lesson, students use a ruler to draw straight lines and to create their own shapes, before trading with a partner. Partners take turns naming and analyzing shapes according to their attributes.

In Lesson 4, students use various attributes (e.g., side length, parallel lines, right angles) to identify different quadrilaterals. Along with recognizing trapezoids and rhombuses, seen in Grade 1, students are introduced to parallelograms. They learn to recognize parallel sides and square corners and to name quadrilaterals based on these attributes. For example, students might be questioned and guided as follows: "Draw a quadrilateral with both pairs of opposite sides parallel. We call this a parallelogram." Next, "Now, draw a quadrilateral with both pairs of opposite sides parallel and four square angles. We call this a rectangle." Then, the teacher might continue with, "Can you draw another quadrilateral that also has opposite sides parallel, but this time use your ruler to show that all sides are equal? We call this a rhombus." While students learn the various names of shapes, the emphasis remains on analyzing shapes based on their varied attributes. In doing so, students begin to notice the similarities and differences between various quadrilaterals.

Finally, in Lesson 5, students focus solely on three-dimensional solids. They classify and sort solids as they discuss attributes using academic language (**2.8B**).

A Teaching Sequence Toward Mastery of Attributes of Geometric Shapes

Objective 1: Describe two-dimensional shapes based on attributes.
(Lesson 1)

Objective 2: Build, identify, and analyze two-dimensional shapes with specified attributes.
(Lesson 2)

Objective 3: Use attributes to draw different polygons including triangles, quadrilaterals, pentagons, and hexagons.
(Lesson 3)

Objective 4: Use attributes to identify and draw different quadrilaterals including rectangles, rhombuses, parallelograms, and trapezoids.
(Lesson 4)

Objective 5: Classify and sort three-dimensional shapes by their attributes.
(Lesson 5)

Lesson 1

Objective: Describe two-dimensional shapes based on attributes.

Suggested Lesson Structure

- Fluency Practice   (12 minutes)
- Application Problem (6 minutes)
- Concept Development (32 minutes)
- Student Debrief   (10 minutes)

Total Time   **(60 minutes)**

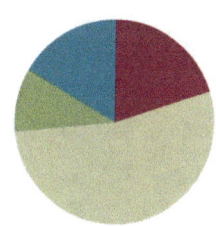

Fluency Practice (12 minutes)

- Rename for the Larger Unit **2.2A**   (3 minutes)
- Sprint: Adding Across a Ten **2.4B**   (9 minutes)

Rename for the Larger Unit (3 minutes)

Note: This fluency activity reviews place value foundations.

- T: I'll tell you a number of ones. Make as many tens as you can, and then tell how many tens and ones. If there are no ones, only say the tens. Ready?
- T: 10 ones.
- S: 1 ten.
- T: 30 ones.
- S: 3 tens.
- T: 41 ones.
- S: 4 tens 1 one.

Continue with the following possible sequence: 50 ones, 54 ones, 80 ones, 85 ones, 99 ones, 100 ones, 105 ones, and 120 ones.

Sprint: Adding Across a Ten (9 minutes)

Materials: (S) Adding Across a Ten Sprint

Note: This Sprint gives practice with the grade level fluency of adding within 20 and applies it to larger numbers.

Application Problem (6 minutes)

Materials: (S) 12 toothpicks

Terrence is making shapes with 12 toothpicks. Using all of the toothpicks, create 3 different shapes he could make. How many other combinations can you find?

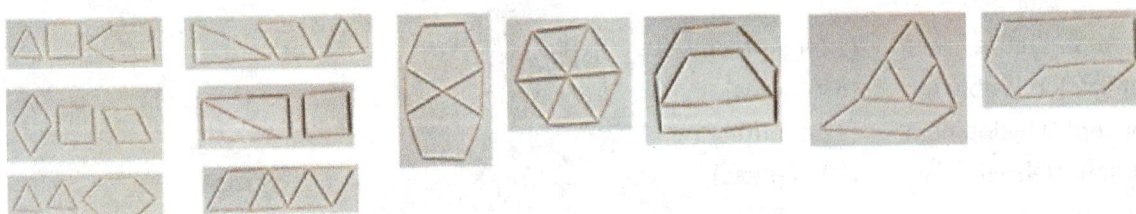

Note: This problem is designed to spark thought about the number of sides needed to produce different shapes. Encourage students to examine one another's work and expand their ideas about combination possibilities. Clarification may be necessary for students to explain that two or more toothpicks may be used to make one side.

Concept Development (32 minutes)

Materials: (T) Chart paper, marker, ruler (S) Personal white board, 1 rubber band, geoboard, 2 pencils

Display seven empty charts labeled Chart 1, Chart 2, Chart 3, Chart 4, Chart 5, Chart 6, and Chart 7. Distribute one geoboard and rubber band per student. Note: These charts are used again in future lessons.

- T: Let's look at this shape. (Draw a triangle on Chart 1 as shown at the top of the next page.) How would you describe this shape without using its name?
- S: It has three sides. → It has three corners. → The sides are different lengths. → The sides are straight lines.
- T: Good. If a figure has three corners, then it also has three angles. An angle is the figure formed when two sides meet. Watch as I trace the sides of the angle, and then mark the angles on the triangle. (Trace the sides of the angle, and then draw a semicircle to show the angles on the triangle.) The point where the two sides meet is the vertex. This triangle has 3 vertices. (Point to a vertex.) An angle has 2 sides and one vertex.
- T: Use your geoboards to create a shape with three sides and three angles that looks different from mine. (Circulate to check for understanding.)
- S: (Create a three-sided shape on the geoboard, illustrated on the next page.)
- T: I'm going to record some of your shapes on Chart 1. (Use a ruler to draw three more shapes.)
- T: (Point to the shapes on Chart 1.) Although these shapes look different, all of them have some attributes, or characteristics, in common. What are they?
- S: They all have three sides, three vertices, and three angles. → They all have straight sides and no curves.

Lesson 1: Describe two-dimensional shapes based on attributes.

T: These shapes are also closed shapes. That means there are no gaps or overlaps between the straight sides. This shape is open. (Draw an open shape.)

T: All of these shapes have common attributes. They all have three straight sides, three angles and three vertices.

T: (Write 3 sides, 3 angles and three vertices at the top of Chart 1, as shown below.)

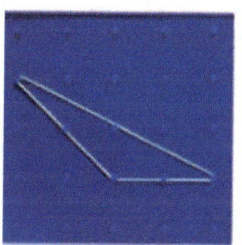 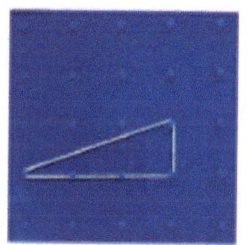 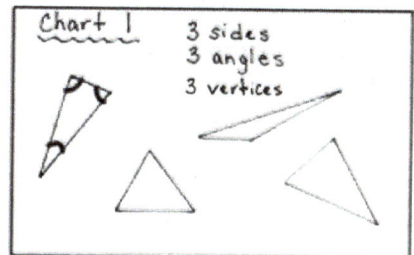

T: Now, let's look at another shape. (Draw a quadrilateral with a concave angle on Chart 2, as shown below.) How would you describe this shape without using its name?

S: It has four straight sides. → Some of the sides are different lengths. → It has four angles. → If it has 4 angles, it has 4 vertices.

T: Yes! Is this an angle? It looks different. (Point to the concave angle on the quadrilateral.)

S: Yes. I think of an angle like a mouth; this one opens on the outside.

T: You're right. It is an angle. Where is the vertex of this angle?

S: The vertex is where the sides of the angle meet.

T: Let's count the angles. If we count the vertices, are we also counting the angles? How do you know?

S: Yes. Each angle has to have a vertex.

T: Put your finger next to the first vertex you count, and continue counting the vertices as you go around the shape. That way you won't count the same vertex twice. Count with me.

S: 1 vertex, 2 vertex, 3 vertex, 4 vertex.

T: Now, it's your turn. On your geoboard, create a shape with four sides and four angles that looks different from mine. (Circulate to check for understanding.)

S: (Create a four-sided shape, as shown to the right.)

T: I'm going to record some of your shapes on Chart 2. (Choose various quadrilaterals, such as rectangles of varied lengths, trapezoids, or parallelograms. Include shapes that cannot be easily named. See the image to the right.)

NOTES ON MULTIPLE MEANS OF REPRESENTATION:

Some students find visual discrimination challenging, particularly when they are not looking at the exemplars of a given shape. Provide encouragement to support students' perseverance. Invite students forward to circle the angles on each shape as a way to confirm the attributes discussed. Allow students to continue the use of this strategy on their Problem Sets.

 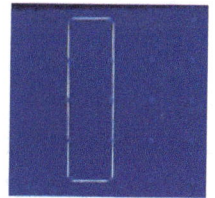

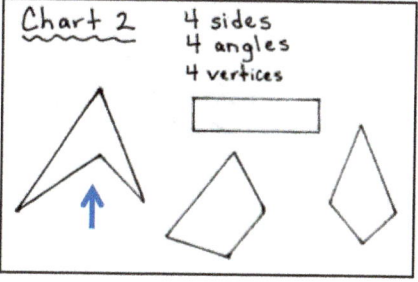

Lesson 1: Describe two-dimensional shapes based on attributes.

T: (Point to the shapes on Chart 2.) Although these shapes look different, all of them have what attributes?

S: Four straight sides, four angles and four vertices! → They are all closed! → They all have straight lines.

T: You're right. All of these shapes share attributes. (Write 4 sides, 4 angles and four vertices at the top of Chart 2, as shown to the right.)

Continue the above process for shapes as shown below. As the sides become more numerous, have the students mark the starting points of the counts by placing their fingers on the sides. Again, highlight many variations of these shapes, drawing attention to various angles.

- five sides, five angles, and five vertices (Chart 3)
- six sides, six angles, and six vertices (Chart 4)
- seven sides, seven angles, and 7 vertices (Chart 5)
- eight sides, eight angles, and 8 vertices (Chart 6)
- nine sides, nine angles, and 9 vertices (Chart 7)

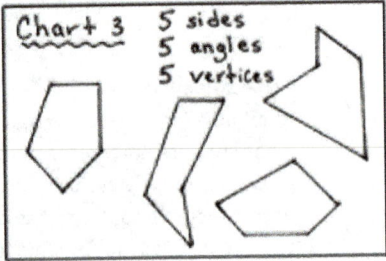
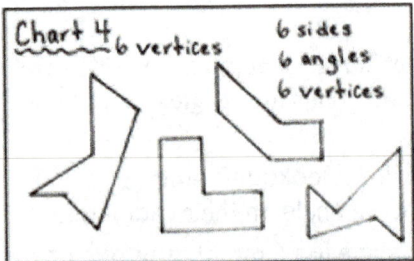
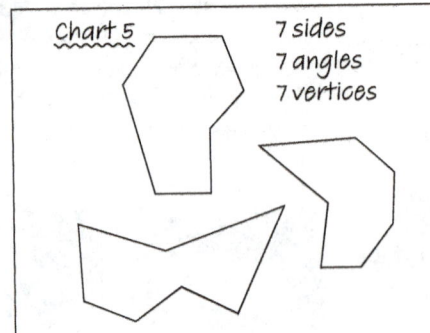
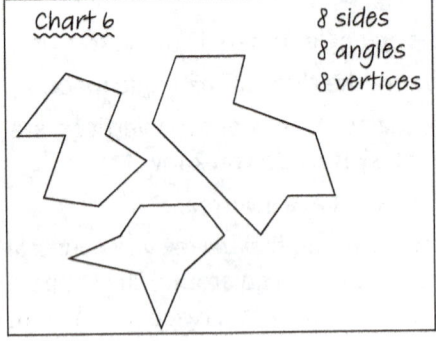
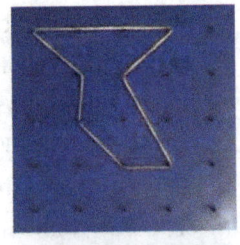
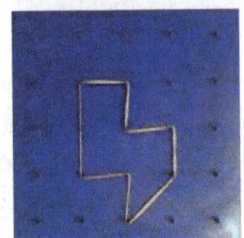
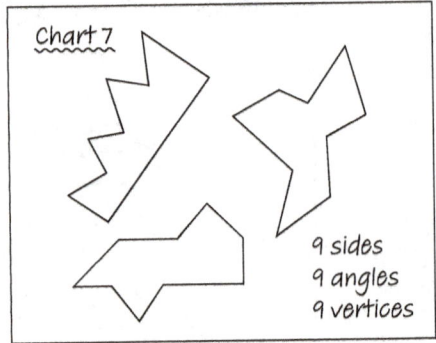

Lesson 1: Describe two-dimensional shapes based on attributes.

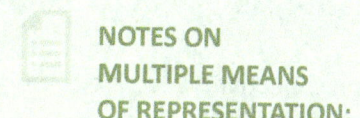

T: Now that we have done so much work with different shapes, how would you describe a vertex? Talk to your partner.

S: It is the place in the corner where the lines meet. → It's the point where the sides of the angle meet.

T: How would you describe an angle? Talk to your partner.

S: An angle is two sides of a shape. → An angle has two sides and a vertex.

T: Yes. Those are all good observations. An angle is formed when sections of lines meet at a vertex. (Point to an acute angle on a triangle.) Show me this angle with two pencils. With your finger, trace the angle you made with the pencils. Point to the vertex of this angle.

S: (Work.)

T: (Repeat the process for an obtuse angle and a right angle.)

NOTES ON MULTIPLE MEANS OF REPRESENTATION:

To support English language learners, write the key terms of the lesson (e.g., *angle, side*, vertex/vertices, and *attribute*), and post them on the word wall as they are introduced within the meaningful context of the instruction. Students who need the extra support are able to refer to them whenever needed.

Note: It is not necessary for students to know the terms *obtuse, acute,* and *right* for angles at this stage. This topic focuses instead on naming and describing shapes.

Problem Set (10 minutes)

Students should do their personal best to complete the Problem Set within the allotted 10 minutes. Some problems do not specify a method for solving. This is an intentional reduction of scaffolding that invokes MPS(C), selecting tools as appropriate to solve problems. Students should solve these problems using the RDW approach used for Application Problems.

For some classes, it may be appropriate to modify the assignment by specifying which problems students should work on first. With this option, let the purposeful sequencing of the Problem Set guide your selections so that problems continue to be scaffolded. Balance word problems with other problem types to ensure a range of practice. Assign incomplete problems for homework or at another time during the day.

Note: Problem 2(e) can be interpreted in different ways. Each shape has the same number of sides and angles (e.g., Problem 2(a) has three sides and three angles), so a possible correct answer is all of them. Another possible answer is B and C since both shapes have seven sides and seven angles. Problem (d) on the Exit Ticket and Problem 2(e) on the Homework can be interpreted similarly.

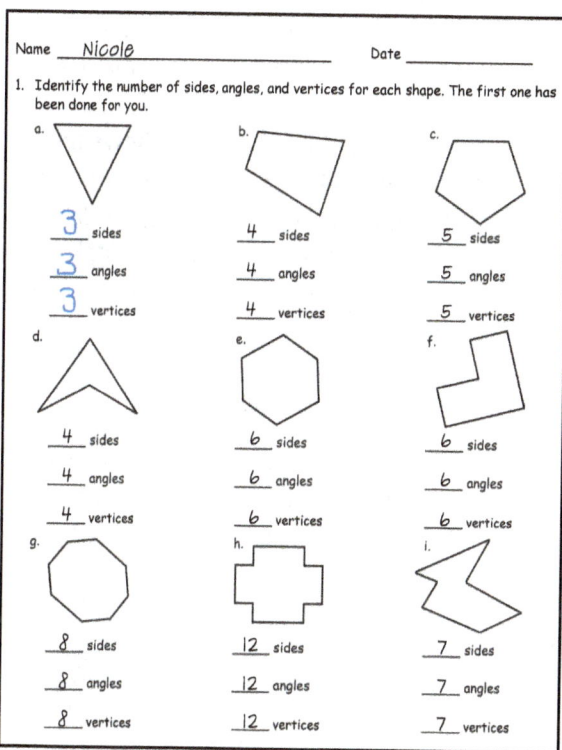

Lesson 1: Describe two-dimensional shapes based on attributes.

Student Debrief (10 minutes)

2. Study the shapes below. Then, answer the questions.

A B C D E F

a. Which shape has the most sides? E

b. Which shape has 3 more angles than shape C? F

c. Which shape has 3 fewer sides than shape B? D

d. How many more angles does shape C have than shape A? 4

e. Which of these shapes have the same number of sides and angles? all

f. Which of these shapes have the same number of angles and vertices? B and C

3. Ethan said the two shapes below are both hexagons, but just different sizes. Explain why he is incorrect.

The two shapes have a different number of sides. One figure has 6 sides and the other has 8 sides.

Lesson Objective: Describe two-dimensional shapes based on attributes.

The Student Debrief is intended to invite reflection and active processing of the total lesson experience.

Invite students to review their solutions for the Problem Set. They should check work by comparing answers with a partner. Look for misconceptions or misunderstandings that can be addressed in the Debrief. Guide students in a conversation to debrief the Problem Set and process the lesson.

Any combination of the questions below may be used to lead the discussion.

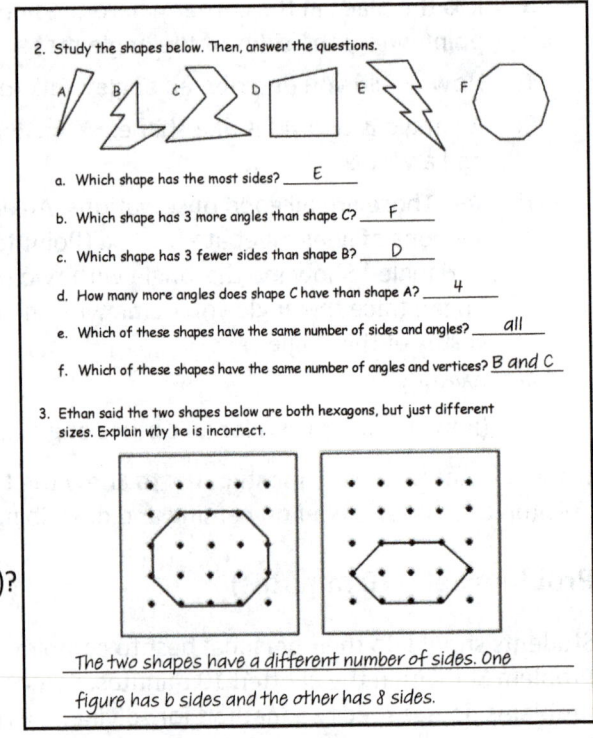

- Look at the Problem Set. What did you notice about the number of **angles**, sides, and vertices in each shape? How did you answer Problem 2(e)? 2(f)?
- Look at all the shapes on the first page of the Problem Set. With your partner, group the shapes based on the number of sides and angles each shape has.
- Look at Problem 3, which shows the two shapes on the geoboards. Tell your partner the names of both shapes. What would make the smaller shape the same as the larger shape?
- When Ethan first counted the sides on the first shape in Problem 3, he thought that it had 10 sides. How would you explain his mistake to him? How is this like the problem we began with today?
- Tell your partner why you need to pay attention to more than how a shape looks when grouping shapes.

Exit Ticket (3 minutes)

After the Student Debrief, instruct students to complete the Exit Ticket. A review of their work will help with assessing students' understanding of the concepts that were presented in today's lesson and planning more effectively for future lessons. The questions may be read aloud to the students.

© Great Minds PBC
TEKS Edition | greatminds.org/texas

A

Adding Across a Ten

Number Correct: _____

1.	8 + 1 =		23.	50 + 30 =	
2.	18 + 1 =		24.	58 + 30 =	
3.	28 + 1 =		25.	9 + 3 =	
4.	58 + 1 =		26.	90 + 30 =	
5.	7 + 2 =		27.	97 + 30 =	
6.	17 + 2 =		28.	8 + 4 =	
7.	27 + 2 =		29.	80 + 40 =	
8.	57 + 2 =		30.	83 + 40 =	
9.	6 + 3 =		31.	83 + 4 =	
10.	36 + 3 =		32.	7 + 6 =	
11.	5 + 4 =		33.	70 + 60 =	
12.	45 + 4 =		34.	74 + 60 =	
13.	30 + 9 =		35.	74 + 5 =	
14.	9 + 2 =		36.	73 + 6 =	
15.	39 + 2 =		37.	58 + 7 =	
16.	50 + 8 =		38.	76 + 5 =	
17.	8 + 4 =		39.	30 + 40 =	
18.	58 + 4 =		40.	20 + 70 =	
19.	50 + 20 =		41.	80 + 70 =	
20.	54 + 20 =		42.	34 + 40 =	
21.	70 + 20 =		43.	23 + 50 =	
22.	76 + 20 =		44.	97 + 60 =	

Lesson 1: Describe two-dimensional shapes based on attributes.

B

Adding Across a Ten

Number Correct: _____

Improvement: _____

1.	7 + 1 =		23.	50 + 30 =	
2.	17 + 1 =		24.	57 + 30 =	
3.	27 + 1 =		25.	8 + 3 =	
4.	47 + 1 =		26.	80 + 30 =	
5.	6 + 2 =		27.	87 + 30 =	
6.	16 + 2 =		28.	9 + 4 =	
7.	26 + 2 =		29.	90 + 40 =	
8.	46 + 2 =		30.	93 + 40 =	
9.	5 + 3 =		31.	93 + 4 =	
10.	75 + 3 =		32.	8 + 6 =	
11.	5 + 4 =		33.	80 + 60 =	
12.	75 + 4 =		34.	84 + 60 =	
13.	40 + 9 =		35.	84 + 5 =	
14.	9 + 2 =		36.	83 + 6 =	
15.	49 + 2 =		37.	68 + 7 =	
16.	60 + 8 =		38.	86 + 5 =	
17.	8 + 4 =		39.	20 + 30 =	
18.	68 + 4 =		40.	30 + 60 =	
19.	50 + 20 =		41.	90 + 70 =	
20.	56 + 20 =		42.	36 + 40 =	
21.	70 + 20 =		43.	27 + 50 =	
22.	74 + 20 =		44.	94 + 70 =	

Name _____ Date _____

1. Identify the number of sides, angles, and vertices for each shape. The first one has been done for you.

a.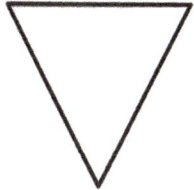

____3____ sides

____3____ angles

____3____ vertices

b.

_____ sides

_____ angles

_____ vertices

c.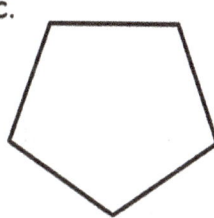

_____ sides

_____ angles

_____ vertices

d.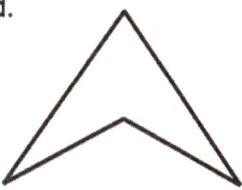

_____ sides

_____ angles

_____ vertices

e.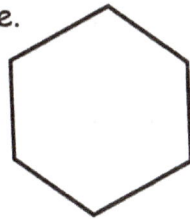

_____ sides

_____ angles

_____ vertices

f.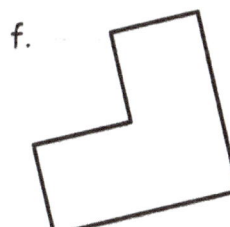

_____ sides

_____ angles

_____ vertices

g.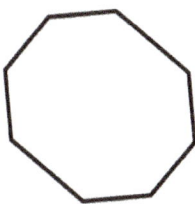

_____ sides

_____ angles

_____ vertices

h.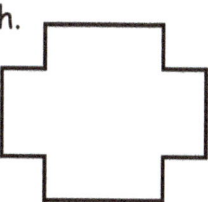

_____ sides

_____ angles

_____ vertices

i.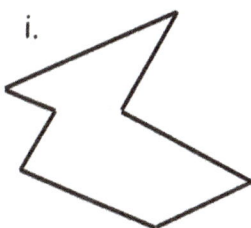

_____ sides

_____ angles

_____ vertices

Lesson 1: Describe two-dimensional shapes based on attributes.

2. Study the shapes below. Then, answer the questions.

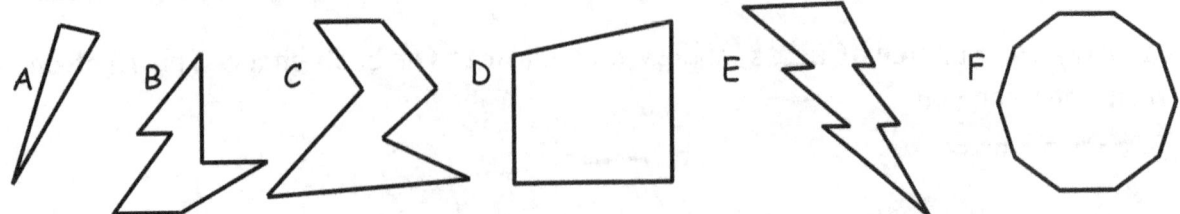

a. Which shape has the most sides? _____

b. Which shape has 3 more angles than shape C? _____

c. Which shape has 3 fewer sides than shape B? _____

d. How many more angles does shape C have than shape A? _____

e. Which of these shapes have the same number of sides and angles? _____

f. Which of these shapes have the same number of angles and vertices? _____

3. Ethan said the two shapes below are both hexagons, but just different sizes. Explain why he is incorrect.

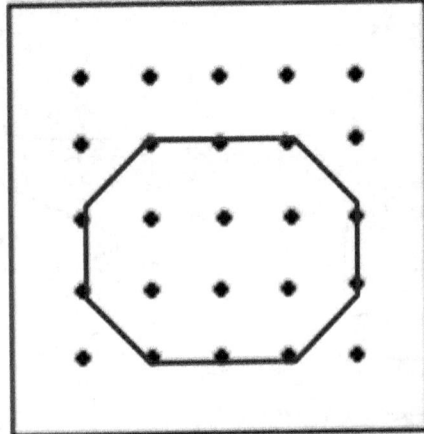 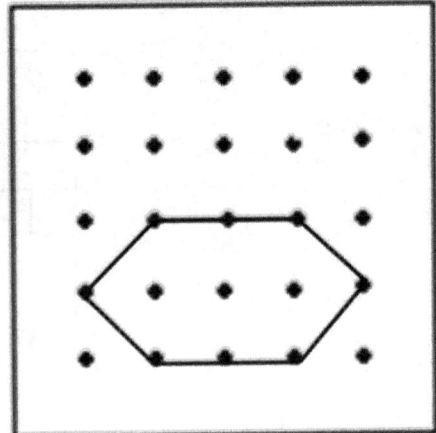

_____

_____

Name _____ Date _____

Study the shapes below. Then, answer the questions.

A 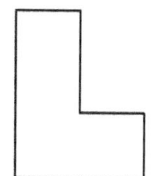 B  C 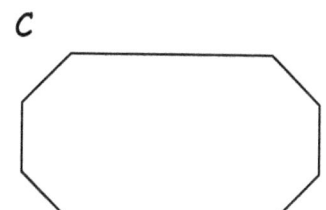 D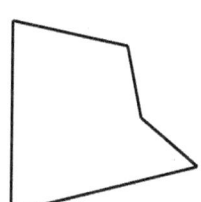

1. Which shape has the most sides? _____

2. Which shape has 3 fewer angles than shape C? _____

3. Which shape has 3 more sides than shape B? _____

4. Which of these shapes have the same number of sides and angles? _____

5. Which of these shapes have the same number of sides and vertices? _____

Lesson 1: Describe two-dimensional shapes based on attributes.

A STORY OF UNITS – TEKS EDITION

Lesson 1 Homework 2•8

Name _____ Date _____

1. Identify the number of sides, angles, and vertices for each shape.

a.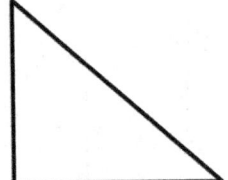

_____ sides

_____ angles

_____ vertices

b.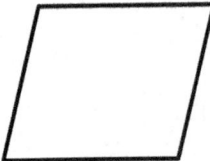

_____ sides

_____ angles

_____ vertices

c.

_____ sides

_____ angles

_____ vertices

d.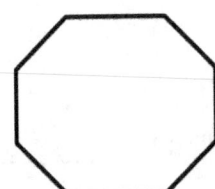

_____ sides

_____ angles

_____ vertices

e.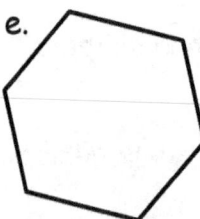

_____ sides

_____ angles

_____ vertices

f.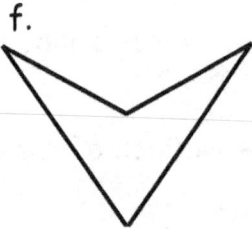

_____ sides

_____ angles

_____ vertices

g.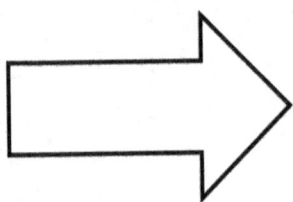

_____ sides

_____ angles

_____ vertices

h.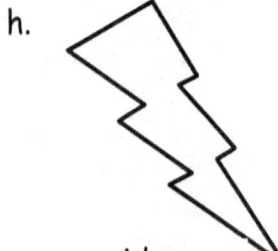

_____ sides

_____ angles

_____ vertices

i.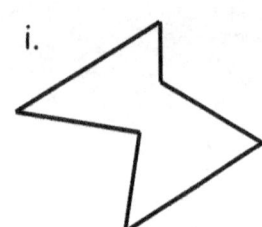

_____ sides

_____ angles

_____ vertices

Lesson 1: Describe two-dimensional shapes based on attributes.

2. Study the shapes below. Then, answer the questions.

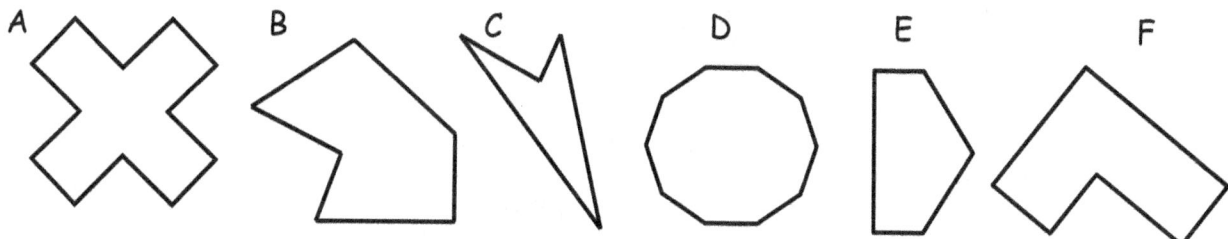

a. Which shape has the most angles? _____

b. Which shape has 4 more angles than shape F? _____

c. Which shape has 5 fewer sides than shape D? _____

d. How many more angles does shape A have than shape B? _____

e. Which of these shapes have the same number of sides and angles? _____

3. Joseph's teacher said to make shapes with 6 sides and 6 angles on his geoboard. Shade the shapes that share these attributes, and circle the shape that does not belong. Explain why it does not belong.

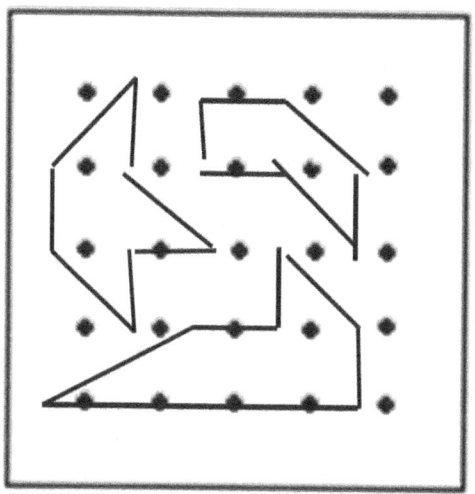

_____

_____

Lesson 2

Objective: Build, identify, and analyze two-dimensional shapes with specified attributes.

Suggested Lesson Structure

- Fluency Practice   (9 minutes)
- Application Problem   (5 minutes)
- Concept Development   (36 minutes)
- Student Debrief   (10 minutes)
- **Total Time**   **(60 minutes)**

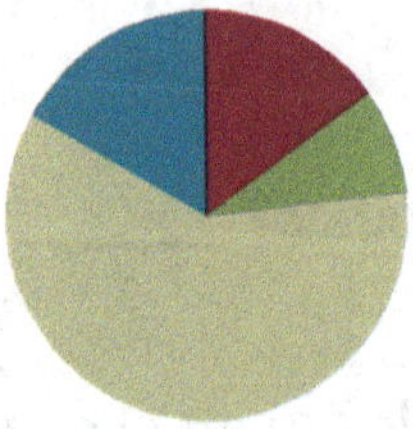

Fluency Practice (9 minutes)

- Sprint: Make a Hundred to Add **2.4B**   (9 minutes)

Sprint: Make a Hundred to Add (9 minutes)

Materials: (S) Make a Hundred to Add Sprint

Note: Students review compensation to make a hundred when adding to gain automaticity.

Application Problem (5 minutes)

Materials: (S) Find the triangles (Application Template)

How many triangles can you find? (Hint: If you only found 10, keep looking!)

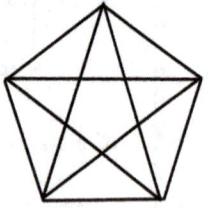

Note: This brainteaser challenges students to search for a familiar shape, the triangle, in a different way. Students are encouraged to think creatively as they find triangles of various sizes and orientations. There are 35 triangles. Hint: There are five of each variation of triangle as students track them around the pentagon. Each student needs both pages of the template.

> **NOTES ON MULTIPLE MEANS OF ACTION AND EXPRESSION:**
>
> Offer students having difficulty seeing the solution a strategy to solve the triangle Application Problem. They can write the numbers inside the most obvious triangles and then lightly shade the larger triangles within the pentagon.
>
> Another option is to print the whole page and have students shade one triangle at a time on each separate image.

A STORY OF UNITS – TEKS EDITION

Lesson 2 2•8

Concept Development (36 minutes)

Materials: (T) 7 charts from Lesson 1, tape, sentence strips with shape names (triangle, quadrilateral, pentagon, hexagon, heptagon, octagon, nonagon, decagon) (S) Container of uncooked spaghetti of differing lengths per group of four students, 1 piece of dark construction paper per student

Note: The polygon is described first, as the other listed descriptions stem from it. The descriptions provided here provide a solid foundation to the definitions that are a part of students' experience in later grades.

When introducing the term *polygon*, show images of polygons, and summarize by saying that they are closed shapes that are made up of some number of straight sides. Polygon and other shape descriptions are given below.

Polygon: A closed figure with three or more straight sides. Every side meets exactly two other sides at the vertices. A polygon always has the same number of angles and vertices as sides.

Triangle: A three-sided polygon with three angles.

Quadrilateral: A four-sided polygon with four angles.

Pentagon: A five-sided polygon with five angles.

Hexagon: A six-sided polygon with six angles.

Heptagon: A seven-sided polygon with seven angles.

Octagon: An eight-sided polygon with eight angles.

Nonagon: A nine-sided polygon with nine angles.

Decagon: A ten-sided polygon with ten angles.

Prior to the lesson, arrange students in groups of four with a container of spaghetti for building shapes and 1 piece of dark construction paper per student.

> **NOTES ON MULTIPLE MEANS OF ACTION AND EXPRESSION:**
>
> Tap into the culture of English language learners by asking them to contribute the words for polygon, triangle, rectangle, pentagon, hexagon, heptagon, octagon, nonagon, and decagon in their native language (Parents can help). Add the names in the students' languages to the charts. This not only helps students to bridge the languages but enriches the whole class's experience as well, since in Latin-based languages these are generally cognates. For example, in Spanish, they are *polígano, triangulo, rectangulo, pentagono, hexagono, heptágona, octagono nonágono,* and *decágono.*

T: Take two pieces of spaghetti of any length out of the container. Let's call these our sides. On your paper, arrange the spaghetti so that the two sides meet to make an angle.

S: (Arrange the spaghetti pieces into an open shape, shown to the right.)

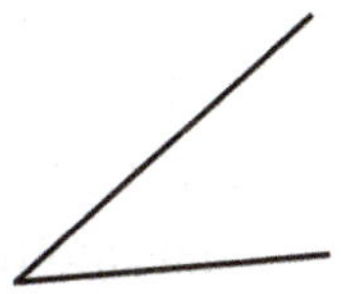

T: Take another piece of spaghetti, and close the shape, creating two more angles.

S: (Complete the shape.)

T: Name the shape you just made.

S: Triangle.

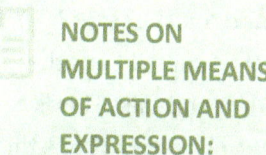

Lesson 2: Build, identify, and analyze two-dimensional shapes with specified attributes.

T: Yes. Shapes can be described with more than one name. We can also use the word **polygon** to describe the triangle. A polygon is a closed shape with three or more angles, so a triangle is the smallest polygon.

T: Can you think of other shapes that are polygons?

S: Hexagon. → Rectangle. → Square.

T: (Draw an open shape with two sides on the board, pointing to one side.) How many sides meet this one?

S: Only one.

T: Is this a polygon?

S: No! It only has one angle. → It's not closed!

T: How can we turn this into a polygon?

S: Add another side?

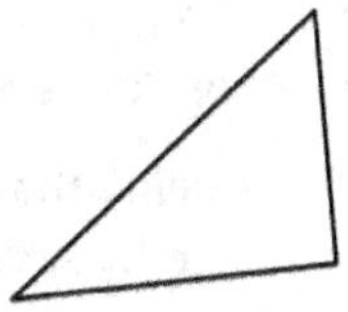

T: Yes. I can add another side to close the shape like this. (Draw a line to complete the triangle.)

T: Turn and talk: This is a polygon. How do we know?

S: It's closed. → It has three angles. → It's a triangle, and that's a polygon.

T: You're right! Today, we are going to name our shapes based on their attributes, or characteristics. (Hold up the word *triangle* on a sentence strip.) Listen carefully: *Tri-* means three. So, a triangle is a shape with …?

S: Three angles!

T: If a polygon has three angles and three sides, what else does it have?

S: It has three vertices.

T: (Reveal Chart 1 from yesterday's lesson.) Here is the chart we made yesterday. A shape with three sides, three angles, and three vertices can be named …?

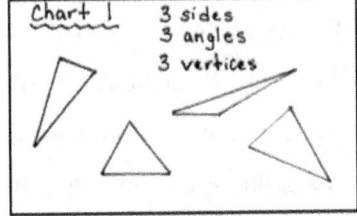

S: A triangle!

T: (Tape the triangle sentence strip to the top of Chart 1.)

T: What do you notice about these triangles and the one on your paper?

S: They don't all look the same. → They all have three sides, three angles, and three vertices. → Not all triangles look like this (points to an equilateral triangle). → I noticed that not all the sides are the same length; some are long, and some are short.

T: Good. So, even though they don't look the same, they are all triangles because they all have three sides and three angles. If they have three angles, they have three …?

S: Vertices!

T: Take another piece of spaghetti, and make a closed shape with four sides.

S: (Build a quadrilateral. Due to the differing lengths of spaghetti, the quadrilateral should be irregular and not as easy to name as a square or rectangle would be.)

T: Can you name the shape you made?

S: No, but it has four sides, four angles, and four vertices.

T: You just built another polygon, called a **quadrilateral**! (Hold up the word *quadrilateral* on a sentence strip.) *Quad-* means four. *Lateral* refers to sides. When we say quadrilateral, we're talking about a polygon with four sides.

T: (Reveal Chart 2 from yesterday's lesson.) What can we label our chart that has shapes with four sides, four angles, and four vertices?

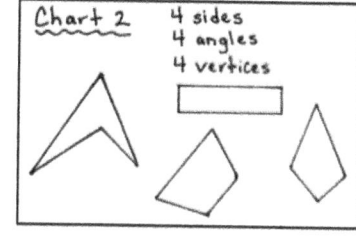

S: Quadrilaterals!

T: (Tape the quadrilateral sentence strip to the top of Chart 2.)

T: What do you notice about these quadrilaterals and the one on your paper?

S: They all have four sides, vertices, and angles. → Some look like shapes I know, but some look different. → Some have equal sides, but some don't.

T: Good. The reason why these shapes are quadrilaterals is because of their shared attributes not because of the way they look. These all have four straight sides, so they are…?

S: Quadrilaterals!

Continue to add a fifth and sixth piece of spaghetti to make a pentagon hexagon, heptagon, octagon, nonagon, and decagon. Follow the pattern above to discuss what students notice about the various shapes. Reveal Charts 3 through 7, labeling the with the appropriate word sentence strips. You may choose to add more pieces of spaghetti, giving students the opportunity to experiment with creating even larger polygons (e.g., heptagon, octagon).

T: Now, we're going to play Complete That Shape. I am going to draw part of a shape on the board, like this (as shown to the right). Then, I will say, "Complete that pentagon." With your spaghetti, start with the part I have drawn, and add more spaghetti sides, corners, and angles until you have built the entire shape. You can break the spaghetti into smaller pieces. Let's play.

T: (Show an obtuse angle, as illustrated to the right.) Complete that quadrilateral!

S: (Add two more pieces of spaghetti of varying lengths to create a quadrilateral.)

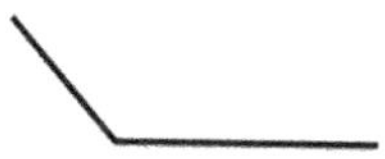

T: How many sides and angles do you have?

S: Four!

Continue playing the game to create more triangles, quadrilaterals, pentagons, hexagons heptagons, octagons, nonagons, and decagons. Once students have had a few minutes to practice building different shapes with spaghetti, instruct them to work independently on the Problem Set.

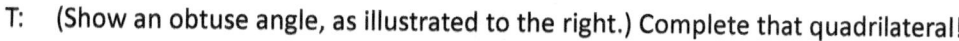

Lesson 2: Build, identify, and analyze two-dimensional shapes with specified attributes.

A STORY OF UNITS – TEKS EDITION

Lesson 2 2•8

Problem Set (10 minutes)

Students should do their personal best to complete the Problem Set within the allotted 10 minutes. For some classes, it may be appropriate to modify the assignment by specifying which problems they work on first. Some problems do not specify a method for solving. Students should solve these problems using the RDW approach used for Application Problems.

Student Debrief (10 minutes)

Lesson Objective: Build, identify, and analyze two-dimensional shapes with specified attributes.

The Student Debrief is intended to invite reflection and active processing of the total lesson experience.

Invite students to review their solutions for the Problem Set. They should check work by comparing answers with a partner. Look for misconceptions or misunderstandings that can be addressed in the Debrief. Guide students in a conversation to debrief the Problem Set and process the lesson.

Any combination of the questions below may be used to lead the discussion.

- Compare your shape names on the first page of your Problem Set with your partner's. Are there any shape names you disagree on? If yes, discuss who is correct and why.
- Look at Problem 1(a) on your Problem Set. What is the name of that shape? Look at 1(c). What is the name of that shape? What is the difference between an **octagon** and a **pentagon**?
- If you closed your eyes and felt a shape with four sides and four corners, could you name it? What would you name it?
- Picture a square in your head. Could you describe a square with another name?
- Could a **polygon** have only two angles? Why or why not?

Lesson 2: Build, identify, and analyze two-dimensional shapes with specified attributes.

28

- Polygons have many angles. *Poly-* means many, and *-gon* means angle. What is the smallest number of angles a polygon can have? What do you think the largest number of angles could be?

Exit Ticket (3 minutes)

After the Student Debrief, instruct students to complete the Exit Ticket. A review of their work will help with assessing students' understanding of the concepts that were presented in today's lesson and planning more effectively for future lessons. The questions may be read aloud to the students.

A

Make a Hundred to Add

Number Correct: _____

1.	98 + 3 =		23.	99 + 12 =	
2.	98 + 4 =		24.	99 + 23 =	
3.	98 + 5 =		25.	99 + 34 =	
4.	98 + 8 =		26.	99 + 45 =	
5.	98 + 6 =		27.	99 + 56 =	
6.	98 + 9 =		28.	99 + 67 =	
7.	98 + 7 =		29.	99 + 78 =	
8.	99 + 2 =		30.	35 + 99 =	
9.	99 + 3 =		31.	45 + 98 =	
10.	99 + 4 =		32.	46 + 99 =	
11.	99 + 9 =		33.	56 + 98 =	
12.	99 + 6 =		34.	67 + 99 =	
13.	99 + 8 =		35.	77 + 98 =	
14.	99 + 5 =		36.	68 + 99 =	
15.	99 + 7 =		37.	78 + 98 =	
16.	98 + 13 =		38.	99 + 95 =	
17.	98 + 24 =		39.	93 + 99 =	
18.	98 + 35 =		40.	99 + 95 =	
19.	98 + 46 =		41.	94 + 99 =	
20.	98 + 57 =		42.	98 + 96 =	
21.	98 + 68 =		43.	94 + 98 =	
22.	98 + 79 =		44.	98 + 88 =	

B

Number Correct: _____

Improvement: _____

Make a Hundred to Add

1.	99 + 2 =		23.	98 + 13 =	
2.	99 + 3 =		24.	98 + 24 =	
3.	99 + 4 =		25.	98 + 35 =	
4.	99 + 8 =		26.	98 + 46 =	
5.	99 + 6 =		27.	98 + 57 =	
6.	99 + 9 =		28.	98 + 68 =	
7.	99 + 5 =		29.	98 + 79 =	
8.	99 + 7 =		30.	25 + 99 =	
9.	98 + 3 =		31.	35 + 98 =	
10.	98 + 4 =		32.	36 + 99 =	
11.	98 + 5 =		33.	46 + 98 =	
12.	98 + 9 =		34.	57 + 99 =	
13.	98 + 7 =		35.	67 + 98 =	
14.	98 + 8 =		36.	78 + 99 =	
15.	98 + 6 =		37.	88 + 98 =	
16.	99 + 12 =		38.	99 + 93 =	
17.	99 + 23 =		39.	95 + 99 =	
18.	99 + 34 =		40.	99 + 97 =	
19.	99 + 45 =		41.	92 + 99 =	
20.	99 + 56 =		42.	98 + 94 =	
21.	99 + 67 =		43.	96 + 98 =	
22.	99 + 78 =		44.	98 + 86 =	

Lesson 2: Build, identify, and analyze two-dimensional shapes with specified attributes.

A STORY OF UNITS – TEKS EDITION

Lesson 2 Problem Set 2•8

Name _____ Date _____

1. Count the number of sides and angles for each shape to identify each polygon. The polygon names in the word bank may be used more than once.

| Hexagon | Quadrilateral | Triangle | Pentagon |
| Nonagon | Octagon | Decagon | Heptagon |

a. _____

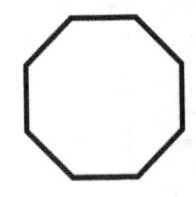

b. _____

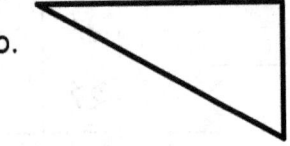

c. _____

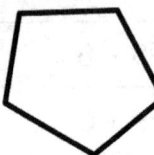

d. _____

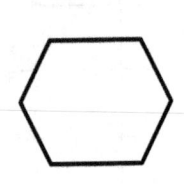

e. _____

f. _____

g. _____

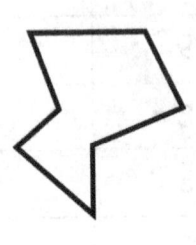

h. _____

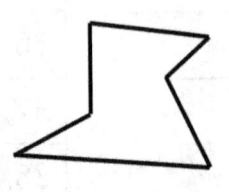

i. _____

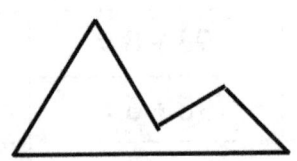

j. _____

k. _____

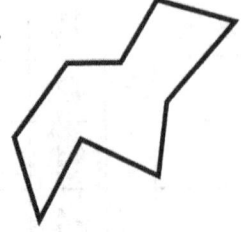

l. _____

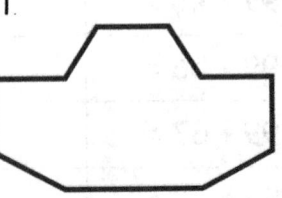

Lesson 2: Build, identify, and analyze two-dimensional shapes with specified attributes.

2. Draw more sides to complete 2 examples of each polygon.

	Example 1	Example 2
a. **Triangle** For each example, _____ line was added. A triangle has _____ total sides.		
b. **Hexagon** For each example, _____ lines were added. A hexagon has _____ total sides.		
c. **Quadrilateral** For each example, _____ lines were added. A quadrilateral has _____ total sides.		
d. **Pentagon** For each example, _____ lines were added. A pentagon has _____ total sides.		

3. a. Explain why both polygons A and B are hexagons.

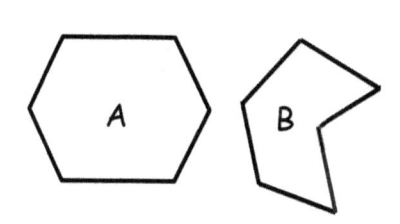

   _____

   _____

   b. Draw a different hexagon than the two that are shown.

4. Explain why both polygons C and D are quadrilaterals.

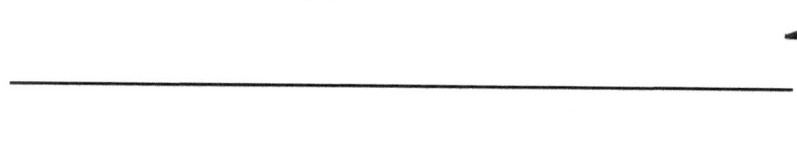

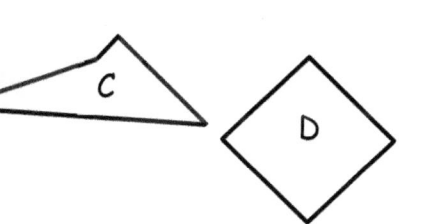

   _____

   _____

Lesson 2: Build, identify, and analyze two-dimensional shapes with specified attributes.

A STORY OF UNITS – TEKS EDITION   Lesson 2 Exit Ticket 2•8

Name _____   Date _____

Count the number of sides and angles for each shape to identify each polygon. The polygon names in the word bank may be used more than once.

| Hexagon | Quadrilateral | Triangle | Pentagon |

1.

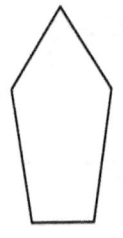

_____

2.

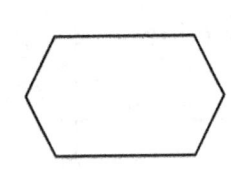

_____

3.

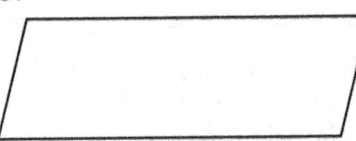

_____

4.

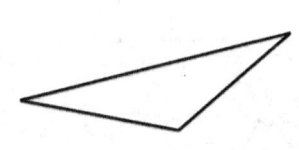

_____

5.

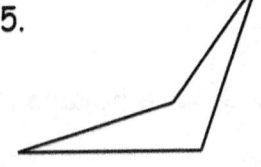

_____

6.

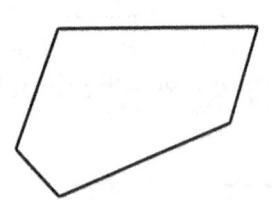

_____

Name _____   Date _____

1. Count the number of sides and angles for each shape to identify each polygon. The polygon names in the word bank may be used more than once.

| Hexagon | Quadrilateral | Triangle | Pentagon |
| Decagon | Heptagon | Nonagon | Octagon |

a. _____

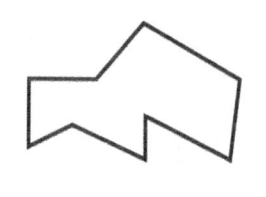

b. _____

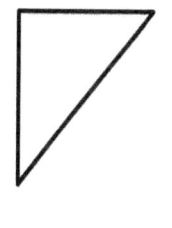

c. _____

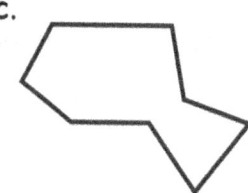

d. _____

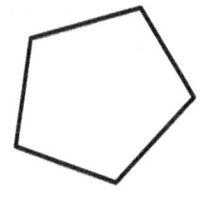

e. _____

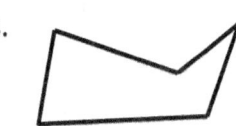

f. _____

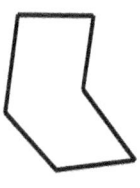

g. _____

h. _____

i. _____

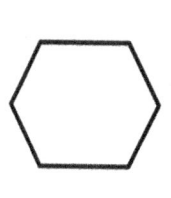

j. _____

k. _____

l. _____

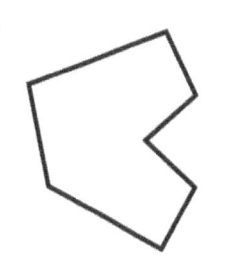

Lesson 2: Build, identify, and analyze two-dimensional shapes with specified attributes.

35

2. Draw more sides to complete 2 examples of each polygon.

	Example 1	Example 2
a. **Quadrilateral** For each example, ___ lines were added. A quadrilateral has ___ total sides.	∟	∧
b. **Pentagon** For each example, ___ lines were added. A pentagon has ___ total sides.	∟	∧
c. **Triangle** For each example, ___ line was added. A triangle has ___ total sides.	∟	∧
d. **Hexagon** For each example, ___ lines were added. A hexagon has ___ total sides.	∟	∧

3. Explain why both polygons A and B are pentagons.

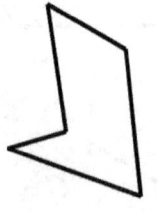

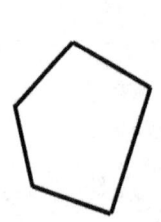

   _____

   _____

4. Explain why both polygons C and D are triangles.

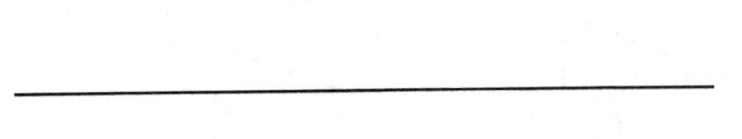

   _____

   _____

Lesson 2: Build, identify, and analyze two-dimensional shapes with specified attributes.

A STORY OF UNITS – TEKS EDITION

Lesson 2 Application Template   2•8

find the triangles

Lesson 2: Build, identify, and analyze two-dimensional shapes with specified attributes.

A STORY OF UNITS – TEKS EDITION — Lesson 2 Application Template — 2•8

find the triangles

Lesson 2: Build, identify, and analyze two-dimensional shapes with specified attributes.

Lesson 3

Objective: Use attributes to draw different polygons including triangles, quadrilaterals, pentagons, and hexagons.

Suggested Lesson Structure

- Fluency Practice   (5 minutes)
- Application Problem   (6 minutes)
- Concept Development   (39 minutes)
- Student Debrief   (10 minutes)
- **Total Time**   **(60 minutes)**

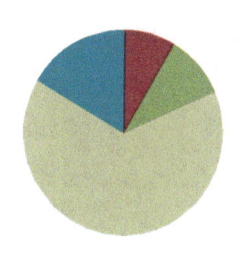

Fluency Practice (5 minutes)

- Grade 2 Fluency Differentiated Practice Sets **2.4A**   (5 minutes)

Grade 2 Fluency Differentiated Practice Sets (5 minutes)

Materials: (S) Fluency Practice Sets

Note: During Topic A and for the remainder of the year, each day's Fluency Practice includes an opportunity for review and mastery of the sums and differences with totals through 20 by means of the Fluency Practice Sets or Sprints. Five options are provided in this lesson for the Fluency Practice Set, with Sheet A being the most simple addition fluency of the grade to Sheet E being the most complex. Start all students on Sheet A. Keep a record of student progress so that you can move students to more complex sheets when they are ready.

Students complete as many problems as they can in 120 seconds. We recommend 100% accuracy and completion before moving to the next level. Collect any Practice Sheets that have been completed within the 120 seconds, and check the answers. The next time Fluency Practice Sets are used, students who have successfully completed their set today can be provided with the next level.

Consider assigning early finishers a counting pattern and start number. Celebrate improvement as well as advancement. Students should be encouraged to compete with themselves rather than their peers. Discuss possible strategies to solve with students. Notify caring adults of each student's progress.

A STORY OF UNITS – TEKS EDITION   Lesson 3   2•8

Application Problem (6 minutes)

Three sides of a quadrilateral have the following lengths: 19 cm, 23 cm, and 26 cm. If the total distance around the shape is 86 cm, what is the length of the fourth side?

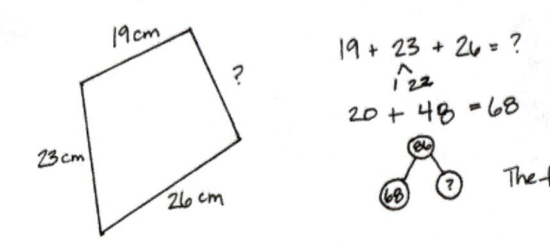

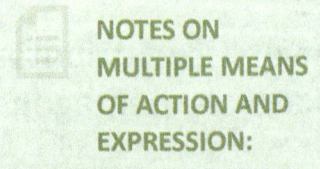

> **NOTES ON MULTIPLE MEANS OF ACTION AND EXPRESSION:**
>
> To help students working below grade level engage with the Application Problem, offer a version with simpler numbers (e.g., sides of 3 cm, 9 cm, and 2 cm with a perimeter of 20 cm). Students can then solve the word problem without getting bogged down by the numbers.

Note: This problem allows students to solve a two-step measurement word problem involving length in the context of geometric shapes using the RDW process. Encourage students to share their solution methods. For example, some may subtract, while others might count up to find the unknown side length.

Concept Development (32 minutes)

Materials: (T) Document camera (if available), large piece of chart paper for a polygon sort
(S) Straightedge, scissors, 2 pieces of white 8½" x 11" inch paper

Part 1: Drawing Polygons

Distribute one straightedge and piece of white paper to each student. Instruct students to follow you as they fold their papers in half twice (as shown to the right) so that they have four sections on both sides of the paper for drawing. For precision, students should use a pencil so that they have the option to erase as they draw the shapes.

T: (On the board, draw a shape with a curve and two straight sides, as shown below.)
T: Is this a polygon?
S: No!
T: What attribute is it missing?
S: Straight sides!
T: How about this shape? (Draw a pentagon, as shown to the right.)
S: Yes, it's a polygon because the sides are straight. → It has the same number of sides, angles, and vertices.

Lesson 3: Use attributes to draw different polygons including triangles, quadrilaterals, pentagons, and hexagons.

T: Since polygons have straight sides, and the sides meet neatly at vertices to form angles, let's use our straightedges to be precise when drawing different polygons today.

T: In one section on the paper you folded earlier, use your straightedge to draw a polygon with four straight sides. (Allow students time to draw.)

T: Describe your shape to your partner. (Listen and facilitate the descriptions below.)

S: Mine has four straight sides. → I have a polygon with four sides and four angles. → My quadrilateral has two little angles and two bigger angles. → Two of my shape's sides are short, and two are long.

T: (Circulate and observe student work.) Nice! I can see that some of your shapes look very different, even though they all have four sides and four angles. What do we call a polygon with four sides and four angles?

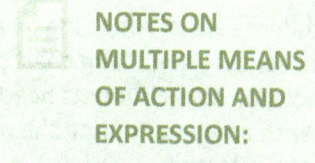

S: A quadrilateral!

T: In the next section of your paper, use your straightedge to draw a polygon with six angles.

S: (Draw a hexagon with six angles and six straight sides.)

T: Show your partner the six vertices, of your polygon by circling them.

S: (Circle and count the vertices while showing a partner.)

T: Good. Now, show your partner the six straight sides of your polygon. Remember to place your finger at the starting point so you don't count the same side twice as you count around the figure.

S: (Count sides while showing a partner.)

T: (Circulate and observe students sharing.) Great thinking! What is the same about all of your shapes?

S: They all have six sides. → They are all called *hexagons*. → They have six angles and six vertices.

T: Yes, and what is different?

S: The sides have different lengths. → Some are big, and some are little. → They all look a little different.

> **NOTES ON MULTIPLE MEANS OF ACTION AND EXPRESSION:**
>
> Throughout the lesson, point to visuals posted on the board to help English language learners follow along. For instance, when asking students, "What do you know about the sides of the polygon?" point first to a side and then to a drawn pentagon.

Instruct students to fill in the remaining two sections of their papers with a polygon with *three* sides and then a polygon with *five* angles (see the examples to the right) using the above vignette as necessary or appropriate. Continue with the second piece of white paper. Instruct students to fold the second piece of paper into 4 sections as previously done. Instruct students to fill one section with a polygon with eight sides, another section with a polygon that has seven vertices, another with ten angles, and, lastly, a polygon with nine vertices.

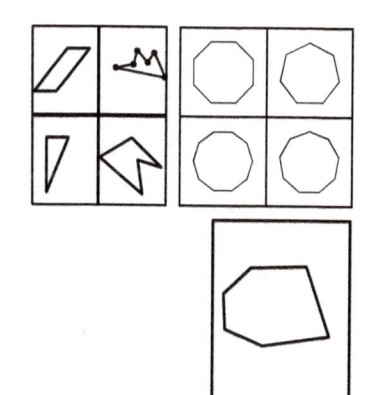

Lesson 3: Use attributes to draw different polygons including triangles, quadrilaterals, pentagons, and hexagons.

41

Find a Friend: Instruct students to quietly walk to find a friend with a different looking polygon with three, four, five, and six sides: "Find a friend with a triangle that looks different from yours."

Part 2: Sorting Polygons

While students are playing Find a Friend, distribute scissors, and hang chart paper for the polygon sort. Students need to work with a partner during the next portion of the lesson.

Polygons!

triangles	quadrilaterals	pentagons	hexagons	heptagons	octagons	nonagons	decagons

T: Now that you have drawn eight polygons on your papers, use your scissors to cut on the folded lines so that you have eight pieces of paper. (See the image above.)

T: Trade shapes with a partner, and take turns describing the shapes' attributes. Then, name them by writing the words *triangle, quadrilateral, pentagon, hexagon, heptagon, octagon, nonagon,* or *decagon*.

T: Choose one polygon to put on our chart. (Display the polygon chart.) Place it on the edge of your desk, so I can add it to the chart while you complete your Problem Set.

As students work on the Problem Set, place student cards on the chart based on how students named the shapes. Mistakes are anonymous and can lead to interesting discussions in the Student Debrief.

Problem Set (10 minutes)

Students should do their personal best to complete the Problem Set within the allotted 10 minutes. For some classes, it may be appropriate to modify the assignment by specifying which problems they work on first. Some problems do not specify a method for solving. Students should solve these problems using the RDW approach used for Application Problems.

Student Debrief (10 minutes)

Lesson Objective: Use attributes to draw different polygons including triangles, quadrilaterals, pentagons, and hexagons.

The Student Debrief is intended to invite reflection and active processing of the total lesson experience.

Invite students to review their solutions for the Problem Set. They should check work by comparing answers with a partner. Look for misconceptions or misunderstandings that can be addressed in the Debrief. Guide students in a conversation to debrief the Problem Set and process the lesson.

Any combination of the questions below may be used to lead the discussion.

- Look at Problems 1(b) and 2(b). How are these problems similar? How are they different?
- Look at Problems 1(d) and 2(d). Do all of your six-sided polygons look alike? What can we call a six-sided polygon? Can hexagons have five sides? Why not?
- If you know how many vertices a polygon has, what else do you know about that polygon?
- Why is it important to use a straightedge when drawing polygons?
- Look closely at our polygon chart. Do you agree with the way that we sorted and named all of the polygons? If not, which do you disagree with and why?
- Pick a polygon that is not yours, and tell your partner why it is in the correct column.
- Did our polygon chart remind you of other work we have done in Grade 2?
- Tell your partner one word that you learned today that you did not know before.

Name ___Nydia___ Date _____

1. Use a straightedge to draw the polygon with the given attributes in the space to the right.

    a. Draw a polygon with 3 angles.
       Number of sides: __3__
       Name of polygon: __triangle__

    b. Draw a five-sided polygon.
       Number of vertices: __5__
       Name of polygon: __pentagon__

    c. Draw a polygon with 4 angles.
       Number of sides: __4__
       Name of polygon: __quadrilateral__

    d. Draw a polygon with six vertices.
       Number of angles: __6__
       Name of polygon: __hexagon__

    e. Draw a polygon with 8 vertices.
       Number of sides: __8__
       Name of polygon: __octagon__

    f. Draw a polygon with 10 angles.
       Number of vertices: __10__
       Name of polygon: __decagon__

    g. Draw a 9-sided polygon.
       Number of angles: __9__
       Name of polygon: __nonagon__

    h. Draw a polygon with 7 vertices.
       Number of angles: __7__
       Name of polygon: __heptagon__

2. Use your straightedge to draw 2 new examples of each polygon that are different from those you drew on the first page.

    a. Triangle

    b. Pentagon

    c. Quadrilateral

    d. Hexagon

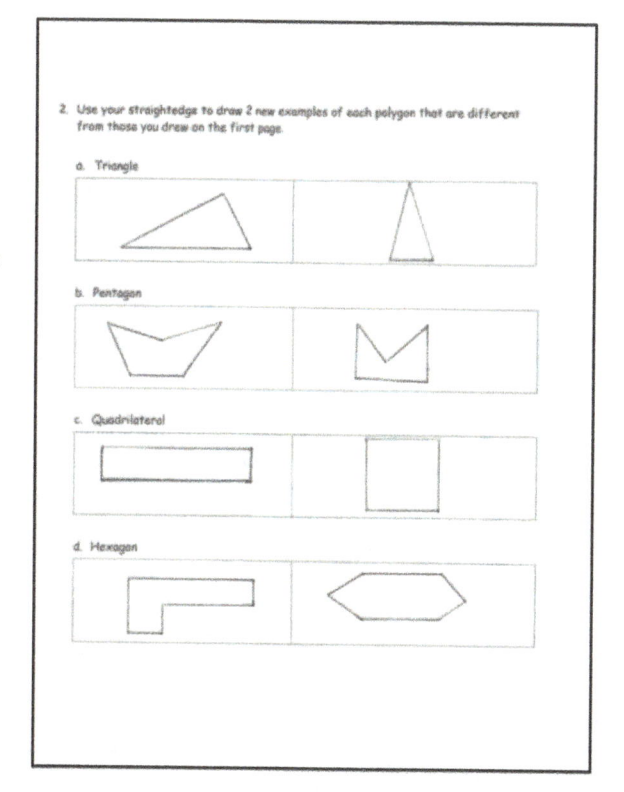

Exit Ticket (3 minutes)

After the Student Debrief, instruct students to complete the Exit Ticket. A review of their work will help assessing students' understanding of the concepts that were presented in today's lesson and planning more effectively for future lessons. The questions may be read aloud to the students.

Name _____ Date _____

1.	10 + 9 =	21.	3 + 9 =
2.	10 + 1 =	22.	4 + 8 =
3.	11 + 2 =	23.	5 + 9 =
4.	13 + 6 =	24.	8 + 8 =
5.	15 + 5 =	25.	7 + 5 =
6.	14 + 3 =	26.	5 + 8 =
7.	13 + 5 =	27.	8 + 3 =
8.	12 + 4 =	28.	6 + 8 =
9.	16 + 2 =	29.	4 + 6 =
10.	18 + 1 =	30.	7 + 6 =
11.	11 + 7 =	31.	7 + 4 =
12.	13 + 4 =	32.	7 + 9 =
13.	14 + 5 =	33.	7 + 7 =
14.	9 + 4 =	34.	8 + 6 =
15.	9 + 2 =	35.	6 + 9 =
16.	9 + 9 =	36.	8 + 5 =
17.	6 + 9 =	37.	4 + 7 =
18.	8 + 9 =	38.	3 + 9 =
19	7 + 8 =	39.	8 + 6 =
20.	8 + 8 =	40.	9 + 4 =

Lesson 3: Use attributes to draw different polygons including triangles, quadrilaterals, pentagons, and hexagons.

Name _____ Date _____

1.	10 + 8 =	21.	5 + 8 =
2.	4 + 10 =	22.	6 + 7 =
3.	9 + 10 =	23.	___ + 4 = 12
4.	11 + 5 =	24.	___ + 7 = 13
5.	13 + 3 =	25.	6 + ___ = 14
6.	12 + 4 =	26.	7 + ___ = 15
7.	16 + 3 =	27.	___ = 9 + 8
8.	15 + ___ = 19	28.	___ = 7 + 5
9.	18 + ___ = 20	29.	___ = 4 + 8
10.	13 + 5 =	30.	3 + 9 =
11.	___ = 4 + 16	31.	6 + 7 =
12.	___ = 6 + 12	32.	8 + ___ = 13
13.	___ = 14 + 6	33.	___ = 7 + 9
14.	9 + 3 =	34.	6 + 6 =
15.	7 + 9 =	35.	___ = 7 + 5
16.	___ + 4 = 11	36.	___ = 4 + 8
17.	___ + 6 = 13	37.	20 = 13 + ___
18.	___ + 5 = 12	38.	18 = ___ + 9
19.	___ + 8 = 14	39.	16 = ___ + 7
20.	___ + 9 = 15	40.	20 = 9 + ___

Lesson 3: Use attributes to draw different polygons including triangles, quadrilaterals, pentagons, and hexagons.

Name _____   Date _____

1.	19 - 9 =	21.	15 - 7 =
2.	19 - 11 =	22.	18 - 9 =
3.	17 - 10 =	23.	16 - 8 =
4.	12 - 2 =	24.	15 - 6 =
5.	15 - 12 =	25.	17 - 8 =
6.	18 - 10 =	26.	14 - 6 =
7.	17 - 5 =	27.	16 - 9 =
8.	20 - 9 =	28.	13 - 8 =
9.	14 - 4 =	29.	12 - 5 =
10.	16 - 13 =	30.	19 - 8 =
11.	11 - 2 =	31.	17 - 9 =
12.	12 - 3 =	32.	16 - 7 =
13.	14 - 2 =	33.	14 - 8 =
14.	13 - 4 =	34.	15 - 9 =
15.	11 - 3 =	35.	13 - 7 =
16.	12 - 4 =	36.	12 - 8 =
17.	13 - 2 =	37.	15 - 8 =
18.	14 - 5 =	38.	14 - 9 =
19	11 - 4 =	39.	12 - 7 =
20.	12 - 5 =	40.	11 - 9 =

Lesson 3: Use attributes to draw different polygons including triangles, quadrilaterals, pentagons, and hexagons.

Name _____ Date _____

1.	12 - 3 =	21.	13 - 7 =
2.	13 - 5 =	22.	15 - 9 =
3.	11 - 2 =	23.	18 - 7 =
4.	12 - 5 =	24.	14 - 7 =
5.	13 - 4 =	25.	17 - 9 =
6.	13 - 2 =	26.	12 - 9 =
7.	11 - 4 =	27.	13 - 6 =
8.	12 - 6 =	28.	15 - 7 =
9.	11 - 3 =	29.	16 - 8 =
10.	13 - 6 =	30.	12 - 6 =
11.	____ = 11 - 9	31.	____ = 13 - 9
12.	____ = 13 - 8	32.	____ = 17 - 8
13.	____ = 12 - 7	33.	____ = 14 - 9
14.	____ = 11 - 6	34.	____ = 13 - 5
15.	____ = 13 - 9	35.	____ = 15 - 8
16.	____ = 14 - 8	36.	____ = 18 - 9
17.	____ = 11 - 7	37.	____ = 16 - 7
18.	____ = 15 - 6	38.	____ = 20 - 12
19.	____ = 16 - 9	39.	____ = 20 - 6
20.	____ = 12 - 8	40.	____ = 20 - 17

Lesson 3: Use attributes to draw different polygons including triangles, quadrilaterals, pentagons, and hexagons.

Name _____ Date _____

1.	13 - 4 =	21.	8 + 4 =
2.	15 - 8 =	22.	6 + 7 =
3.	19 - 5 =	23.	9 + 9 =
4.	11 - 7 =	24.	12 - 6 =
5.	9 + 6 =	25.	16 - 7 =
6.	7 + 8 =	26.	13 - 5 =
7.	4 + 7 =	27.	11 - 8 =
8.	13 + 6 =	28.	7 + 9 =
9.	12 - 8 =	29.	5 + 7 =
10.	17 - 9 =	30.	8 + 7 =
11.	14 - 6 =	31.	9 + 8 =
12.	16 - 7 =	32.	11 + 9 =
13.	6 + 8 =	33.	12 - 3 =
14.	7 + 6 =	34.	14 - 5 =
15.	4 + 9 =	35.	20 - 13 =
16.	5 + 7 =	36.	8 - 5 =
17.	9 - 5 =	37.	7 + 4 =
18.	13 - 7 =	38.	13 + 5 =
19	16 - 9 =	39.	7 + 9 =
20.	14 - 8 =	40.	8 + 11 =

Lesson 3: Use attributes to draw different polygons including triangles, quadrilaterals, pentagons, and hexagons.

Name _____   Date _____

1. Use a straightedge to draw the polygon with the given attributes in the space to the right.

    a. Draw a polygon with 3 angles.
       Number of sides: _____
       Name of polygon: _____

    b. Draw a five-sided polygon.
       Number of vertices: _____
       Name of polygon: _____

    c. Draw a polygon with 4 angles.
       Number of sides: _____
       Name of polygon: _____

    d. Draw a polygon with six vertices.
       Number of angles: _____
       Name of polygon: _____

    e. Draw a polygon with 8 vertices.
       Number of sides: _____
       Name of polygon: _____

    f. Draw a polygon with 10 angles.
       Number of vertices: _____
       Name of polygon: _____

    g. Draw a 9-sided polygon.
       Number of angles: _____
       Name of polygon: _____

    h. Draw a polygon with 7 vertices.
       Number of angles: _____
       Name of polygon: _____

2. Use your straightedge to draw 2 new examples of each polygon that are different from those you drew on the first page.

   a. Triangle

   b. Pentagon

   c. Quadrilateral

   d. Hexagon

Name _____   Date _____

Use a straightedge to draw the polygon with the given attributes in the space to the right.

Draw a five-sided polygon.

Number of angles: _____

Name of polygon: _____

Name _____   Date _____

1. Use a straightedge to draw the polygon with the given attributes in the space to the right.

    a. Draw a polygon with 4 vertices.

       Number of sides: _____

       Name of polygon: _____

    b. Draw a six-sided polygon.

       Number of angles: _____

       Name of polygon: _____

    c. Draw a polygon with 3 angles.

       Number of sides: _____

       Name of polygon: _____

    d. Draw a polygon with 5 vertices.

       Number of angles: _____

       Name of polygon: _____

    e. Draw a ten-sided polygon.

       Number of vertices: _____

       Name of polygon: _____

    f. Draw a polygon with 9 vertices.

       Number of sides: _____

       Name of polygon: _____

    g. Draw a polygon with 7 angles.

       Number of vertices: _____

       Name of polygon: _____

    h. Draw a polygon with 8 vertices.

       Number of angles: _____

       Name of polygon: _____

Lesson 3: Use attributes to draw different polygons including triangles, quadrilaterals, pentagons, and hexagons.

2. Use your straightedge to draw 2 new examples of each polygon that are different from those you drew on the first page.

   a. Quadrilateral

   b. Hexagon

   c. Pentagon

   d. Triangle

Lesson 4

Objective: Use attributes to identify and draw different quadrilaterals including rectangles, rhombuses, parallelograms, and trapezoids.

Suggested Lesson Structure

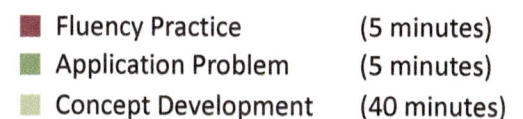

- Fluency Practice   (5 minutes)
- Application Problem   (5 minutes)
- Concept Development   (40 minutes)
- Student Debrief   (10 minutes)
- **Total Time**   **(60 minutes)**

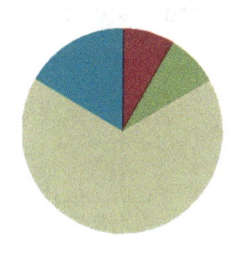

Fluency Practice (5 minutes)

- Addition with Renaming **2.4B**   (5 minutes)

Addition with Renaming (5 minutes)

Materials: (S) Personal white board, hundreds place value chart (Fluency Template)

Note: This fluency activity reviews the application of a chip model while recording with the algorithm. Allow students work time between each problem, and reinforce place value understandings by having students say their answers in both unit form and in standard form. Students use their personal white boards and a place value chart to solve.

- T: Slide the place value chart template into your personal white board.
- T: (Write 167 + 47 vertically on the board.) Let's use a chip model to add. On your personal white board, record your work using the algorithm.
- S: (Solve.)
- T: 1 hundred 6 tens 7 ones plus 4 tens 7 ones is...?
- S: 2 hundreds 1 ten 4 ones!
- T: 167 + 47 is...?
- S: 214.

Continue with the following possible sequence: 285 + 38, 234 + 67, 317 + 94, and 367 + 55.

A STORY OF UNITS – TEKS EDITION　　　　　　　　　　　　　　　　　Lesson 4　2•8

Application Problem (5 minutes)

Juanita earns $22 walking dogs. She spends $6 on a coloring book and $3 on crayons. Juanita deposits the rest of the money in her bank account. How much money does Juanita deposit in her bank account?

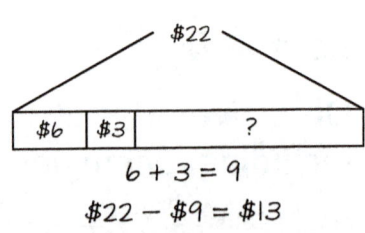

$6 | $3 | ? ←—— $22

6 + 3 = 9
$22 − $9 = $13
Juanita deposits $13.

Note: This problem allows students to solve a two-step word problem about personal financial literacy. Encourage students to share how they solved the problem.

Concept Development (40 minutes)

Materials:　(T) Chart 2 from Lesson 1, index card, square tile, drawing of rhombus (S) 1 piece of 8½" x 11" white paper, centimeter rulers (Template), index card, highlighter

Note: Students need crayons or colored pencils for the homework.

Note: The shape descriptions below provide a solid foundation to the definitions that are a part of students' experience in later grades. Students are not expected to memorize these but rather to have an experience drawing different quadrilaterals using the new attributes of square angles and parallel sides.

　　　Quadrilateral: A four-sided polygon with four angles.
　　　Trapezoid: A quadrilateral with exactly one pair of parallel sides. (See the UDL box.)
　　　Parallelogram: A quadrilateral with two pairs of parallel sides.
　　　Rectangle: A quadrilateral with four square angles.
　　　Square: A special rectangle with sides that are all the same length.
　　　Rhombus: A quadrilateral with four sides that are all the same length.

Distribute a piece of 8½" x 11" white paper, a centimeter ruler, and an index card to each student. Instruct students to follow you as they fold their papers in half twice, such that they have four sections on both sides of the paper for drawing. (See the image to the right.) For precision, students should use a pencil so that they have the option to erase as they draw the shapes.

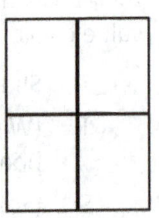

Part 1: Drawing Square Corners and Parallel Lines

T:　Look at your index card. How many angles does it have?
S:　Four!
T:　Yes. Let's look at our chart with other shapes that have four sides and four angles. (Circle the shape on the chart with three acute angles, as shown.)
T:　How are the angles on your index card different from those of this shape?
S:　The ones on my index card are all the same. → The angles on my card are in the shape of an L. → The ones on the chart are big and small.
T:　We call the angles on our index cards **square angles**.

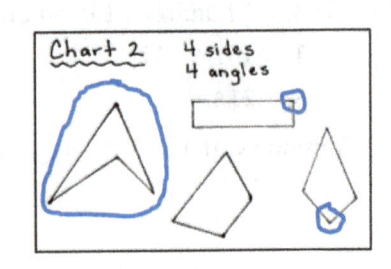

56　　Lesson 4:　Use attributes to identify and draw different quadrilaterals including rectangles, rhombuses, parallelograms, and trapezoids.

EUREKA MATH　TEKS EDITION

© Great Minds PBC
TEKS Edition | greatminds.org/texas

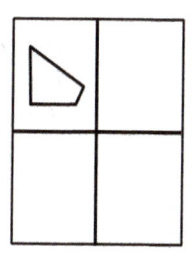

T: Look at Chart 2 again. Student A, come up and circle a square angle.
S: (Uses a marker to identify and circle a square angle.)
T: Thumbs up if you agree. Let's use our index card to check to see if Student A found a square angle. (Put the angle of the index card in the angle of the shape, and show students how to check by seeing if the lines of the shape line up with the edges of the index card.)
T: Good job, Student A! This is a square angle. (Find and check other square angles.)
T: Let's use our index cards as a tool to help us draw a quadrilateral with one square angle.
T: In one of the sections on your paper, draw a square angle using your index card as a guide. Then, use the straightedge of your card to draw two more lines to complete your quadrilateral.

As time permits, students practice how to make other quadrilaterals.

T: Place your centimeter ruler vertically in the next section on your paper. Use your centimeter ruler to draw a straight line within the section. 
S: (Draw a vertical line using a pencil.)
T: Without moving your ruler, use the opposite edge to draw a second straight line of any length. (See the image to the right.)
S: (Draw a second straight line parallel to the first one using a pencil.)
T: What do you notice about these lines?
S: One is shorter than the other one. → They don't touch. → They don't make an angle. → They are the same distance apart. The lines never come closer or get farther away from each other. → They look like the sides of an H.
T: If I used a really long ruler and a really long piece of paper and kept drawing these lines, they would never cross or touch.
T: We call these **parallel** lines. (Write *parallel* on the board.) Look at the word *parallel*. The two L's in the middle of the word are parallel.
T: In the next section, position your ruler in different ways—horizontally, diagonally—and practice making more pairs of parallel lines.
S: (Practice making parallel lines with rulers in different positions.)

As time permits, direct students to Chart 2 again to answer the question, "Which of these shapes has a pair of parallel lines?"

Part 2: Drawing and Identifying a Trapezoid

T: Position your ruler horizontally in a new section on your paper. Use your ruler to draw a straight line that is 8 cm long.
S: (Draw an 8 cm horizontal line using a pencil.)

> **NOTES ON STANDARDS ALIGNMENT:**
>
> The term *trapezoid* may have two meanings, depending on an exclusive or inclusive definition.
>
> - Exclusive: A trapezoid is a quadrilateral with exactly one pair of parallel sides.
> - Inclusive: A trapezoid is a quadrilateral with at least one pair of parallel sides.
>
> While both definitions are legitimate, this curriculum, aligned to Texas Essential Knowledge and Skills, uses the exclusive definition.

Lesson 4: Use attributes to identify and draw different quadrilaterals including rectangles, rhombuses, parallelograms, and trapezoids.

T: Without moving your ruler, use the opposite edge of the ruler to draw a second straight line shorter or longer than the first line you drew. Then, with your ruler, join the ends of both lines. (See the three examples shown to the right.)

S: (Use rulers to join the ends of both lines, forming a trapezoid.)

T: You made a four-sided polygon. What do we call it?

S: A quadrilateral!

T: Compare your quadrilateral with those of your neighbors.

T: Turn and talk: What new attribute do you notice about the sides of these quadrilaterals?

S: They all have one pair of parallel sides. → Two opposite sides are parallel, but the other two aren't. → The opposite sides are different lengths. → They all have exactly one pair of parallel sides.

T: If the quadrilateral has more than 1 pair of parallel sides, it is not a trapezoid. Does this quadrilateral have exactly one pair of parallel sides?

S: Yes!

T: (Point to a different trapezoid.) How about this quadrilateral?

S: Yes!

T: Your quadrilaterals are trapezoids if they have exactly one pair of parallel sides. What is our new word?

S: **Trapezoid**!

Part 3: Drawing and Identifying a Parallelogram

T: Turn your paper over. In another section, use both sides of your ruler to draw two parallel lines that are each 8 cm long. Draw one line starting at zero and stopping at 8 cm. Draw the other starting at any number but advancing 8 centimeters, like this. (Demonstrate.) Now, it's your turn.

S: (Draw two parallel lines, each 8 cm in length.)

T: Use these parallel lines to make another quadrilateral by joining the ends of the parallel sides.

S: (Use a ruler to join the ends of both lines, forming a parallelogram, as shown to the right.)

T: What do you notice about the connecting sides?

S: They are also parallel.

T: How can you be sure?

S: They look like they won't touch if they keep going. → I can put my ruler down that way and see that the other line runs along it without getting any closer.

T: Since this quadrilateral has two pairs of parallel sides (point to the parallel sides), we call it a **parallelogram**. What's it called?

S: A parallelogram!

> **NOTES ON MULTIPLE MEANS OF ENGAGEMENT:**
>
> Some students might have difficulty drawing the different shapes. Support their learning by providing them with a template for their personal white boards that has some of the lines already drawn so that all they have to do is extend their drawings to connect the sides. This is especially useful for creating the trapezoid. Students may also be offered the use of a geoboard.

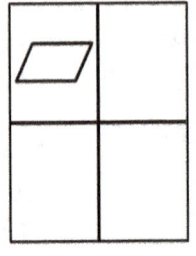

Lesson 4: Use attributes to identify and draw different quadrilaterals including rectangles, rhombuses, parallelograms, and trapezoids.

Part 4: Drawing and Identifying a Rectangle and Square and Relating the Rhombus to a Square

T: Now, let's draw another quadrilateral. In another section on your paper you are going to draw two congruent lines. Congruent means they are exactly the same. If these two lines are congruent, and one line is 8 cm long how long will the second line be?

S: 8 cm long.

T: Use both sides of your ruler to draw 2 congruent lines. They should be parallel lines that are 8 cm long. This time, start both lines at zero on your ruler.

S: (Measure and draw two parallel lines, each beginning at zero and extending 8 cm in length.)

T: Complete the quadrilateral by drawing two more lines.

S: (Use a ruler to join the ends of both lines, forming a rectangle, as shown to the right.)

T: Turn and talk: What do you notice about the angles of this special quadrilateral?

S: They make square angles!

T: You already know this shape. What is it?

S: A rectangle!

T: Yes! A quadrilateral with four square angles is a rectangle.

T: There is a special rectangle, too. It is special because it has four square angles and four sides that are the same length. What do you think it is?

S: A square!

T: Watch as I draw a square. (Draw a square on the board.)

T: Let's double-check to see if it is a rectangle. Student B, use your index card to check the angles to see if they are all square angles.

S: (Student B checks angles.) Yes! They are all square angles.

T: Good. Finally, let's check to see if the sides are all the same length. Student C, use your ruler to measure each side of the square.

S: (Student C measures sides.) All the sides are 10 cm! It is a angles.

T: Just like a square, there is another quadrilateral that has four equal sides. It looks like this. (Draw a rhombus on the board.)

T: What do you notice?

S: It looks like a square leaning over. → I don't think it has square angles. → I think the sides are all equal, like a square. → I see that both pairs of opposite sides are parallel.

T: Yes! We call a quadrilateral with four equal sides a **rhombus**. It does have equal sides like a square, but it doesn't have to have square angles.

T: You've really flexed your geometry muscles today! On to the Problem Set!

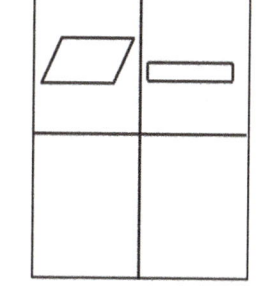

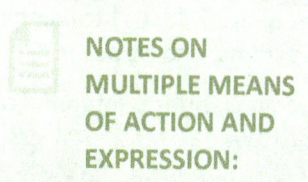

> **NOTES ON MULTIPLE MEANS OF ACTION AND EXPRESSION:**
>
> Help English language learners practice using the new geometric vocabulary. Make a game of it. Show students the shape, and ask them to say its name, or ask them to match shapes with their names and say the names as they do.

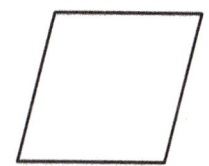

Lesson 4: Use attributes to identify and draw different quadrilaterals including rectangles, rhombuses, parallelograms, and trapezoids.

Problem Set (10 minutes)

Students should do their personal best to complete the Problem Set within the allotted 10 minutes. For some classes, it may be appropriate to modify the assignment by specifying which problems they work on first. Some problems do not specify a method for solving. Students should solve these problems using the RDW approach used for Application Problems.

Note: It is possible that there will not be enough time today for the Problem Set. If just a few minutes remain, consider having students instead draw different quadrilaterals with the attributes of parallel lines and square corners, and see if they can identify which names apply to their shapes.

Student Debrief (10 minutes)

Lesson Objective: Use attributes to identify and draw different quadrilaterals including rectangles, rhombuses, parallelograms, and trapezoids.

The Student Debrief is intended to invite reflection and active processing of the total lesson experience.

Invite students to review their solutions for the Problem Set. They should check work by comparing answers with a partner. Look for misconceptions or mis understandings that can be addressed in the Debrief. Guide students in a conversation to debrief the Problem Set and process the lesson.

Any combination of the questions below may be used to lead the discussion.

- Turn and talk: What do you know about **parallel** lines? Where do you see some in our classroom?
- Can a shape have different names? Tell your partner other names that a quadrilateral can be called.
- Use your fingers to show your partner a **square corner**. Use your fingers to show your partner an angle that is not square.

- What did all the shapes we talked about today have in common? (They all were quadrilaterals, or four-sided polygons, with four sides and four angles.)
- Use some of the new vocabulary words you learned today to describe to your partner the attributes of a rectangle. A trapezoid. A **parallelogram**. A square. A rhombus.
- What makes a square a special rectangle? Explain how you know.

Exit Ticket (3 minutes)

After the Student Debrief, instruct students to complete the Exit Ticket. A review of their work will help with assessing students' understanding of the concepts that were presented in today's lesson and planning more effectively for future lessons. The questions may be read aloud to the students.

Name _____   Date _____

1. Use your ruler to draw 2 parallel lines that are not the same length.

2. Use your ruler to draw 2 parallel lines that are the same length.

3. Trace the parallel lines on each quadrilateral using a crayon. For each shape with two sets of parallel lines, use two different colors. Use your index card to find each square angle, and box it.

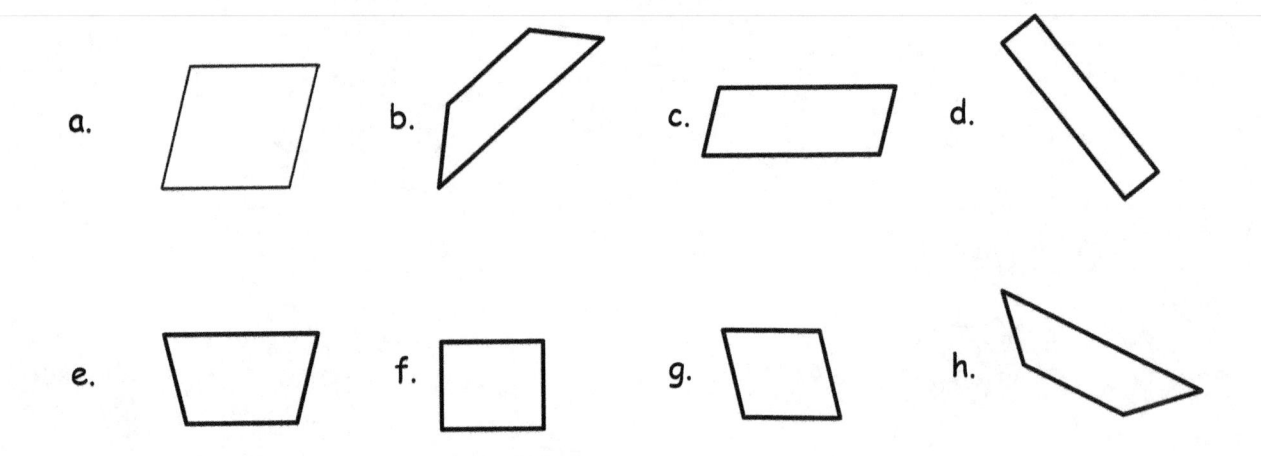

a.   b.   c.   d.

e.   f.   g.   h.

4. Draw a parallelogram with no square angles.

5. Draw a quadrilateral with 4 square angles.

6. Measure and label the sides of the figure to the right with your centimeter ruler. What do you notice? Be ready to talk about the attributes of this quadrilateral. Can you remember what this polygon is called?

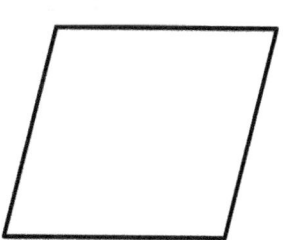

7. A square is a special rectangle. What makes it special?

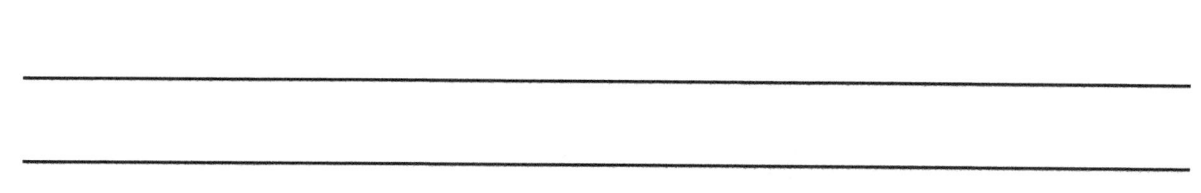

_____

_____

A STORY OF UNITS – TEKS EDITION   Lesson 4 Exit Ticket   2•8

Name _____   Date _____

Use crayons to trace the parallel sides on each quadrilateral. Use your index card to find each square angle, and box it.

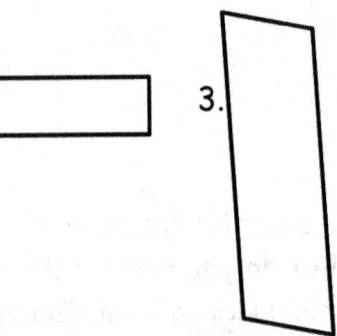

1.   2.   3.   4.

Name _____   Date _____

1. Use your ruler to draw 2 parallel lines that are not the same length.

2. Use your ruler to draw 2 parallel lines that are the same length.

3. Draw a quadrilateral with two sets of parallel sides. What is the name of this quadrilateral?

4. Draw a quadrilateral with 4 square angles and opposite sides the same length. What is the name of this quadrilateral?

5. A square is a special rectangle. What makes it special?

   _____

   _____

6. Color each quadrilateral with 4 square angles and two sets of parallel sides red.
   Color each quadrilateral with no square angles and no parallel sides blue.
   Color each quadrilateral with exactly one set of parallel sides green.

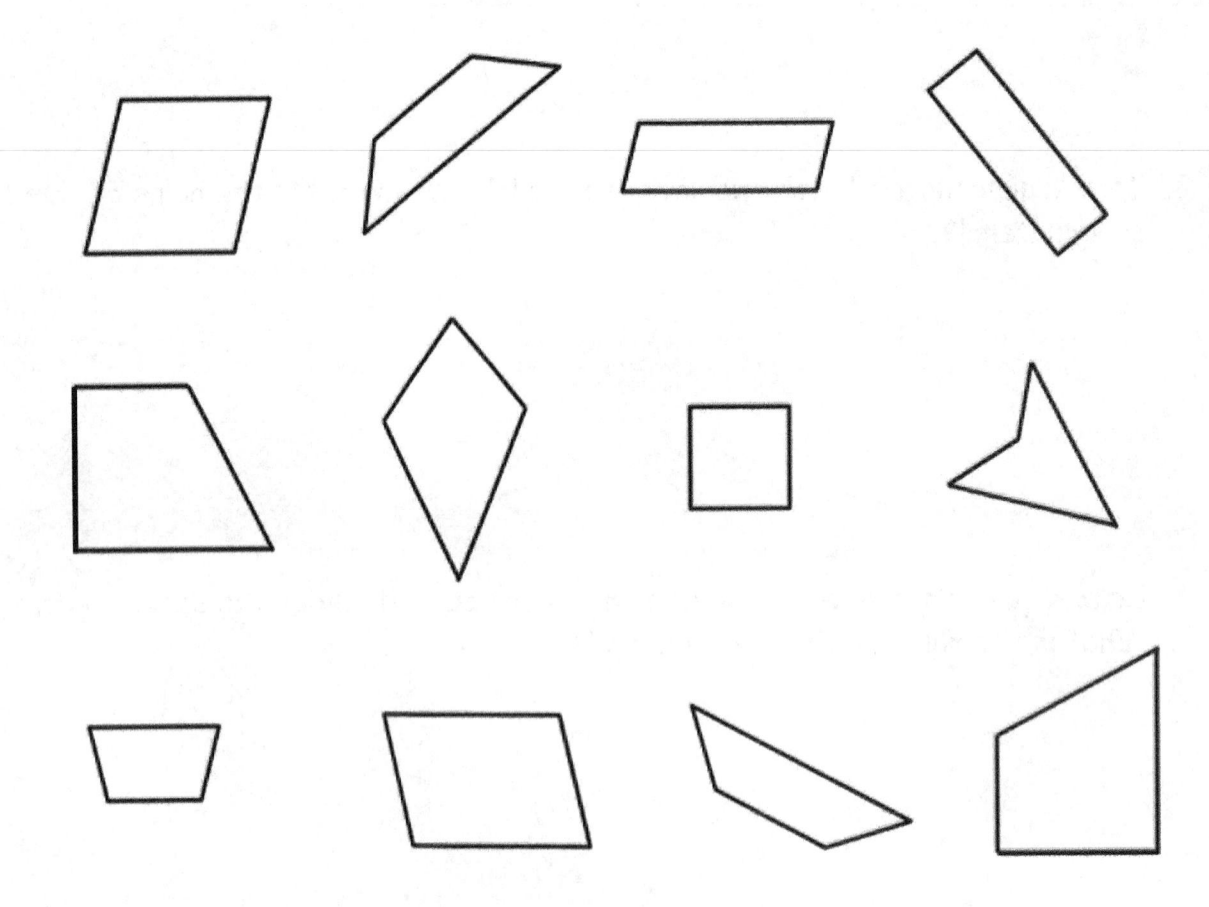

Hundreds	Tens	Ones

Workspace:

hundreds place value chart

Copy onto heavy tag board and cut.

centimeter rulers

Lesson 5

Objective: Classify and sort three-dimensional figures according to their attributes.

Suggested Lesson Structure

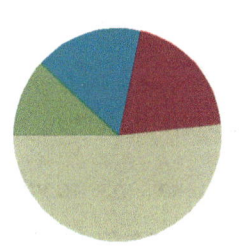

- Fluency Practice   (12 minutes)
- Application Problem   (7 minutes)
- Concept Development   (31 minutes)
- Student Debrief   (10 minutes)
- **Total Time**   **(60 minutes)**

Fluency Practice (12 minutes)

- Rename for the Smaller Unit **2.2A**   (3 minutes)
- Sprint: Subtraction Patterns **2.4A, 2.4B** (9 minutes)

Rename for the Smaller Unit (3 minutes)

Note: This fluency activity reviews using place value understanding to rename units in preparation for subtraction with chips and the algorithm during Fluency Practice in Lessons 7 and 8.

- T: (Write 1 hundred = ____ tens.)
- T: I'm going to give you a number in unit form. I want you to rename 1 of the hundreds for 10 tens and then tell me how many hundreds, tens, or ones. Ready?
- T: Say the number sentence.
- S: 1 hundred = 10 tens.
- T: (Write 1 hundred 1 ten = ____ tens.) Say the number sentence.
- S: 1 hundred 1 ten = 11 tens.
- T: (Write 2 hundreds = 1 hundred ____ tens.) Say the number sentence.
- S: 2 hundreds = 1 hundred 10 tens.
- T: (Write 2 hundreds 1 ten = 1 hundred ____ tens.) Say the number sentence.
- S: 2 hundreds 1 ten = 1 hundred 11 tens.
- T: (Write 2 hundreds = 1 hundred 9 tens ____ ones.) Say the number sentence.
- S: 2 hundreds = 1 hundred 9 tens 10 ones.

Continue with the following possible sequence: 1 hundred 3 tens, 2 hundreds 3 tens, 3 hundreds 4 tens, and 5 hundreds 7 tens.

A STORY OF UNITS – TEKS EDITION   Lesson 5   2•8

Sprint: Subtraction Patterns (9 minutes)

Materials: (S) Subtraction Patterns Sprint

Note: Students practice subtraction in order to gain mastery of the sums and differences within 20 and identify relationships with higher numbers.

Application Problem (7 minutes)

Materials: (S) Set of geometric solids (cone, cube, cylinder, rectangular prism, sphere, and triangular prism) or a constructed set of solids from the lesson templates

a. Sort the solids into three groups that make sense to you.

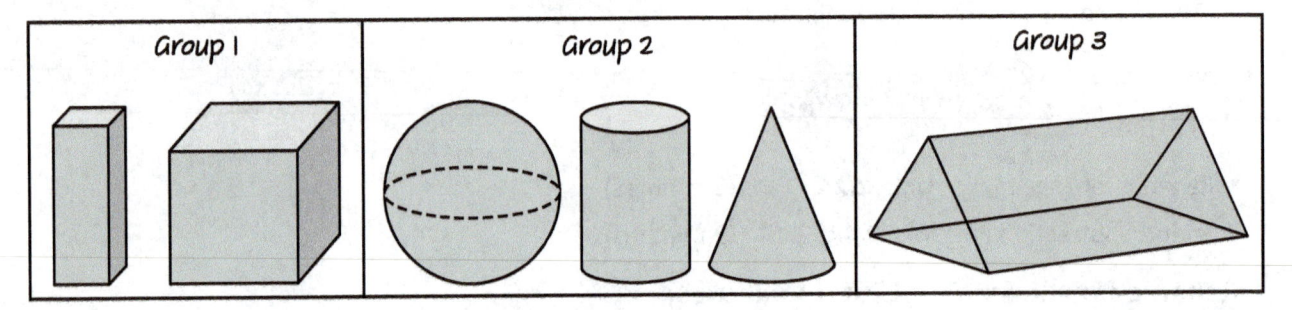

Group 1	Group 2	Group 3
(rectangular prism, cube)	(sphere, cylinder, cone)	(triangular prism)

Student answers will vary.

b. Describe how your solids are sorted.

Group 1	Group 2	Group 3
same number of sides each side looks like a quadrilateral	can be rolled reminds me of circles	made with triangles

Student answers will vary.

Note: This application problem introduces students to the characteristics of solid figures in an open-ended format. Have students share their work, but there should be little discussion. This is an opportunity to determine what students recall about the solids and formatively assess the vocabulary students use. The problem builds on the knowledge of the attributes of plane figures from previous lessons, bridging to this lesson's objective of identifying, describing, comparing, and contrasting solid figures according to their attributes. Commercial solids are encouraged for the lesson, but templates are provided if actual geometric solids are not available.

Lesson 5:   Classify and sort three-dimensional figures according to their attributes.

Concept Development (31 minutes)

Materials: (S) Set of geometric solids (cone, cube, cylinder, rectangular prism, sphere, and triangular prism) or a constructed set of solids from the Lesson Templates

Problem 1: Define attributes of solid figures.

T: You sorted some shapes in our Application Problem. How are these shapes different from the shapes we've been working with in previous lessons? Turn and talk to your partner.

S: They are 3-D shapes. → They are still made from plane shapes like circles and rectangles, but they aren't flat.

T: Find the cube. What do you know about a cube?

S: All of the sides are squares. → There are 6 sides. → All of the sides are the same size. → A cube has 6 faces.

T: Put your hand on one of the cube's sides. When we talk about geometric solids, any flat surface is called a face. How many faces does this cube have?

S: 6.

T: How are the faces the same?

S: They are the same size and shape.

T: What is a word we can use to describe shapes that are the same?

S: Congruent!

T: Find another solid in our collection that has 6 faces. What is it called?

S: Rectangular prism.

T: Compare the cube with the rectangular prism. How are they alike? How are they different?

S: The faces on both are all rectangles. The cube just has special rectangles called squares. → They both have 6 faces. → The rectangular prism has 4 rectangles and 2 squares, but the cube has 6 squares.

T: What else can you tell about the faces?

S: The square faces are congruent and the rectangular faces are congruent.

T: Find a solid that has only 2 faces. Explain your thinking.

S: (Find the cylinder.) This has 2 flat surfaces and a round part.

T: What can we say about the faces/bases of a cylinder?

S: They are congruent.

T: Tell your partner the name of this solid. Then tell your partner where you might have seen this solid outside of our classroom. Turn and talk.

T: Find a solid in the collection that has no faces. Remind me what it is called.

S: Sphere.

T: Why do we say a sphere has no faces?

S: A sphere has a round shape and no flat parts. → A face has to be a flat surface. A sphere has a curved surface.

Lesson 5: Classify and sort three-dimensional figures according to their attributes.

T: Work with your partner to find a solid that has only 1 face. Explain your thinking.

S: (Find the cone.) This only has 1 face because it's round like the sphere. → It only has one flat surface so it only has one face.

T: What is the name of this geometric solid?. Where might we see this solid in the real world?

S: This solid is a cone. Ice cream can be served in cones. → Party hats look like cones. → Sometimes they use things that look like cones to mark roadwork, like traffic cones. → Some animal horns look like cones. → Snowcones are served in cone-shaped paper cups.

S: This is a cylinder. → I've seen cylinders at the grocery store. Cans of soup are cylinders. → Tennis balls come in containers that are cylinders.

T: Now look for another solid that has an odd number of faces.

S: (Find the triangular prism.)

T: How is this solid similar to and different from other solids in our collection? Turn and talk.

S: → It's like a cube because it has some rectangular faces, but it only has 3 and a cube has 6. → It's the only solid we have that has some triangles for faces. → It also has a some rectangular faces, like a rectangular prism.

T: Tell the name of this three dimensional solid.

S This is a triangular prism.

T: Place your hands on 2 faces of the cube that touch each other. (Demonstrate as necessary.) Notice where your hands meet.

T: What do we call the line segment where 2 flat faces of a three dimensional shape meet?

S: An edge.

T: How many edges does a cube have?

S: 12 edges.

T: What other solid in our collection has the same number of edges as a cube? Work with your partner to count its edges to verify your thinking.

S: (Count.) The rectangular prism has the same number of edges as a cube.

T: How many edges does a cone have? How about a cylinder? Turn and talk.

S: I see that the round part meets the face that is a circle on the cone, but we said a cone only has 1 face. I don't think this can be an edge because 2 flat faces don't meet here. → The cylinder has 2 faces, but they don't touch each other. I don't think cylinders have any edges.

T: You're showing some great thinking. Because cones and cylinders don't have flat faces that touch other flat faces, we say that neither cones nor cylinders have edges.

T: (Point to a vertex on a cube.) What is the name for the point where straight edges meet?

S: A vertex.

T: When we talk about geometric solids, we call the place where 3 or more line segments meet a **vertex**. When we speak about more than one vertex, we say *vertices*. Work together to find all the places on the cube where there are vertices. How many vertices does a cube have?

S: 8.

T: Pick up another solid and count the number of vertices.

Lesson 5: Classify and sort three-dimensional figures according to their attributes.

S: (Count.)

T: How many vertices does a cylinder have? How about a cone? Turn and talk.

S: A cylinder doesn't have any line segments that meet up anywhere. So a cylinder has no vertices. → A cone has lots of line segments that go from the face and meet up at the pointy part, so a cone has 1 vertex.

Problem 2: Compare and contrast solid figures by their attributes.

T: Compare a cylinder with a cone. Turn and talk about how they are alike and how they are different. Be sure to use the words *face*, *edge*, and *vertex* in your conversation.

T: How are the rectangular prism, triangular prism, and cube alike?

S: All these solids have two congruent bases that are across from each other and flat sides. → This is a triangular prism. Its bases are congruent triangles. → All the prisms have rectangles for the other faces. → A cube is a prism too. It has congruent bases and rectangles for its other faces.

T: Yes, these shapes are all prisms because prisms have two congruent bases that are opposite one another and flat faces that are quadrilaterals. I notice that a cylinder has two congruent bases as well. Should a cylinder also be classified as a prism? Why or why not?

S: No. A cylinder is not a prism. It does not have quadrilaterals as faces.

Continue the sequence by having students compare the following: cone, cylinder and sphere rectangular prism and cylinder.

Ask students to sort the solids again, using *edge*, *face*, and *vertex* as part of their sorting categories.

> **NOTES ON MULTIPLE MEANS OF ACTION AND EXPRESSION:**
>
> The current lesson allows many opportunities for English language learners to practice spoken language as they interact with a partner.
>
> The use of the physical solids also allows for full participation by these students as they can gesture using the shapes to make their meaning clear.

Problem Set (10 minutes)

Students should do their personal best to complete the Problem Set within the allotted 10 minutes. Be sure to provide each student or group of students with a sphere or spherical item in order for them to complete the Problem Set. Students may struggle when describing the attributes of the cone and sphere. Let them struggle, and address their questions or misconceptions during the Student Debrief.

Name_____ Date_____

1. Use your geometric solids to complete the table.

Solid Figure	Number of Faces	Shape of Faces	Number of Edges	Number of Vertices
Cube	6	square	12	8
Rectangular Prism	6	rectangles	12	8
Triangular prism	5	rectangle/ triangle	9	6
Cone	1	circle	0	1
Cylinder	2	circle	0	0
Sphere	0	n/a	0	0

Student Debrief (10 minutes)

Lesson Objective: Classify and sort three-dimensional figures according to their attributes.

The Student Debrief is intended to invite reflection and active processing of the total lesson experience.

Invite students to review their solutions for the Problem Set. They should check work by comparing answers with a partner. Look for misconceptions or misunderstandings that can be addressed in the Student Debrief. Guide students in a conversation to debrief the Problem Set and process the lesson.

Any combination of the questions below may be used to lead the discussion.

- How are a rectangular prism and a cube similar?
- Why doesn't a sphere have faces?
- Why do spheres, cones, and cylinders not have edges?
- How many parts of a solid must touch to form an edge? What are those parts called?
- How many parts of a solid must touch to form a vertex? What are those parts called?
- How did the Application Problem connect to today's lesson?

2. Sort the geometric solids into three groups using their names. Give each group a title that explains why you grouped the geometric solids together. Be sure to use the words *face*, *edge*, and *vertex*.

solids with vertices	solids with circle faces	solids with curved surfaces
cube	cone	cylinder
rectangular prism	cylinder	cone
triangular prism		sphere
cone		

3. Jim drew a cone and labeled it. Explain Jim's mistake.

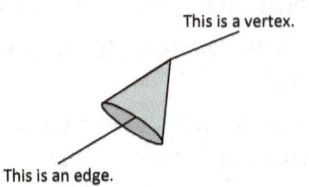

This is a vertex.
This is an edge.

A cone does not have an edge because an edge is where 2 faces meet and a cone only has 1 face.

Exit Ticket (3 minutes)

After the Student Debrief, instruct students to complete the Exit Ticket. A review of their work will help with assessing students' understanding of the concepts that were presented in today's lesson and planning more effectively for future lessons. The questions may be read aloud to the students.

A

Subtraction Patterns

Number Correct: _____

1.	8 - 1 =		23.	41 - 20 =	
2.	18 - 1 =		24.	46 - 20 =	
3.	8 - 2 =		25.	7 - 5 =	
4.	18 - 2 =		26.	70 - 50 =	
5.	8 - 5 =		27.	71 - 50 =	
6.	18 - 5 =		28.	78 - 50 =	
7.	28 - 5 =		29.	80 - 40 =	
8.	58 - 5 =		30.	84 - 40 =	
9.	58 - 7 =		31.	90 - 60 =	
10.	10 - 2 =		32.	97 - 60 =	
11.	11 - 2 =		33.	70 - 40 =	
12.	21 - 2 =		34.	72 - 40 =	
13.	61 - 2 =		35.	56 - 4 =	
14.	61 - 3 =		36.	52 - 4 =	
15.	61 - 5 =		37.	50 - 4 =	
16.	10 - 5 =		38.	60 - 30 =	
17.	20 - 5 =		39.	90 - 70 =	
18.	30 - 5 =		40.	80 - 60 =	
19.	70 - 5 =		41.	96 - 40 =	
20.	72 - 5 =		42.	63 - 40 =	
21.	4 - 2 =		43.	79 - 30 =	
22.	40 - 20 =		44.	76 - 9 =	

Lesson 5: Classify and sort three-dimensional figures according to their attributes.

B

Subtraction Patterns

Number Correct: _____

Improvement: _____

1.	7 - 1 =	
2.	17 - 1 =	
3.	7 - 2 =	
4.	17 - 2 =	
5.	7 - 5 =	
6.	17 - 5 =	
7.	27 - 5 =	
8.	57 - 5 =	
9.	57 - 6 =	
10.	10 - 5 =	
11.	11 - 5 =	
12.	21 - 5 =	
13.	61 - 5 =	
14.	61 - 4 =	
15.	61 - 2 =	
16.	10 - 2 =	
17.	20 - 2 =	
18.	30 - 2 =	
19.	70 - 2 =	
20.	71 - 2 =	
21.	5 - 2 =	
22.	50 - 20 =	

23.	51 - 20 =	
24.	56 - 20 =	
25.	8 - 5 =	
26.	80 - 50 =	
27.	81 - 50 =	
28.	87 - 50 =	
29.	60 - 30 =	
30.	64 - 30 =	
31.	80 - 60 =	
32.	85 - 60 =	
33.	70 - 30 =	
34.	72 - 30 =	
35.	76 - 4 =	
36.	72 - 4 =	
37.	70 - 4 =	
38.	80 - 40 =	
39.	90 - 60 =	
40.	60 - 40 =	
41.	93 - 40 =	
42.	67 - 40 =	
43.	78 - 30 =	
44.	56 - 9 =	

Lesson 5: Classify and sort three-dimensional figures according to their attributes.

Name _____   Date _____

1. Use your geometric solids to complete the table.

Solid Figure	Number of Faces	Shape of Faces	Number of Edges	Number of Vertices
Cube				
Rectangular Prism				
Triangular Prism				
Cone				
Cylinder				
Sphere				

2. Sort the geometric solids into three groups using their names. Give each group a title that explains why you grouped the geometric solids together. Be sure to use the words *face*, *edge*, and *vertex*.

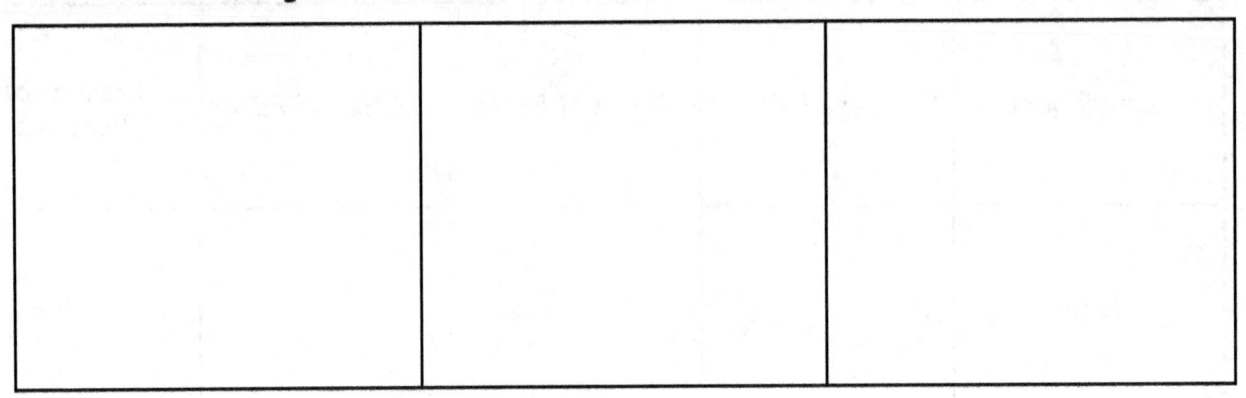

3. Jim drew a cone and labeled it. Explain Jim's mistake.

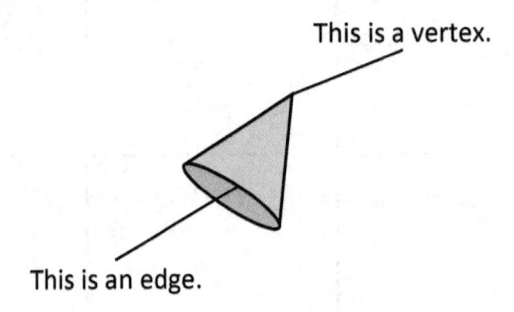

This is a vertex.

This is an edge.

Name _____   Date _____

1. Fill in the blanks to label the characteristics of the rectangular prism.

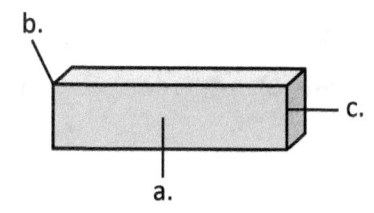

   a. _____

   b. _____

   c. _____

2. Explain why a cylinder is not a prism.

Name _____ Date _____

Use the clues to identify each of the solid figures described.

1. I have 2 circular faces that are the same size. They are joined by a curved surface. I do not have any edges or vertices. I can roll. What am I?

2. I am perfectly round. I do not have any faces or edges. What am I?

3. I have 5 faces total. Three of my faces are rectangles. My other two faces are triangles. What am I?

4. I have 6 square faces, 12 edges, and 8 vertices. All of my edges are the same length. What am I?

5. I have 1 face that is a circle and 1 curved surface. I have no edges and 1 vertex. What am I?

6. Hal says that a cylinder is a prism because it has two congruent bases that are opposite each other. Explain why Hal is incorrect.

Cube

Cut out the net below. Fold along the dotted lines. Use the tabs to glue or tape the solid together.

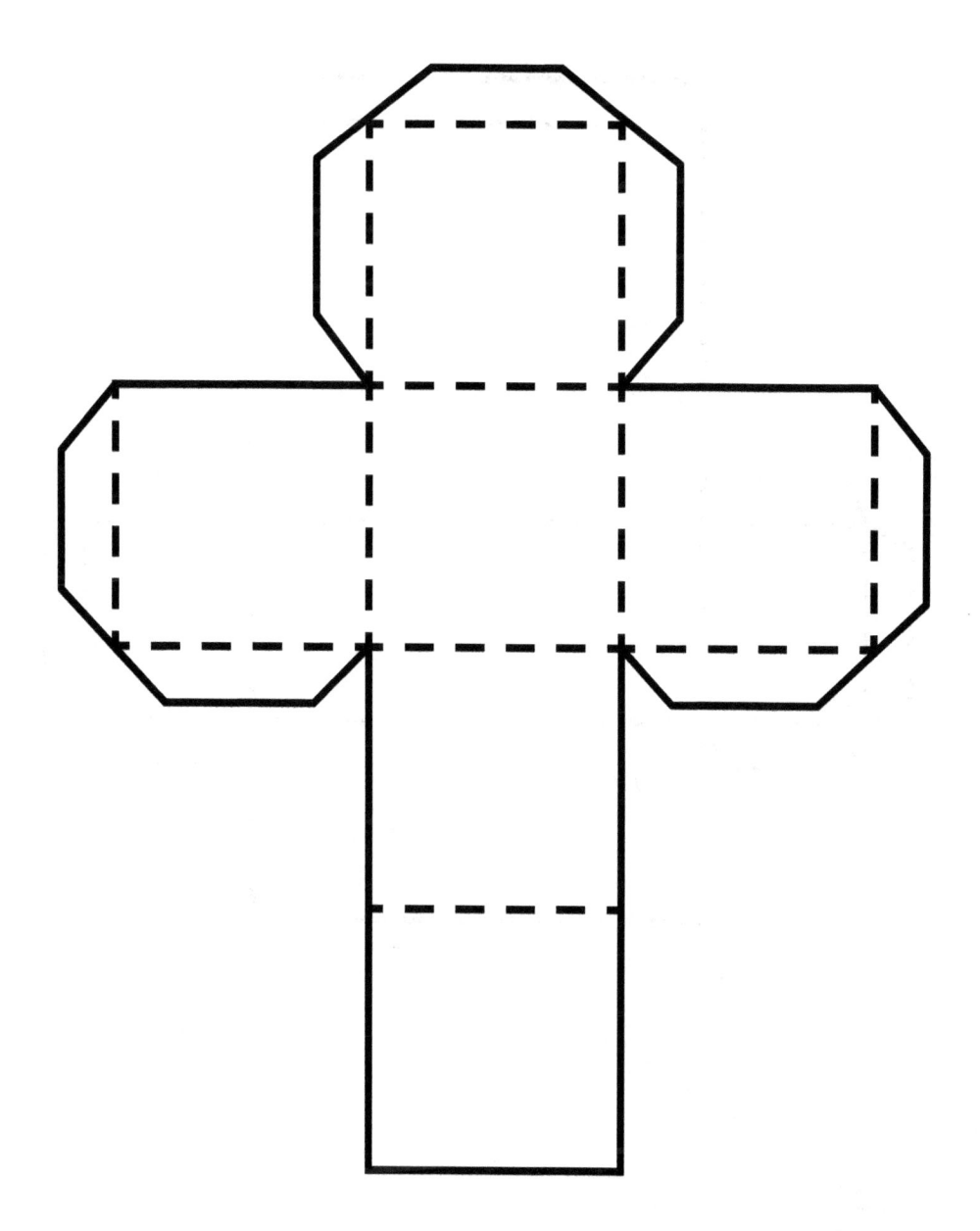

A STORY OF UNITS – TEKS EDITION

Lesson 5 Template 2   2•8

Rectangular Prism

Cut out the net below. Fold along the dotted lines. Use the tabs to glue or tape the solid together.

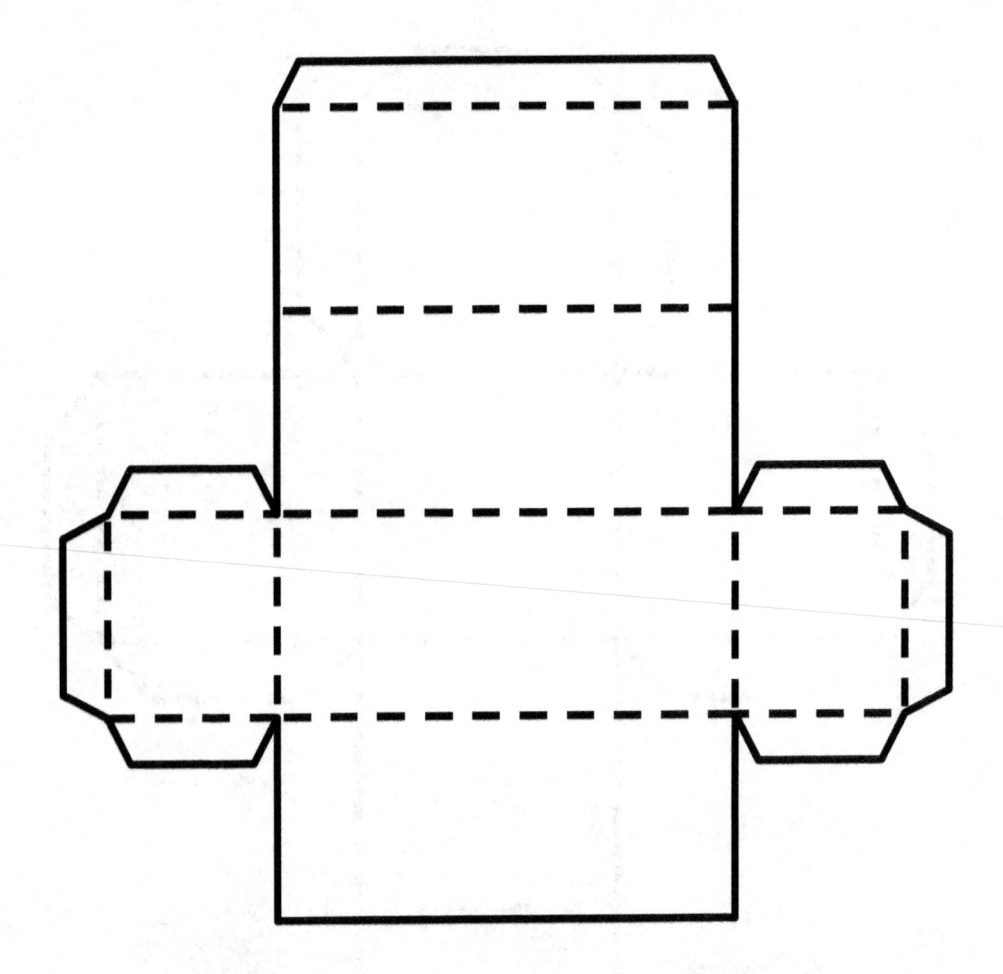

Triangular Prism

Cut out the net below. Fold along the dotted lines. Use the tabs to glue or tape the solid together.

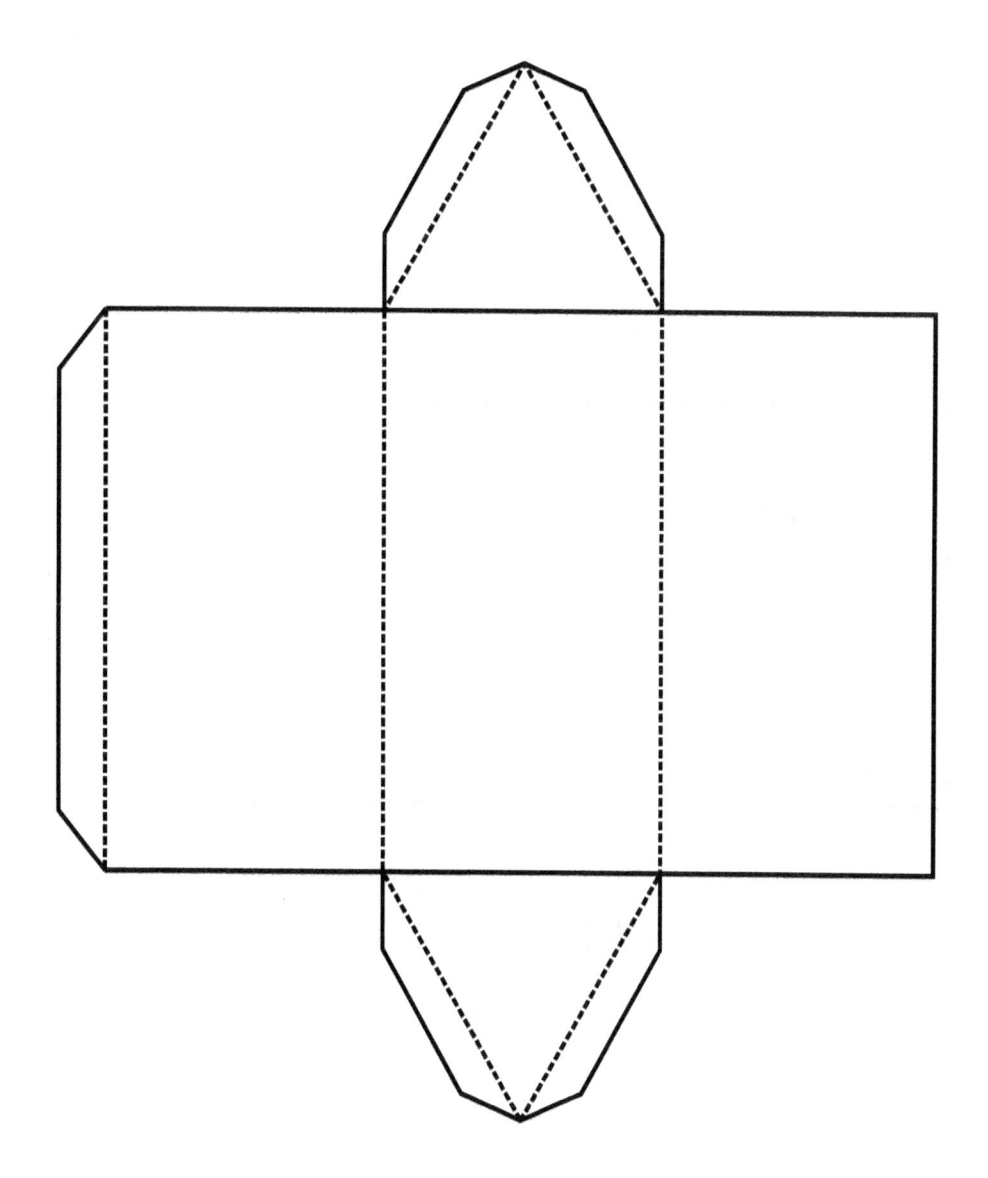

Cylinder

Cut out the net below. Fold along the dotted lines. Use the tabs to glue or tape the solid together.

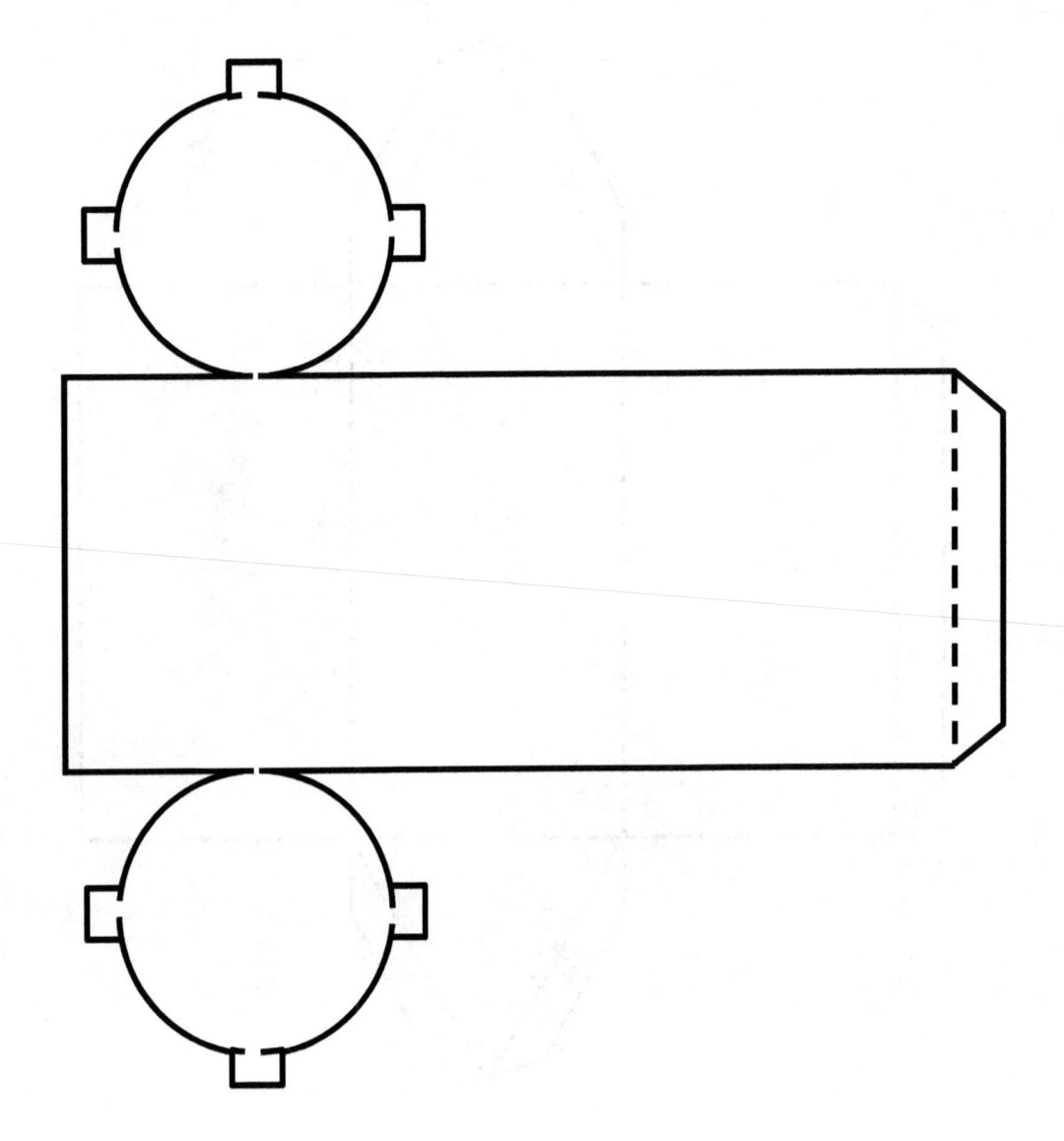

Cone

Cut out the net below. Fold along the dotted lines. Use the tabs to glue or tape the solid together.

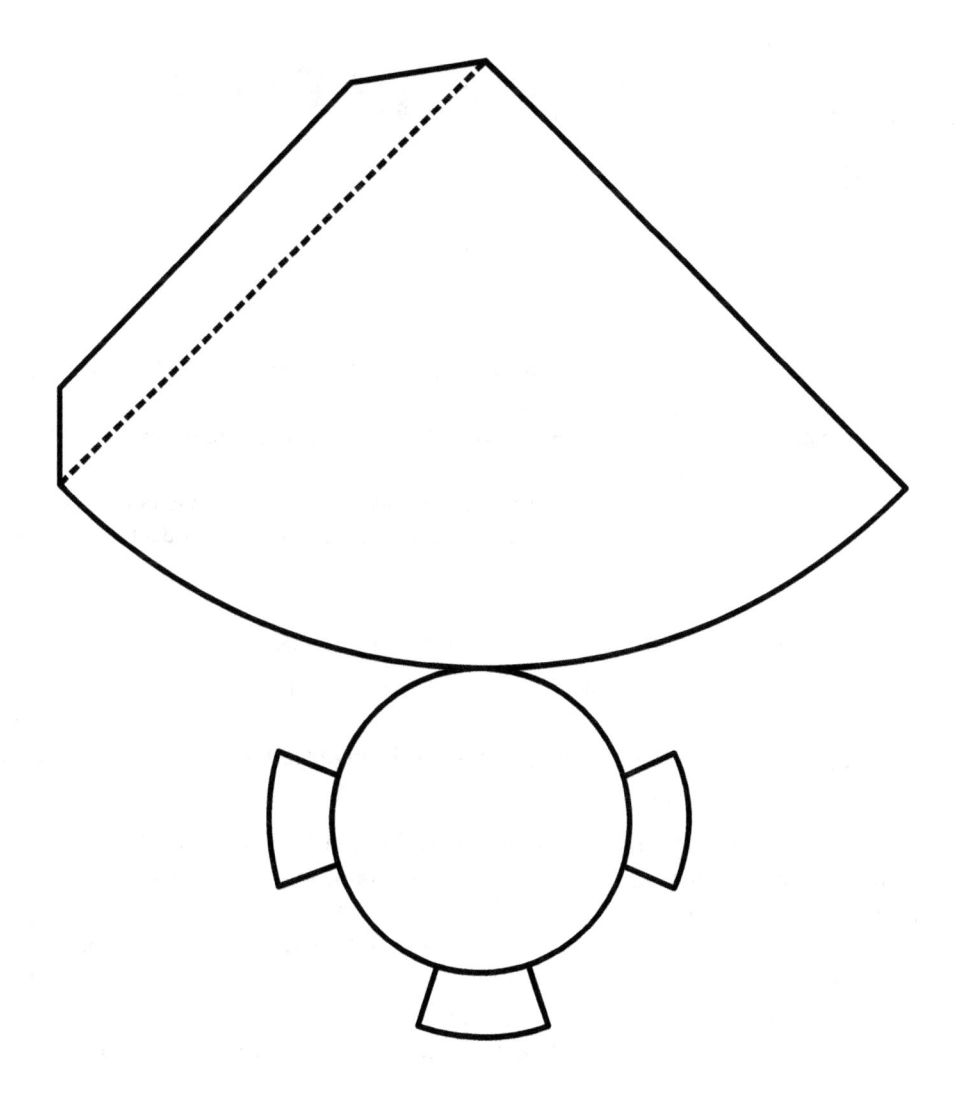

Lesson 5: Classify and sort three-dimensional figures according to their attributes.

A STORY OF UNITS — TEKS EDITION

Mathematics Curriculum

GRADE 2 • MODULE 8

Topic B
Composite Shapes and Fraction Concepts

2.3A, 2.8D, 2.8E, 2.3C, 2.3D, 2.8A, 2.8C

Focus Standards:	2.3A	Partition objects into equal parts and name the parts, including halves, fourths, and eighths, using words.
	2.8D	Compose two-dimensional shapes and three-dimensional solids with given properties or attributes.
	2.8E	Decompose two-dimensional shapes such as cutting out a square from a rectangle, dividing a shape in half, or partitioning a rectangle into identical triangles and identify the resulting geometric parts.
Instructional Days:	3	
Coherence -Links from:	G1–M5	Identifying, Composing, and Partitioning Shapes
-Links to:	G3–M7	Geometry and Measurement Word Problems

In Topic B, students build and partition composite shapes, exploring fraction concepts as they identify the relationships between parts and wholes.

Students see in Lesson 6 that the tangram puzzle (shown on the right) is composed of many smaller two-dimensional shapes. As students cut out the various shapes within the tangram, they name them. They explore the variety of ways they can compose new shapes by repositioning the pieces. For example, students see that a larger triangle can be composed of two right triangles and a square, which can also be repositioned to form a trapezoid, parallelogram, or rectangle (as shown below). Further, students see that the composite triangle pictured below can be placed next to another triangle to form a larger square.

A STORY OF UNITS – TEKS EDITION

Topic B 2•8

In Lesson 7, students interpret equal shares within composite shapes. They begin by using the tangram pieces from the previous day to show how the two smallest triangles can be positioned to form a larger triangle, parallelogram, or square (as shown on the right). Each of these composite shapes is composed of two equal shares, described as halves. By the end of Lesson 7, students experiment with pattern blocks to see, for example, how three triangle blocks can be combined to form a trapezoid.

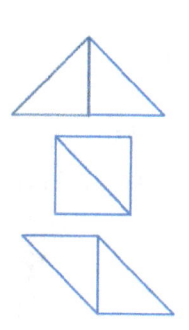

Thus, the trapezoid can be partitioned into three equal shares, with each share described as a third of the whole, as shown below.

In Lesson 8, students continue to use pattern blocks to build composite shapes from equal parts. For example, they see that a regular hexagon can be composed from two trapezoids, representing two equal shares, or halves. Alternatively, the hexagon can also be composed of three rhombuses (as shown below), described as thirds, or six same-size equilateral triangles. Students also use four square-inch tiles to compose a larger square and describe each part as a fourth. The Texas Essential Knowledge and Skills require students to explore halves, fourths, and eighths (**2.3A, 2.3D**). In addition to exploring halves and fourths, the lessons in this topic also explore thirds and sixths using pattern blocks. Pattern blocks are an excellent first manipulative for exploring equal parts, and they clearly show thirds and sixths. These additional units (thirds and sixths) help solidify and extend the understanding of equal parts using examples and non-examples. The problems in these lessons that go beyond the requirements of the TEKS can be considered optional. However, they give an excellent foundation to a first exposure to fractional units. Thirds and sixths are not assessed.

A Teaching Sequence Toward Mastery of Composite Shapes and Fraction Concepts
Objective 1: Combine shapes to create a composite shape; create a new shape from composite shapes. (Lesson 6)
Objective 2: Interpret equal shares in composite shapes as halves, thirds, and fourths. (Lessons 7–8)

Topic B: Composite Shapes and Fraction Concepts

Lesson 6

Objective: Combine shapes to create a composite shape; create a new shape from composite shapes.

Suggested Lesson Structure

- **Fluency Practice** (12 minutes)
- **Application Problem** (5 minutes)
- **Concept Development** (33 minutes)
- **Student Debrief** (10 minutes)
- **Total Time** **(60 minutes)**

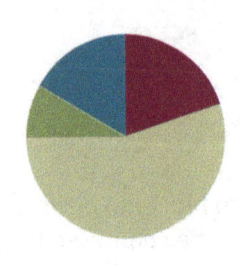

Fluency Practice (12 minutes)

- Rename for the Smaller Unit 2.2A   (3 minutes)
- Sprint: Addition and Subtraction Patterns 2.4A   (9 minutes)

Rename for the Smaller Unit (3 minutes)

Note: This fluency activity reviews place value foundations.

- T: (Write 101 = ____ tens ____ ones.)
- T: I'm going to give you a number in unit form. I want you to rename 1 of the hundreds as 10 tens and then tell me how many hundreds, tens, or ones. Ready?
- S: 10 tens 1 one.
- T: (Write 121 = ____ tens ____ one.) Say the number sentence.
- S: 121 = 12 tens 1 one.
- T: 203.
- S: 203 = 1 hundred 10 tens 3 ones.
- T: 213.
- S: 213 = 1 hundred 11 tens 3 ones.

Continue with the following possible sequence: 305, 315; 204, 224; 108, 158; and 908, 968.

Sprint: Addition and Subtraction Patterns (9 minutes)

Materials: (S) Addition and Subtraction Patterns Sprint

Note: Students practice adding and subtracting to gain mastery of the sums and differences within 20.

A STORY OF UNITS – TEKS EDITION   Lesson 6   2•8

Application Problem (5 minutes)

Frank has 19 fewer cubes than Josie. Frank has 56 cubes. They want to use all of their cubes to build a tower. How many cubes will they use?

Note: This is a two-step problem with a *compare with bigger unknown* type problem as one step. Encourage students to draw a strip diagram to help visualize the comparison.

$56 + 19 = 55 + 20 = 75$

$75 + 56 = 131$

They will use 131 cubes.

Concept Development (33 minutes)

Materials: (T) Tangram (Template), scissors, document camera (if available) (S) Tangram (Template), scissors, personal white board

Note: Students previously worked with tangrams in Grade 1 Module 5 Lesson 5. If time allows, refresh students' memory by reading *Grandfather Tang's Story* by Ann Tompert during story time.

Distribute the materials. (Students will also need the cut-out tangram pieces for the Problem Set, Homework, and Lesson 8.)

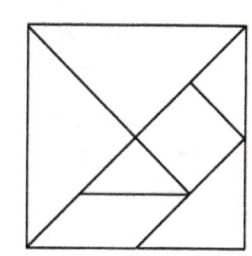

Part 1: Cutting the Tangram and Analyzing the Polygons

T: (Hold up the tangram.) Who remembers what this is called?
S: A tangram!
T: Let's describe the polygons as we cut them out.
T: First, cut out the large square. (Cut out a large square from the tangram as students do the same.)
T: (Hold up the tangram backward so students do not see the lines within.) As you cut, talk to your partner: What are the attributes, or characteristics, of a square?
S: A square has four straight sides and four square angles. → It's a special rectangle because its sides are all the same length. → It's a quadrilateral. → It has parallel sides.
T: Good descriptions! Watch how I fold my large square down the diagonal line that goes through the middle. (Fold the paper.) What polygon do you see in the top half?
S: A triangle!
T: As you cut out the triangle, tell your partner the attributes of a triangle.
S: A triangle has three straight sides. → It has three angles. → It has three vertices. This triangle has a square angle.

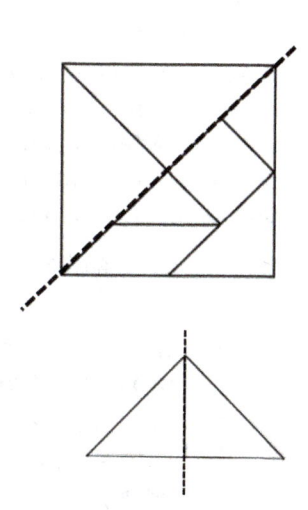

Lesson 6: Combine shapes to create a composite shape; create a new shape from composite shapes.

T: (Hold up the triangle.) How many triangles make up this **whole** triangle?
S: Two!
T: So we can make larger polygons out of smaller ones.
T: Cut apart the two smaller triangles, and set them aside. (Model as students do the same.) 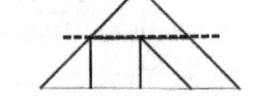
T: Look at the other half. (Hold up the other large triangle, pictured to the right.) What polygons do you see inside this triangle?
S: I see two smaller triangles and one bigger triangle. → There's a square. → There's a parallelogram.
T: Which of the shapes are quadrilaterals? Hold them up as you say their names.
S: The square. → The parallelogram.
T: Let's cut off the triangle on top and place that with the other two. (Model as students do the same.)
T: Now we have the large trapezoid. What are the attributes of this trapezoid?
S: It has four straight sides, but they're not all the same length. → This trapezoid has four angles, but they're not square angles. → It has exactly one pair of parallel sides which makes it a trapezoid.

Next, cut off the parallelogram and trace, touch, and count its sides and angles. Cut out the remaining square and two triangles.

T: How many polygons make up the tangram?
S: Seven!

> **NOTES ON MULTIPLE MEANS OF ENGAGEMENT:**
>
> Support English language learners' oral language production by providing sentence frames such as, "I see _____ parallelograms because I see a _____," to use in partner turn and talks.

Part 2: Creating Composite Shapes

Allow time for students to explore ways to create new shapes. They do not have to be shapes that students can name. Remind students that they can flip, slide, and turn the pieces to make the new shapes.

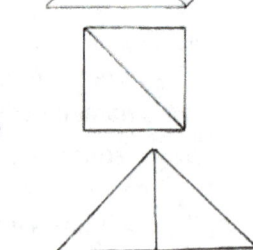

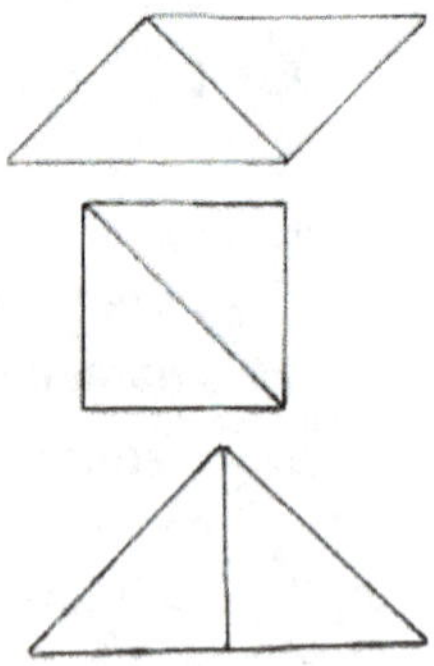

Next, direct student pairs to create three shapes, a triangle, a square, and a parallelogram with no square corners (as pictured to the right), using the two largest triangles. After creating the shapes, students should draw them on their personal white boards. Circulate to check for understanding, and encourage students to persevere, providing the least direction possible.

Have students gather their square and the two smallest triangles and move to the carpet.

T: Try this! Can you create a triangle out of a square and the two smallest triangles? (Allow students time to work.)
T: Now, combine the triangle you just made with your partner's to make a square. (Allow students time to work.)

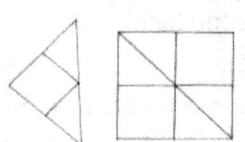

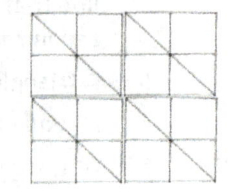

Lesson 6: Combine shapes to create a composite shape; create a new shape from composite shapes.

T: Is it possible for us to make a really big square with all of the squares you just made?

S: I think so. Let's try! → I don't think we have enough.

T: Let's try. (Allow time for students to make the attempt. The ability to make a square depends on the number of students in the class. If it is not possible to make a square, ask what shape could be made, and allow time to make a rectangle.)

Problem Set (10 minutes)

Students should do their personal best to complete the Problem Set within the allotted 10 minutes. For some classes, it may be appropriate to modify the assignment by specifying which problems they work on first. Some problems do not specify a method for solving. Students should solve these problems using the RDW approach used for Application Problems.

Note: Challenge early finishers to reassemble the tangram.

NOTES ON MULTIPLE MEANS OF ACTION AND EXPRESSION:

Challenge students working above grade level by asking them to reconstruct the original square using the seven tangram pieces. A further challenge would be for them to use all seven pieces to make one large rectangle.

Student Debrief (10 minutes)

Lesson Objective: Combine shapes to create a composite shape; create a new shape from composite shapes.

The Student Debrief is intended to invite reflection and active processing of the total lesson experience.

Invite students to review their solutions for the Problem Set. They should check work by comparing answers with a partner. Look for misconceptions or misunderstandings that can be addressed in the Debrief. Guide students in a conversation to debrief the Problem Set and process the lesson.

Any combination of the questions below may be used to lead the discussion.

- Share the polygons you made in Problem 5 with your partner. Describe the attributes of each polygon.
- Why do you think we used tangrams for this lesson?
- Can you think of any real-world objects that are made up of lots of smaller shapes? (Provide an example to get students started if needed: tile floor, window blinds, chain-link fence, interlocking building blocks, brick wall.)
- How is breaking big shapes into smaller shapes kind of like decomposing numbers? Pennies and dimes? Centimeters and meters?

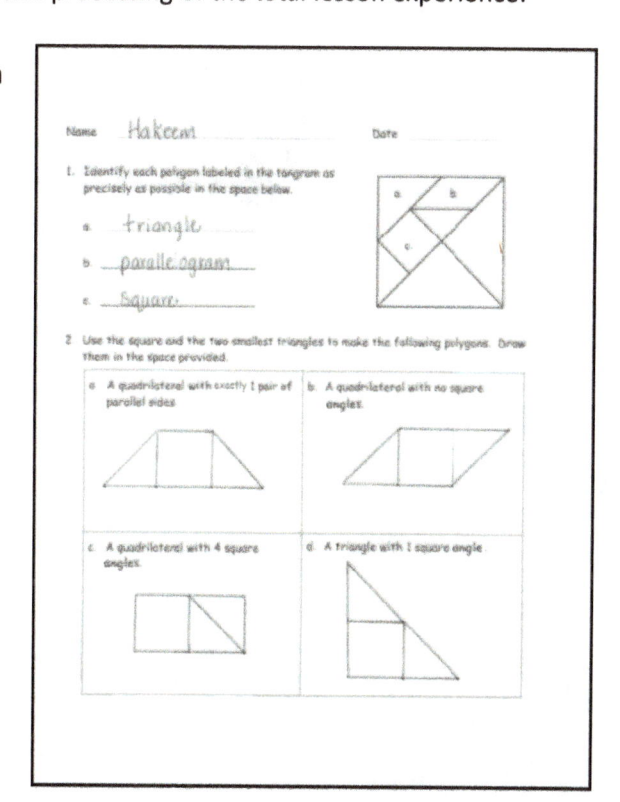

A STORY OF UNITS – TEKS EDITION Lesson 6 2•8

- Are all squares parallelograms? How can you prove that? Are all parallelograms squares?
- How is Frank and Josie's tower of cubes from the Application Problem similar to what we did today?

Exit Ticket (3 minutes)

After the Student Debrief, instruct students to complete the Exit Ticket. A review of their work will help with assessing students' understanding of the concepts that were presented in today's lesson and planning more effectively for future lessons. The questions may be read aloud to the students.

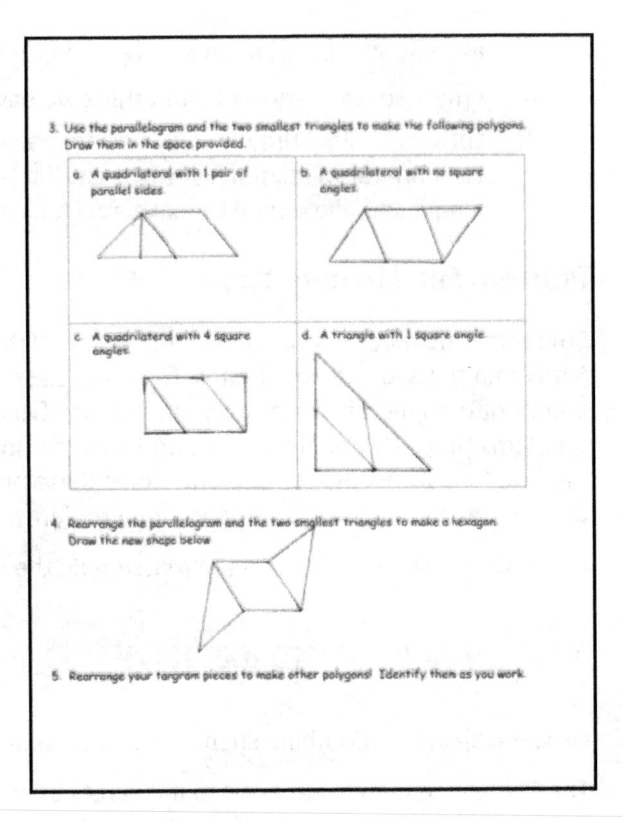

A

Addition and Subtraction Patterns

Number Correct: _____

1.	8 + 3 =		23.	8 + 8 =	
2.	11 - 3 =		24.	16 - 8 =	
3.	9 + 2 =		25.	9 + 6 =	
4.	11 - 2 =		26.	15 - 9 =	
5.	6 + 5 =		27.	9 + 9 =	
6.	11 - 6 =		28.	18 - 9 =	
7.	7 + 4 =		29.	7 + 7 =	
8.	11 - 7 =		30.	14 - 7 =	
9.	8 + 4 =		31.	8 + 9 =	
10.	12 - 4 =		32.	17 - 8 =	
11.	9 + 3 =		33.	7 + 9 =	
12.	12 - 3 =		34.	16 - 7 =	
13.	7 + 5 =		35.	19 - 6 =	
14.	12 - 7 =		36.	6 + 7 =	
15.	6 + 6 =		37.	17 - 6 =	
16.	12 - 6 =		38.	11 - 7 =	
17.	8 + 6 =		39.	7 + 6 =	
18.	14 - 8 =		40.	13 - 7 =	
19.	9 + 4 =		41.	19 - 7 =	
20.	13 - 9 =		42.	3 + 8 =	
21.	8 + 7 =		43.	5 + 8 =	
22.	15 - 8 =		44.	18 - 5 =	

Lesson 6: Combine shapes to create a composite shape; create a new shape from composite shapes.

B

Addition and Subtraction Patterns

Number Correct: _____

Improvement: _____

1.	9 + 2 =		23.	9 + 6 =	
2.	11 - 2 =		24.	15 - 9 =	
3.	8 + 3 =		25.	8 + 8 =	
4.	11 - 3 =		26.	16 - 8 =	
5.	7 + 4 =		27.	7 + 7 =	
6.	11 - 7 =		28.	14 - 7 =	
7.	6 + 5 =		29.	9 + 9 =	
8.	11 - 6 =		30.	18 - 9 =	
9.	9 + 3 =		31.	7 + 9 =	
10.	12 - 3 =		32.	16 - 9 =	
11.	8 + 4 =		33.	8 + 9 =	
12.	12 - 4 =		34.	17 - 9 =	
13.	7 + 5 =		35.	19 - 7 =	
14.	12 - 5 =		36.	5 + 8 =	
15.	6 + 6 =		37.	18 - 5 =	
16.	12 - 6 =		38.	13 - 8 =	
17.	9 + 4 =		39.	6 + 7 =	
18.	13 - 4 =		40.	13 - 6 =	
19.	8 + 6 =		41.	19 - 6 =	
20.	14 - 8 =		42.	3 + 9 =	
21.	7 + 8 =		43.	6 + 9 =	
22.	15 - 7 =		44.	18 - 6 =	

Name _____   Date _____

1. Identify each polygon labeled in the tangram as precisely as possible in the space below.

   a. _____

   b. _____

   c. _____

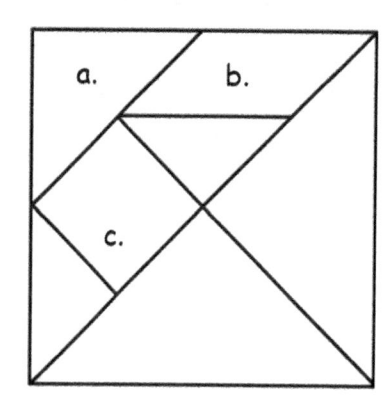

2. Use the square and the two smallest triangles of your tangram pieces to make the following polygons. Draw them in the space provided.

a. A quadrilateral with exactly 1 pair of parallel sides.	b. A quadrilateral with no square angles.
c. A quadrilateral with 4 square angles.	d. A triangle with 1 square angle.

3. Use the parallelogram and the two smallest triangles of your tangram pieces to make the following polygons. Draw them in the space provided.

a. A quadrilateral with 1 pair of parallel sides.	b. A quadrilateral with no square angles.
c. A quadrilateral with 4 square angles.	d. A triangle with 1 square angle.

4. Rearrange the parallelogram and the two smallest triangles to make a hexagon. Draw the new shape below.

5. Rearrange your tangram pieces to make other polygons! Identify them as you work.

A STORY OF UNITS – TEKS EDITION

Lesson 6 Exit Ticket 2•8

Name _____ Date _____

Use your tangram pieces to make two new polygons. Draw a picture of each new polygon, and name them.

1.

2.

Lesson 6: Combine shapes to create a composite shape; create a new shape from composite shapes.

A STORY OF UNITS – TEKS EDITION   Lesson 6 Homework 2•8

Name _____   Date _____

1. Identify each polygon labeled in the tangram as precisely as possible in the space below.

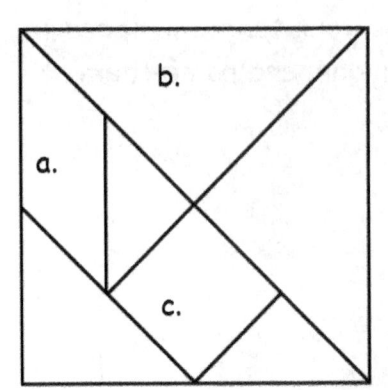

   a. _____

   b. _____

   c. _____

2. Use the square and the two smallest triangles of your tangram pieces to make the following polygons. Draw them in the space provided.

a. A triangle with 1 square angle.	b. A quadrilateral with 4 square angles.
c. A quadrilateral with no square angles.	d. A quadrilateral with exactly 1 pair of parallel sides.

Lesson 6: Combine shapes to create a composite shape; create a new shape from composite shapes.

A STORY OF UNITS – TEKS EDITION
Lesson 6 Homework 2•8

3. Rearrange the parallelogram and the two smallest triangles of your tangram pieces to make a hexagon. Draw the new shape below.

4. Rearrange your tangram pieces to make at least 6 other polygons! Draw and name them below.

Lesson 6: Combine shapes to create a composite shape; create a new shape from composite shapes.

Cut the tangram into 7 puzzle pieces.

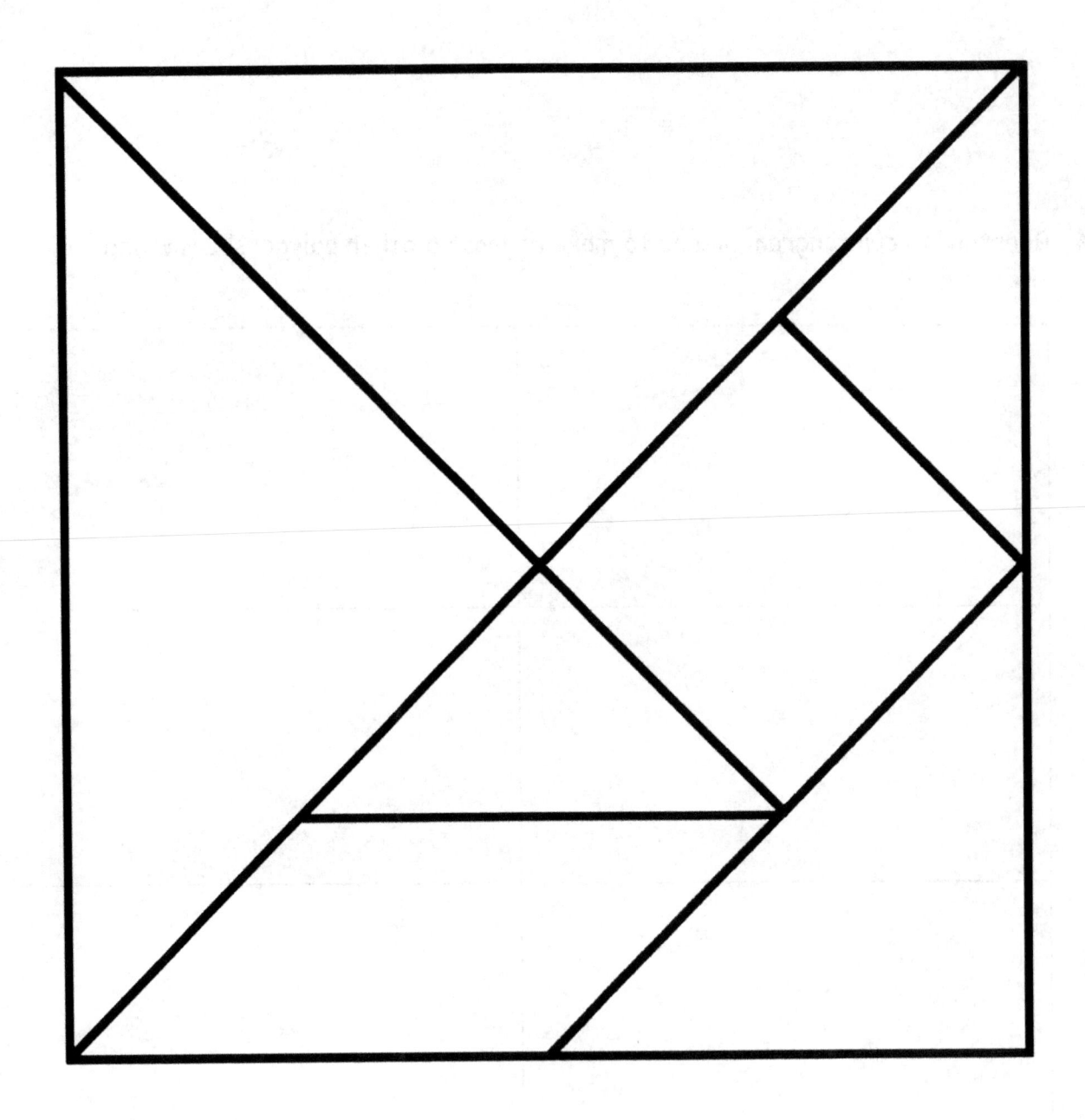

tangram

Lesson 7

Objective: Interpret equal shares in composite shapes as halves, thirds, and fourths.

Suggested Lesson Structure

- Fluency Practice   (12 minutes)
- Application Problem   (5 minutes)
- Concept Development   (33 minutes)
- Student Debrief   (10 minutes)

Total Time   **(60 minutes)**

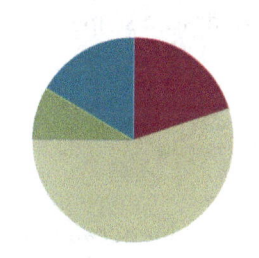

> **NOTES ON STANDARD ALIGNMENT:**
>
> The Texas Essential Knowledge and Skills require students to explore halves, fourths, and eighths (2.3A, 2.3D). The lessons in this topic also explore thirds and sixths. The inclusion of these units helps to extend the understanding of equal parts using examples and non-examples. These units are not assessed.

Fluency Practice (12 minutes)

- Subtraction with Renaming **2.4B**   (7 minutes)
- Grade 2 Fluency Differentiated Practice Sets **2.4A**   (5 minutes)

Subtraction with Renaming (7 minutes)

Materials: (S) Personal white board, hundreds place value chart (Lesson 4 Fluency Template)

Note: This fluency activity reviews the application of a chip model while recording with the algorithm. Allow students work time between each problem. Students use their personal white boards and a place value chart to solve.

- T: Slide the place value chart template into your personal white board.
- T: (Write 161 – 18 horizontally on the board.) Let's use a chip model to subtract. On your personal white board, record your work using the algorithm.
- S: (Solve.)
- T: 161 – 18 is…?
- S: 143.

Continue with the following possible sequence: 152 – 29, 237 – 56, 319 – 28, 463 – 54, and 208 – 57.

Grade 2 Fluency Differentiated Practice Sets (5 minutes)

Materials: (S) Fluency Practice Sets (Lesson 3)

Note: During Topic B and for the remainder of the year, each day's Fluency Practice includes an opportunity for review and mastery of the sums and differences with totals through 20 by means of the Fluency Practice Sets or Sprints. The process is detailed, with Practice Sets provided, in Lesson 3.

A STORY OF UNITS – TEKS EDITION   Lesson 7   2•8

Application Problem (5 minutes)

Vishal saves $3 each week. After 7 weeks, how much money does Vishal save?

Note: This problem gives students the opportunity to review their understanding of personal financial literacy concepts learned in Module 7. Encourage students to draw a strip diagram to solve the problem.

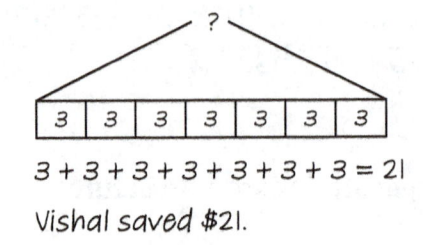

| 3 | 3 | 3 | 3 | 3 | 3 | 3 |

3 + 3 + 3 + 3 + 3 + 3 + 3 = 21

Vishal saved $21.

Concept Development (33 minutes)

Materials: (T) Tangram pieces (Lesson 6), document camera, chart paper, pattern blocks
(S) Tangram pieces (Lesson 6), pattern blocks in individual plastic bags (set of 1 hexagon, 4 squares, 3 triangles, 2 trapezoids, 3 wide (not thin) rhombuses)

Have students take out their tangram pieces. Distribute individual bags of pattern block pieces for later use.

Part 1: Using Tangrams to Create Composite Shapes Described as Halves

T: Let's continue exploring ways to compose new shapes using our tangram pieces.

T: Start with just the two smallest triangles. What shapes can you make that you can name? (Allow students time to work.)

Circulate as students move the pieces to make new shapes. Choose three students to place their shapes under the document camera to show a larger triangle, a parallelogram with no square corners, and a parallelogram that is a square, respectively.

T: What is the name of this polygon?
S: Triangle!
T: How many parts are in this large triangle?
S: Two parts!
T: Are the parts equal?
S: Yes!
T: We can say this triangle is made up of two equal shares, or parts, called halves.
T: Let's record this. (Draw the shape on chart paper, partitioned to show the pieces used.)

Repeat this process for the parallelogram and square, and record the shapes.

T: Let's label this chart *Halves, or 2 Equal Parts*. (Label the chart.)

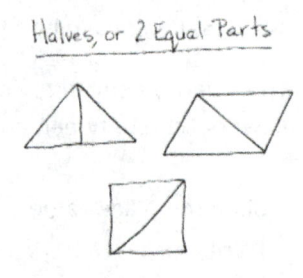

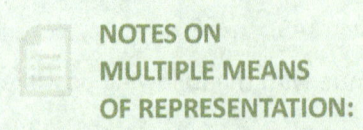

NOTES ON MULTIPLE MEANS OF REPRESENTATION:

Support English language learners by showing pictures of halves, thirds, and fourths, or by cutting an apple in half while saying "half." Post the pictures with the words underneath on the word wall.

Lesson 7: Interpret equal shares in composite shapes as halves, thirds, and fourths.

T: If you didn't make one of these shapes, move your pieces to make the shape now. If you did make all the shapes, try moving back and forth between them smoothly. (Wait for students to try all three shapes.)

T: Can we make halves by putting together a small triangle and a parallelogram? Why or why not? Discuss with your partner.

S: No, because the parts are different shapes, and the size is not the same. → No, because there are two parts, but they're not equal.

T: That's right. To be halves, the two parts must be equal in size, which means they take up the same amount of space.

T: (Point to each shape.) How many halves make a whole? Give me a complete sentence.

S: Two halves make a whole.

Part 2: Using Pattern Blocks to Create Composite Shapes Described as Halves, Thirds, and Fourths

T: Let's explore halves using pattern blocks. Start with a hexagon. (Place a hexagon under the document camera as students get a hexagon from among their shapes.)

T: What smaller polygon could you use to cover half of the hexagon? (Allow students time to experiment and find the trapezoid.)

S: A trapezoid!

T: Yes. One trapezoid covers half the hexagon. Put another trapezoid on top to cover the whole hexagon. (Place two trapezoids on top of the hexagon under the document camera as students do the same.)

T: How many trapezoids make a whole hexagon?

S: Two!

T: Are they equal shares?

S: Yes!

T: How many halves are in the hexagon?

S: Two halves!

T: Let's record this on our *Halves* chart. (Record on the chart.)

Repeat this process for a rhombus, covering it with two equilateral triangles, and record on the chart.

T: Let's try something different. This time we'll use a trapezoid. (Place a trapezoid under the document camera as students get a trapezoid from among their shapes.)

T: Can you cover the trapezoid with three smaller polygons? (Allow students time to experiment.)

T: What shape did you use?

S: A triangle!

T: Are the shapes equal in size?

S: Yes!

T: How many equal shares compose a whole trapezoid?

S: Three!

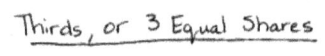

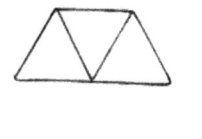

Lesson 7: Interpret equal shares in composite shapes as halves, thirds, and fourths.

T: We call three equal shares, or parts, **thirds**. Let's make a new chart and record this. (Label a new chart *Thirds, or 3 Equal Shares*, and draw the shape on chart paper, partitioned to show the pieces used.)

T: Work with a partner. Leave one triangle on, and cover the rest of the trapezoid with a rhombus. (Model under the document camera as students do the same.)

T: Talk with your partner: Are these halves? Why or why not?

S: They're not halves because there are two parts, but they're different shapes and sizes. → The two parts aren't equal because one is a triangle, and the other is a rhombus.

T: Correct. Is it thirds?

S: No, because there are only two parts, not three.

T: Yes!

Repeat the process for a hexagon covered by three rhombuses, and record on the chart.

T: Now, can you make one large square that is created with equal parts? (Allow students time to work with the smaller squares.)

Invite a student to show his or her composite square under the document camera. Have students note how many parts are used to make the square and if they are even. Introduce them to the term fourths, create a new chart labeled *Fourths, or 4 Equal Shares*, and draw the shape, partitioned to show the pieces used.

Allow students who show understanding to move on to the Problem Set.

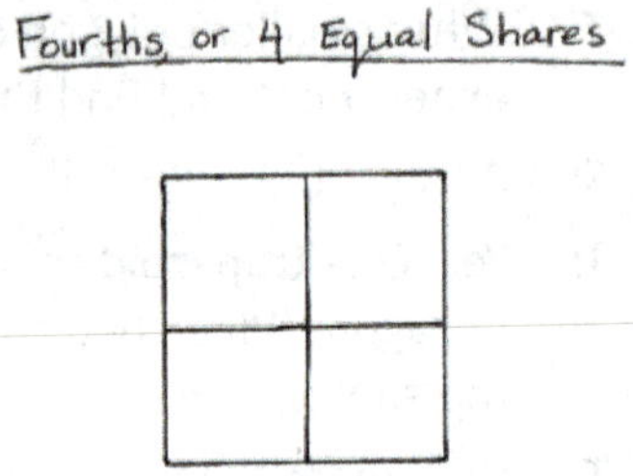

Problem Set (10 minutes)

Students should do their personal best to complete the Problem Set within the allotted 10 minutes. For some classes, it may be appropriate to modify the assignment by specifying which problems they work on first. Some problems do not specify a method for solving. Students should solve these problems using the RDW approach used for Application Problems.

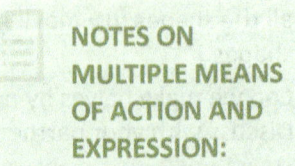

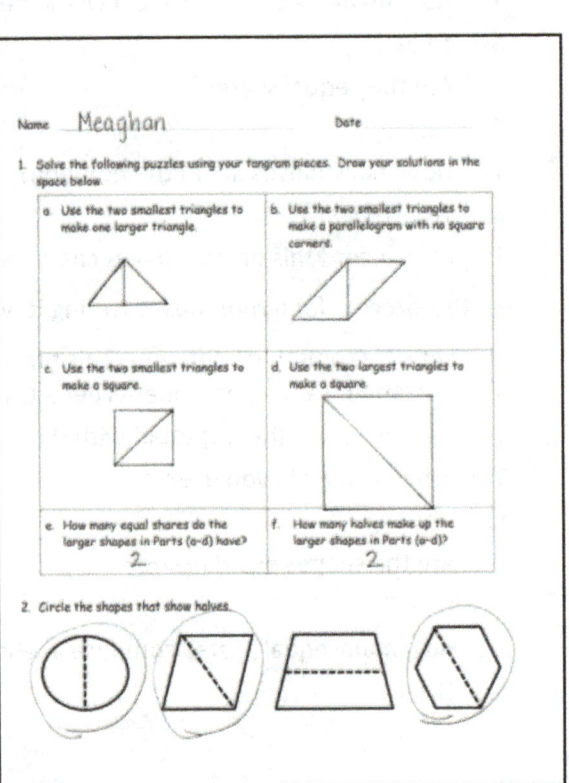

NOTES ON MULTIPLE MEANS OF ACTION AND EXPRESSION:

Challenge students working above grade level by asking them to create a poster for the class with a variety of examples of halves, thirds, and fourths alongside non-examples of the same. Ask them to explain how the examples and non-examples are the same (e.g., they have the same number of pieces) and how they differ (e.g., the pieces are not equal).

A STORY OF UNITS – TEKS EDITION
Lesson 7 2•8

Student Debrief (10 minutes)

Lesson Objective: Interpret equal shares in composite shapes as halves, thirds, and fourths.

The Student Debrief is intended to invite reflection and active processing of the total lesson experience.

Invite students to review their solutions for the Problem Set. They should check work by comparing answers with a partner. Look for misconceptions or misunderstandings that can be addressed in the Debrief. Guide students in a conversation to debrief the Problem Set and process the lesson.

Any combination of the questions below may be used to lead the discussion.

- Look at your Problem Set, and show your partner a shape that has two equal shares. What do we call those shares? (Halves. Repeat with **thirds** and fourths.)
- In Problem 4, does the trapezoid show thirds? Why or why not?
- When would you want to have equal shares of something?
- Use your pattern blocks to show me an example of halves. Show me an example of thirds. Now, show me an example that has three blocks but does not show thirds.

Exit Ticket (3 minutes)

After the Student Debrief, instruct students to complete the Exit Ticket. A review of their work will help with assessing students' understanding of the concepts that were presented in today's lesson and planning more effectively for future lessons. The questions may be read aloud to the students.

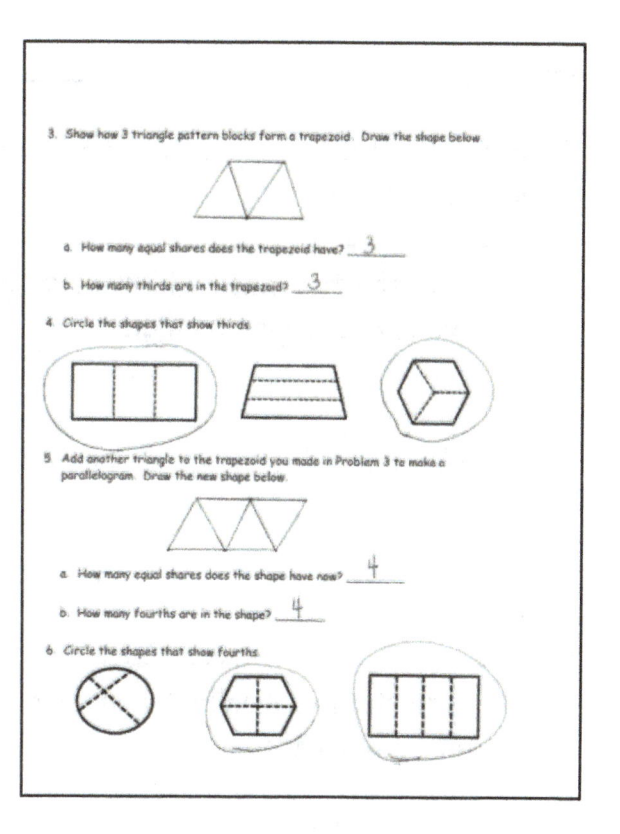

Lesson 7: Interpret equal shares in composite shapes as halves, thirds, and fourths.

Name _____ Date _____

1. Solve the following puzzles using your tangram pieces. Draw your solutions in the space below.

a. Use the two smallest triangles to make one larger triangle.	b. Use the two smallest triangles to make a parallelogram with no square corners.
c. Use the two smallest triangles to make a square.	d. Use the two largest triangles to make a square.
e. How many equal shares do the larger shapes in Parts (a–d) have?	f. How many halves make up the larger shapes in Parts (a–d)?

2. Circle the shapes that show halves.

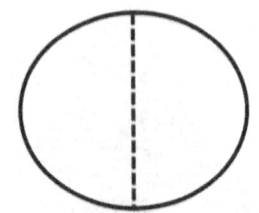

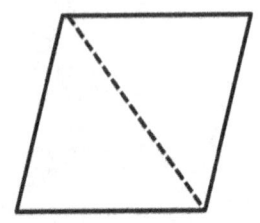

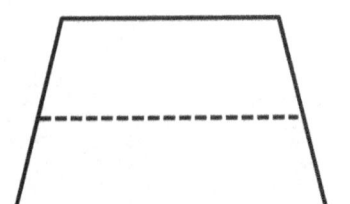

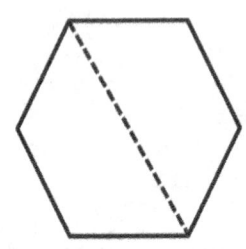

3. Show how 3 triangle pattern blocks form a trapezoid. Draw the shape below.

   a. How many equal shares does the trapezoid have? _____
   b. How many thirds are in the trapezoid? _____

4. Circle the shapes that show thirds.

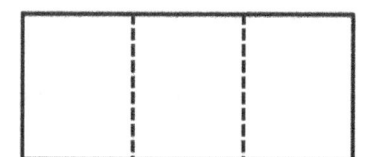

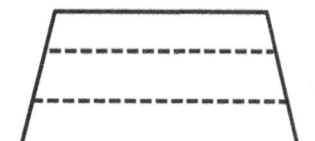

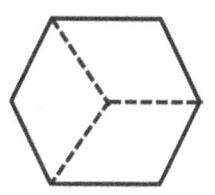

5. Add another triangle to the trapezoid you made in Problem 3 to make a parallelogram. Draw the new shape below.

   a. How many equal shares does the shape have now? _____
   b. How many fourths are in the shape? _____

6. Circle the shapes that show fourths.

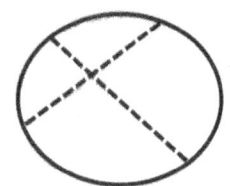

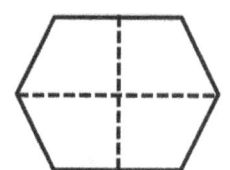

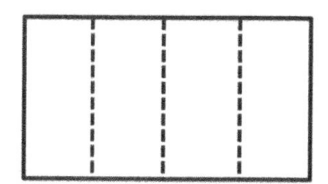

Lesson 7: Interpret equal shares in composite shapes as halves, thirds, and fourths.

Name _____ Date _____

1. Circle the shapes that show thirds.

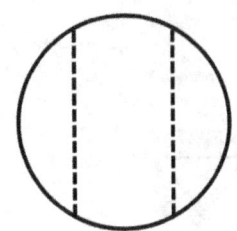

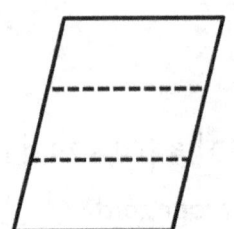

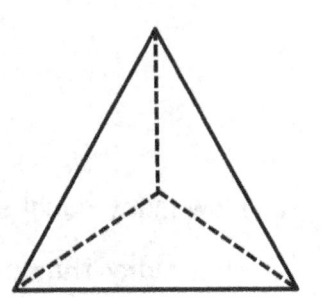

2. Circle the shapes that show fourths.

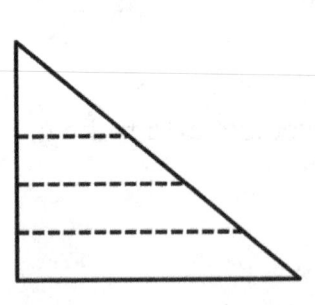

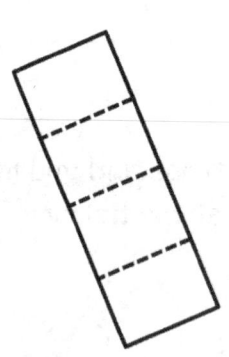

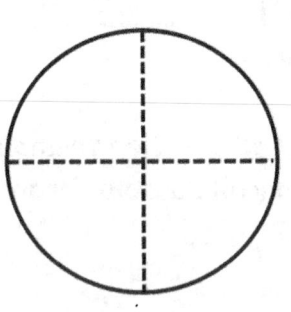

A STORY OF UNITS – TEKS EDITION

Lesson 7 Homework 2•8

Name _____ Date _____

1. Solve the following puzzles using your tangram pieces. Draw your solutions in the space below.

a. Use the two largest triangles to make a square.	b. Use the two smallest triangles to make a square.
c. Use the two smallest triangles to make a parallelogram with no square corners.	d. Use the two smallest triangles to make one larger triangle.
e. How many equal shares do the larger shapes in Parts (a–d) have?	f. How many halves make up the larger shapes in Parts (a–d)?

2. Circle the shapes that show halves.

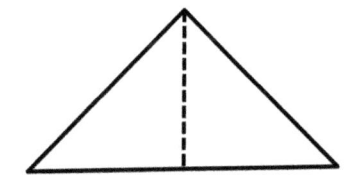

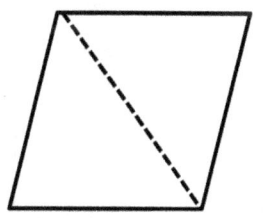

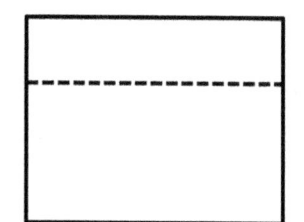

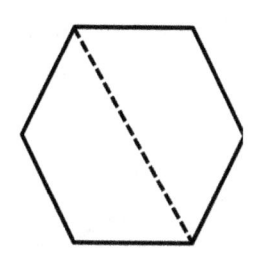

Lesson 7: Interpret equal shares in composite shapes as halves, thirds, and fourths.

3. Examine the trapezoid.

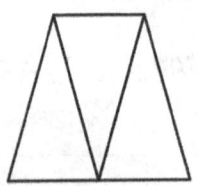

   a. How many equal shares does the trapezoid have? _____
   b. How many thirds are in the trapezoid? _____

4. Circle the shapes that show thirds.

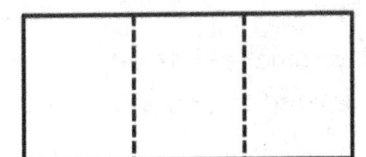

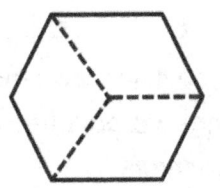

5. Examine the parallelogram.

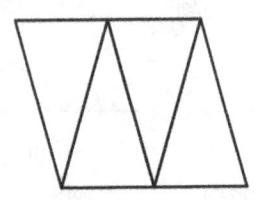

   a. How many equal shares does the shape have? _____
   b. How many fourths are in the shape? _____

6. Circle the shapes that show fourths.

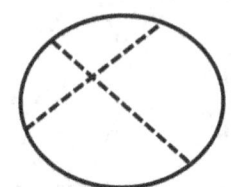

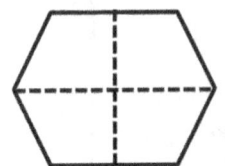

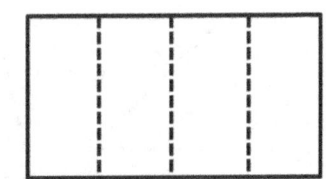

Lesson 8

Objective: Interpret equal shares in composite shapes as halves, thirds, and fourths.

Suggested Lesson Structure

- ■ Fluency Practice   (15 minutes)
- ■ Application Problem   (5 minutes)
- ■ Concept Development   (30 minutes)
- ■ Student Debrief   (10 minutes)
- **Total Time**   **(60 minutes)**

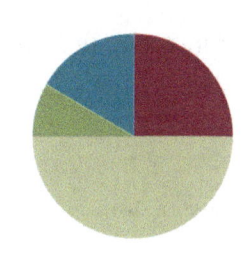

Fluency Practice (15 minutes)

- Rename for the Smaller Unit **2.2A**   (3 minutes)
- Subtraction with Renaming **2.4B**   (7 minutes)
- Grade 2 Fluency Differentiated Practice Sets **2.4A**   (5 minutes)

Rename for the Smaller Unit (3 minutes)

Note: This fluency activity reviews place value foundations.

- T: (Write 121 = ___ tens ___ ones.)
- T: I'm going to give you a number in unit form. I want you to rename 1 of the hundreds as 10 tens and then tell me how many hundreds, tens, or ones. Ready?
- S: 12 tens 1 one.
- T: (Write 158 = ___ tens ___ ones.) Say the number sentence.
- S: 158 = 15 tens 8 ones.
- T: 203.
- S: 203 = 1 hundred 10 tens 3 ones.
- T: 213.
- S: 213 = 1 hundred 11 tens 3 ones.

Continue with the following possible sequence: 305, 315; 204, 224; 108, 158; and 908, 968.

Subtraction with Renaming (7 minutes)

Materials: (S) Personal white board, hundreds place value chart (Lesson 4 Fluency Template)

Note: This fluency activity reviews the application of a chip model while recording with the algorithm. Allow students work time between each problem, and reinforce place value understandings by having students say the answer in both unit form and in standard form. Students use their personal white boards and a place value chart to solve.

- T: Slide the place value chart template into your personal white board.
- T: (Write 123 – 47 horizontally on the board.) Let's use a chip model to subtract. On your personal white board, record your work using the algorithm.
- S: (Solve.)
- T: 1 hundred, 2 tens, 3 ones minus 4 tens, 7 ones is…?
- S: 7 tens, 6 ones!
- T: 123 – 47 is…?
- S: 76.

Continue with the following possible sequence: 132 – 59, 231 – 65, 300 – 26, 446 – 77, and 506 – 187.

Grade 2 Fluency Differentiated Practice Sets (5 minutes)

Materials: (S) Fluency Practice Sets (Lesson 3)

Note: During Topic B and for the remainder of the year, each day's Fluency Practice includes an opportunity for review and mastery of the sums and differences with totals through 20 by means of the Fluency Practice Sets or Sprints. The process is detailed, with Practice Sets provided, in Lesson 3.

Application Problem (5 minutes)

Students were making larger shapes out of triangles and squares. They put away all 72 triangles. There were still 48 squares on the carpet. How many triangles and squares were on the carpet when they started?

Note: This is a *take from with start unknown* type problem. Encourage students to draw a strip diagram to visualize the relationships within the problem.

> **NOTES ON MULTIPLE MEANS OF REPRESENTATION:**
>
> Scaffold the Application Problem for students working below grade level by walking them through the calculation one step at a time. Ask questions such as, "How can we make this problem easier? How many tens are in 72 and 48? What do 2 ones and 8 ones make?" Continue until students come up with the answer.

72 + 48 = 120
11 tens + 1 ten = 12 tens

There were 120 shapes on the carpet when they started.

Lesson 8: Interpret equal shares in composite shapes as halves, thirds, and fourths.

A STORY OF UNITS – TEKS EDITION　　　　　　　　　　　　　　　　　　　　　Lesson 8　2•8

Concept Development (30 minutes)

Materials: (T) Pattern blocks, Problem Set, document camera (S) Problem Set, pattern blocks in individual plastic bags per pair (set of 1 hexagon, 6 squares, 6 triangles, 2 trapezoids, 3 wide (not thin) rhombuses)

Note: The Problem Set is completed throughout the Concept Development.

Note: In this lesson, students work in pairs to encourage math conversations as they explore equal shares using pattern blocks. Students identify and use one pattern block to cover a half, a third, or a fourth of a given shape. They then draw a picture of the composite shape formed by the halves, thirds, and fourths.

For each problem, questions are supplied to support the objective. Post the questions so students can discuss their work in greater detail with a partner or at their tables. Encourage them to close their eyes and visualize how they moved the smaller polygons to create the new shape. Have them describe how they used flips, slides, or turns to move the pieces. This discussion, linked with action, develops spatial visualization skills.

Pass out the Problem Set and the individual bags of pattern blocks.

Problem 1: Use one pattern block to cover half the rhombus.

T: Complete Problem 1. Share your thinking with your partner. Close your eyes and visualize how you moved the smaller polygons to create the rhombus. Describe how you flip, slide, or turn the pieces.

Ask questions such as the following to support deeper analysis of halves:

- How can looking at angles and sides help you find the block that is half a rhombus?
- If the rhombus was made from a piece of paper, how many different ways could you cut it to get two halves? Draw the different ways you could cut the rhombus into two halves.

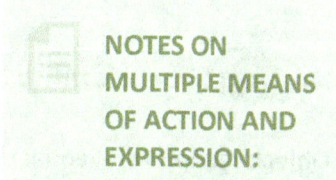

> **NOTES ON MULTIPLE MEANS OF ACTION AND EXPRESSION:**
>
> Support English language learners' ability to follow the lesson by pointing to the rhombus, the hexagon, the trapezoid, and the square. Provide them with appropriate sentence frames to discuss their work with a partner.

Problem 2: Use one pattern block to cover half the hexagon.

Ask questions such as the following to encourage interpreting different representations of a half:

- Cover the bottom half of the hexagon with three triangles. Is it still half covered? Why or why not?
- Cover the bottom half of the hexagon with a rhombus and a triangle. Is it still half covered?

Problem 3: Use one pattern block to cover one-third of the hexagon.

Ask questions such as the following to encourage deeper understanding of thirds:

- How many thirds do you need to fill the whole hexagon?
- Cover one-third with two triangles. Is the hexagon one-third covered?
- What fraction is not covered?

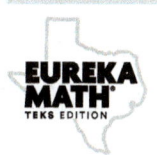

Lesson 8: Interpret equal shares in composite shapes as halves, thirds, and fourths.

Problem 4: Use one pattern block to cover one-third of the trapezoid.

Prompt students to interpret thirds in relationship to a whole:

- Use your drawing of the trapezoid formed by thirds to talk about how many small triangles would make a whole hexagon.
- How many thirds are in the trapezoid? In the hexagon?

Problem 5: Use four pattern blocks to make one larger square.

Prompt students to support different understandings of fourths:

- How many equal shares does the large square have?
- How many fourths make up the large square?
- How many fourths equal one whole square?
- Use your blocks to show that 2 fourths is the same as a half of the large square.

Problem 6: Use one pattern block to cover one-sixth of the hexagon.

Ask questions such as the following to support thinking about sixths:

- How many equal parts does the hexagon have?
- How many **sixths** make up the hexagon?

Student Debrief (10 minutes)

Lesson Objective: Interpret equal shares in composite shapes as halves, thirds, and fourths.

The Student Debrief is intended to invite reflection and active processing of the total lesson experience.

Invite students to review their solutions for the Problem Set. They should check work by comparing answers with a partner. Look for misconceptions or misunderstandings that can be addressed in the Debrief. Guide students in a conversation to debrief the Problem Set and process the lesson.

Any combination of the questions below may be used to lead the discussion. Consider using some of the discussion questions posed to pairs during the Concept Development as part of the Student Debrief. This will give students an opportunity to share their learning and to solidify their understanding if they overcame a misconception.

- Which problem was most difficult to solve? What strategies did you use to solve it? What made you keep trying even when it was hard?

- How did knowing the attributes of each shape help you solve the problems?
- (Show a hexagon covered by a triangle.) Look at Problem 3. What part of the hexagon am I showing? How many more triangles do I need to fill the hexagon?
- (Hold up a pattern block triangle.) Can this triangle be a half, a third, or a fourth? Explain.

Exit Ticket (3 minutes)

After the Student Debrief, instruct students to complete the Exit Ticket. A review of their work will help with assessing students' understanding of the concepts that were presented in today's lesson and planning more effectively for future lessons. The questions may be read aloud to the students.

Name _____ Date _____

1. Use one pattern block to cover half the rhombus.

    a. Identify the pattern block used to cover half of the rhombus. _____

    b. Draw a picture of the rhombus formed by the 2 halves.

2. Use one pattern block to cover half the hexagon.

    a. Identify the pattern block used to cover half of a hexagon. _____

    b. Draw a picture of the hexagon formed by the 2 halves.

3. Use one pattern block to cover 1 third of the hexagon.

    a. Identify the pattern block used to cover 1 third of a hexagon. _____

    b. Draw a picture of the hexagon formed by the 3 thirds.

4. Use one pattern block to cover 1 third of the trapezoid.

    a. Identify the pattern block used to cover 1 third of a trapezoid. _____

    b. Draw a picture of the trapezoid formed by the 3 thirds.

A STORY OF UNITS – TEKS EDITION   Lesson 8 Problem Set 2•8

5. Use 4 pattern block squares to make one larger square.

   a. Draw a picture of the square formed in the space below.

   b. Shade 1 small square. Each small square is 1 _____ (half / third / fourth) of the whole square.

   c. Shade 1 more small square. Now, 2 _____ (halves / thirds / fourths) of the whole square is shaded.

   d. And 2 fourths of the square is the same as 1 _____ (half / third / fourth) of the whole square.

   e. Shade 2 more small squares. ____ fourths is equal to 1 whole.

6. Use one pattern block to cover 1 sixth of the hexagon.

   a. Identify the pattern block used to cover 1 sixth of a hexagon. _____

   b. Draw a picture of the hexagon formed by the 6 sixths.

Lesson 8: Interpret equal shares in composite shapes as halves, thirds, and fourths.

117

A STORY OF UNITS – TEKS EDITION Lesson 8 Exit Ticket 2•8

Name _____ Date _____

Name the pattern block used to cover half the rectangle. _____

Use the shape below to draw the pattern blocks used to cover 2 halves.

Lesson 8: Interpret equal shares in composite shapes as halves, thirds, and fourths.

A STORY OF UNITS – TEKS EDITION　　　　　　　　　Lesson 8 Homework　2•8

Name _____　Date _____

1. Name the pattern block used to cover half the rhombus. _____

   Sketch the 2 pattern blocks used to cover both halves of the rhombus.

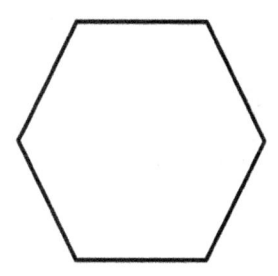

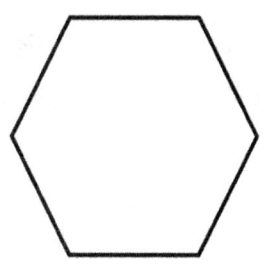

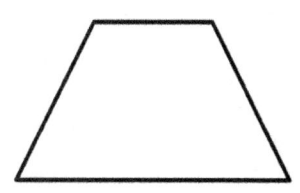

2. Name the pattern block used to cover half the hexagon. _____

   Sketch the 2 pattern blocks used to cover both halves of the hexagon.

3. Name the pattern block used to cover 1 third of the hexagon. _____

   Sketch the 3 pattern blocks used to cover thirds of the hexagon.

4. Name the pattern block used to cover 1 third of the trapezoid. _____

   Sketch the 3 pattern blocks used to cover thirds of the trapezoid.

Lesson 8:　Interpret equal shares in composite shapes as halves, thirds, and fourths.

119

5. Draw 2 lines to make 4 squares in the square below.

   a. Shade 1 small square. Each small square is 1 _____ (half / third / fourth) of the whole square.

   b. Shade 1 more small square. Now, 2 _____ (halves / thirds / fourths) of the whole square are shaded.

   c. And 2 fourths of the square is the same as 1 _____ (half / third / fourth) of the whole square.

   d. Shade 2 more small squares. ____ fourths is equal to 1 whole.

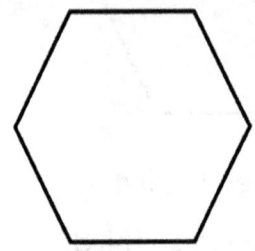

6. Name the pattern block used to cover 1 sixth of the hexagon. _____
   Sketch the 6 pattern blocks used to cover 6 sixths of the hexagon.

A STORY OF UNITS – TEKS EDITION   Mid-Module Assessment Task 2•8

Name _____   Date _____

1. Complete the chart. Use the word bank below to identify the name of each shape. Not all of the names will be used.

a.	b.	c.	d.
(quadrilateral shape)	(pentagon shape)	(triangle shape)	(hexagon shape)
_____ sides	_____ sides	_____ sides	_____ sides
_____ angles	_____ angles	_____ angles	_____ angles
_____ vertices	_____ vertices	_____ vertices	_____ vertices
Name of shape:	Name of shape:	Name of shape:	Name of shape:

Word Bank
hexagon   cube   square   triangle   pentagon   trapezoid

e. Sarah and Henry were asked to draw a hexagon. Sarah believes that only her drawing is correct. Explain why both shapes are hexagons.

Sarah's Hexagon   Henry's Hexagon

_____

_____

_____

Module 8: Time, Shapes, and Fractions as Equal Parts of Shapes

A STORY OF UNITS – TEKS EDITION
Mid-Module Assessment Task 2•8

2. a. Draw a shape with three sides. Make one of the angles of the shape a square angle. Which shape in Problem 1 has the same number of angles?

   b. Draw a shape with 4 square angles. Which shape in Problem 1 has the same number of angles?

3. Solve the following problems.

   a. Draw the shape that is one face of a cube.

   b. How many faces are on a cube? _____

   c. How many vertices are on a cube? _____

   d. How many edges are on a cube? _____

4. Complete each statement by circling the correct answer based on the figure below.

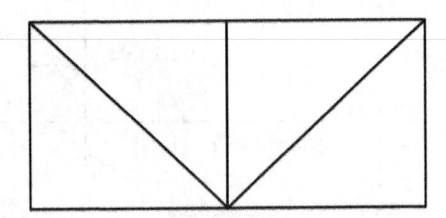

   a. One small triangle is what portion of the figure?
      1 fourth   1 half   1 whole

   b. One square is what portion of the figure?
      1 fourth   1 half   1 whole

   c. One rectangle that is not a square is what portion of the figure?
      1 half   1 fourth   1 whole

5. John cuts two pies into halves.

   a. Draw to show how John cut the pies.

   b. How many halves are in both pies altogether?

   There are _____ halves altogether.

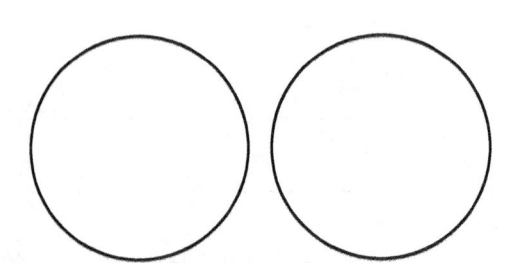

Module 8: Time, Shapes, and Fractions as Equal Parts of Shapes

| A STORY OF UNITS – TEKS EDITION | Mid-Module Assessment Task | 2•8 |

Mid-Module Assessment Task
Standards Addressed
Topics A–B

Number and Operations
The student is expected to:

- **2.3A** partition objects into equal parts and name the parts, including halves, fourths, and eighths, using words;
- **2.3C** use concrete models to count fractional parts beyond one whole using words and recognize how many parts it takes to equal one whole;
- **2.3D** identify examples and non-examples of halves, fourths, and eighths.

Geometry and Measurement
The student is expected to:

- **2.8A** create two-dimensional shapes based on given attributes, including number of sides and vertices;
- **2.8B** classify and sort three-dimensional solids including spheres, cones, cylinders, rectangular prisms (including cubes as special rectangular prisms) and triangular prisms, based on attributes using formal geometric language;
- **2.8C** classify and sort polygons with 12 or fewer sides according to attributes, including identifying the number of sides and number of vertices;
- **2.8E** decompose two-dimensional shapes such as cutting out a square from a rectangle, dividing a shape in half, or partitioning a rectangle into identical triangles and identify the resulting geometric parts.

Evaluating Student Learning Outcomes

A Progression Toward Mastery is provided to describe steps that illuminate the gradually increasing understandings that students develop *on their way to proficiency*. In this chart, this progress is presented from left (Step 1) to right (Step 4). The learning goal for students is to achieve Step 4 mastery. These steps are meant to help teachers and students identify and celebrate what the students CAN do now and what they need to work on next.

A Story of Units – TEKS Edition

Mid-Module Assessment Task 2•8

A Progression Toward Mastery				
Assessment Task Item and Standards Assessed	STEP 1 Little evidence of reasoning without a correct answer. (1 Point)	STEP 2 Evidence of some reasoning without a correct answer. (2 Points)	STEP 3 Evidence of some reasoning with a correct answer or evidence of solid reasoning with an incorrect answer. (3 Points)	STEP 4 Evidence of solid reasoning with a correct answer. (4 Points)
1 2.8C	The student answers one out of five parts correctly.	The student answers two out of five parts correctly.	The student answers three to four out of five parts correctly.	The student correctly answers: a. 4, 4, 4, *trapezoid*. b. 5, 5, 5, *pentagon*. c. 3, 3, 3, *triangle*. d. 6, 6, 6, *hexagon*. e. That both images have 6 sides, 6 angles, and/or 6 vertices.
2 2.8A	The student answers one out of four parts correctly.	The student answers two out of four parts correctly.	The student answers three out of four parts correctly.	The student draws appropriate shapes and correctly answers: a. *Triangle*. b. *Quadrilateral*.
3 2.8A 2.8B 2.8C	The student answers one out of four parts correctly.	The student answers two out of four parts correctly.	The student answers three out of four parts correctly.	The student correctly: a. Draws a square. b. Answers 6. c. Answers 8. d. Answers 12.
4 2.3A 2.3D	The student is unable to answer any of the questions.	The student answers one out of three parts correctly.	The student answers two out of three parts correctly.	The student correctly circles: a. *1 fourth*. b. *1 half*. c. *1 whole*.
5 2.3A 2.3C 2.8E	The student is unable to answer any of the question.	The student is able to partition one circle correctly.	The student is able to either partition the circles or counts the halves correctly.	The student correctly: a. partitions circles into halves. b. Answers 4.

Module 8: Time, Shapes, and Fractions as Equal Parts of Shapes

A STORY OF UNITS – TEKS EDITION Mid-Module Assessment Task 2•8

Name __Sam_____ Date _____

1. Complete the chart. Use the word bank below to identify the name of each shape. Not all of the names will be used.

a.	b.	c.	d.
__4__ sides	__5__ sides	__3__ sides	__6__ sides
__4__ angles	__5__ angles	__3__ angles	__6__ angles
__4__ vertices	__5__ vertices	__3__ vertices	__6__ vertices
Name of shape: trapezoid	Name of shape: pentagon	Name of shape: triangle	Name of shape: hexagon

Word Bank

hexagon   cube   square   triangle   pentagon   trapezoid

e. Sarah and Henry were asked to draw a hexagon. Sarah believes that only her drawing is correct. Explain why both shapes are hexagons.

Sarah's Hexagon   Henry's Hexagon

They both have 6 sides and 6 angles.

Module 8: Time, Shapes, and Fractions as Equal Parts of Shapes

A STORY OF UNITS – TEKS EDITION
Mid-Module Assessment Task 2•8

2. a. Draw a shape with three sides. Make one of the angles of the shape a square angle. Which shape in Problem 1 has the same number of angles?

    triangle

   b. Draw a shape with 4 square angles. Which shape in Problem 1 has the same number of angles?

    trapezoid

3. Solve the following problems.

   a. Draw the shape that is one face of a cube.

   b. How many faces are on a cube? __6__

   c. How many vertices are on a cube? __8__

   d. How many edges are on a cube? __12__

4. Complete each statement by circling the correct answer based on the figure below.

   a. One small triangle is what portion of the figure?
      (**1 fourth**)   1 half   1 whole

   b. One square is what portion of the figure?
      1 fourth   (**1 half**)   1 whole

   c. One rectangle that is not a square is what portion of the figure?
      1 half   1 fourth   (**1 whole**)

5. John cuts two pies into halves.

   a. Draw to show how John cut the pies.

   b. How many halves are in both pies altogether?

   There are __4__ halves altogether.

Module 8: Time, Shapes, and Fractions as Equal Parts of Shapes

A STORY OF UNITS — TEKS EDITION

Mathematics Curriculum

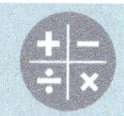

GRADE 2 • MODULE 8

Topic C
Fractions of Circles and Rectangles

2.3A, 2.3B, 2.3C, 2.3D, 2.8E, 2.8A, 2.8C

Focus Standards:	2.3A	Partition objects into equal parts and name the parts, including halves, fourths, and eighths, using words.
	2.3B	Explain that the more fractional parts used to make a whole, the smaller the part; and the fewer the fractional parts, the larger the part.
	2.3C	Use concrete models to count fractional parts beyond one whole using words and recognize how many parts it takes to equal one whole.
	2.3D	Identify examples and non-examples of halves, fourths, and eighths.
	2.8E	Decompose two-dimensional shapes such as cutting out a square from a rectangle, dividing a shape in half, or partitioning a rectangle into identical triangles and identify the resulting geometric parts.
Instructional Days:	3	
Coherence -Links from:	G1–M5	Identifying, Composing, and Partitioning Shapes
-Links to:	G3–M5	Fractions as Numbers on the Number Line

Topic C focuses on partitioning circles and rectangles into equal fractional parts. In Lesson 9, students are introduced to partitioning shapes into two equal shares, or halves, using both circles and rectangles. First, partners choose different ways to fold a sheet of paper in half. Then, they label and share their halves, discovering that though they each folded their rectangle differently, they each have two equal parts of the original whole. Next, they cut out a circle and fold, color, and label one half. They then rotate their circles and discover that halves are determined by equal parts, not by the orientation of the line. Finally, students look at pictures of partitioned shapes and discuss whether the shaded (or unshaded) portion is or is not two equal shares. To encourage student reasoning about equal shares, a variety of partitions and orientations are used.

Lesson 10 continues the same process with fourths and eighths. They create fourths by splitting two halves into two equal parts. They continue the process by decomposing a whole into 8 equal parts, creating eighths. Given a variety of partitioned shapes, students are asked to determine how many fourths and eighths are represented by the shaded (or unshaded) portion. Lesson 10 ends with students synthesizing their understanding of halves, fourths, and eighths by partitioning a pizza and a rectangular sheet cake, making decisions based on their share of the pizza or cake.

In Lesson 11, students build upon their new knowledge by assembling wholes out of fractional parts. Given a circle made of two parts, students see that the whole circle is composed of 2 halves. They count beyond 2 halves, to confirm that the act of counting doesn't change, only the unit changes. Using cutouts, students count beyond 1: 1 half, 2 halves, 3 halves. This is continued with fourths and eighths.

This topic provides a foundation for Topic D, applying what students have learned about fractional parts of a circle, particularly halves and quarters, to telling time on an analog clock.

A Teaching Sequence Toward Mastery of Fractions of Circles and Rectangles
Objective 1: **Partition circles and rectangles into equal parts, and describe those parts as halves, thirds, or fourths.** (Lesson 9)
Objective 2: **Partition circles and rectangles into equal parts, and describe those parts as halves, fourths, and eighths.** (Lesson 10)
Objective 3: **Use concrete models to count fractional parts beyond one whole.** (Lesson 11)

Lesson 9

Objective: Partition circles and rectangles into equal parts, and describe those parts as halves, thirds, or fourths.

Suggested Lesson Structure

- ■ Fluency Practice   (15 minutes)
- ■ Application Problem   (5 minutes)
- ■ Concept Development   (30 minutes)
- ■ Student Debrief   (10 minutes)
- **Total Time**   **(60 minutes)**

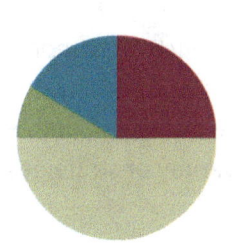

Fluency Practice (15 minutes)

- Rename for the Larger Unit 2.2A   (6 minutes)
- Sprint: Subtraction Patterns 2.4B   (9 minutes)

Rename for the Larger Unit (6 minutes)

Note: This fluency activity reviews place value foundations.

- T: I'm going to tell you a number of ones. Tell me the largest units that can be made. Ready?
- T: (Write 12 ones = ____ ten ____ ones.)
- T: Say the number sentence. (Point to the board.)
- S: 12 ones = 1 ten 2 ones.
- T: (Write 29 ones = ____ tens ____ ones.) Say the number sentence.
- S: 29 ones = 2 tens 9 ones.
- T: (Write 29 ones = 1 ten ____ ones.) Say the number sentence.
- S: 29 ones = 1 ten 19 ones.

Continue with the following possible sequence: 58 ones, 97 ones, 100 ones, 130 ones, 148 ones, 254 ones, 309 ones, and 880 ones.

Sprint: Subtraction Patterns (9 minutes)

Materials: (S) Subtraction Patterns Sprint

Note: Students practice subtracting in order to gain mastery of the sums and differences within 20 and relate those facts to larger numbers.

A STORY OF UNITS – TEKS EDITION   Lesson 9 2•8

Application Problem (5 minutes)

Mr. Thompson's class raised 96 dollars for a field trip. They need to raise a total of 120 dollars.

   a. How much more money do they need to raise in order to reach their goal?

   b. If they raise 86 more dollars, how much extra money will they have?

Note: This Application Problem reviews multi-digit addition and subtraction and invites students to use a variety of strategies to solve.

a. $96 \xrightarrow{+4} 100 \xrightarrow{+20} 120$
They need to raise 24 dollars.

b. $\begin{array}{r}96\\+86\\\hline 182\end{array}$ $182 \xrightarrow{-100} 82 \xrightarrow{-20} 62$

or

$\begin{array}{r}86\\-24\\\hline 62\end{array}$

They will have 62 extra dollars.

Concept Development (30 minutes)

Materials: (T) 1 piece of 8½" × 11" paper, circle (Template 1) shaded shapes (Template 2) (S) 1 piece of 8½" × 11" paper, circle (Template 1), shaded shapes (Template 2), personal white board, scissors, crayons or colored pencils

Distribute 8½" × 11" paper and crayons or colored pencils to each student.

   T: (Hold up a piece of paper.) What shape is this paper?
   S: A rectangle!
   T: How can you prove that?
   S: It has four straight sides and four square corners.
   T: A square corner is called a **right angle**.
   T: Partner A, choose one way to fold your paper in half.
   T: Partner B, fold your paper in half another way. (Circulate to ensure students are folding accurately.)
   T: Once you have folded your paper, open it up and draw straight down the fold line with a crayon. Then, color 1 half, and label it. (Model as students do the same.)
   T: Talk with your partner. Use math language to describe how your papers are alike and different.
   S: We folded them differently, but we both have two equal parts. → We both have two halves. → We both still have a whole piece of paper.
   T: Excellent! You have **partitioned**, or divided, your paper into two equal shares called halves.
   T: And we can describe either part, whether shaded or unshaded, as half, true?
   S: True!

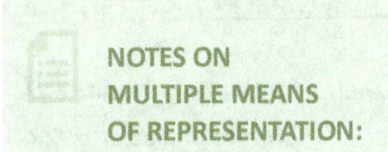

NOTES ON MULTIPLE MEANS OF REPRESENTATION:

Encourage written reflection as students share the strategies they used to arrive at their answers. Ask questions such as, "How did you use the make ten strategy?" or "How did your use of that strategy make the job of subtracting 96 from 120 easier?"

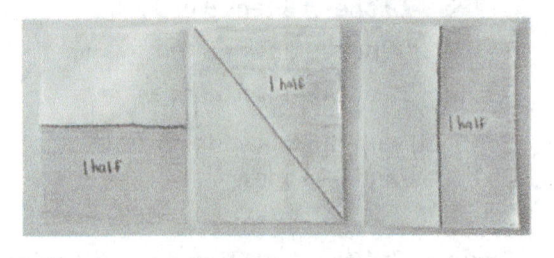

Lesson 9: Partition circles and rectangles into equal parts, and describe those parts as halves, thirds, or fourths.

A STORY OF UNITS – TEKS EDITION
Lesson 9 2•8

T: Cut along your fold line, and then, hold up your papers. (Wait as students do so.)
T: What are you holding?
S: Two halves. → Two equal shares. → Two equal parts that make a whole.
T: Put them together. Now, what do you have?
S: One whole!

Pass out the circle template and scissors. At the end of this activity, have students store their circle in their personal white board to use during Lesson 10.

T: Cut out the circle by cutting right on top of the black line. (Model as students do the same.)
T: Fold your circle in half. Is there more than one way to do that?
S: No.
T: (Hold up the folded circle.) This reminds me of certain foods. Do you know which ones I'm thinking of?
S: An omelet! → A quesadilla! → A taco!
T: Sure! Whether it's eggs or a tortilla, we sometimes take a circle and fold it in half. Yum!
T: Now, open up your circle, and draw straight down the fold line with a crayon. Then, color 1 half, and label it. (Model as students do the same.)
T: How would you describe this circle now?
S: 1 half is shaded, and the other half is unshaded. → We have two equal shares. → We have 2 halves.
T: That is correct!

> **NOTES ON MULTIPLE MEANS OF ACTION AND EXPRESSION:**
>
> English language learners' cultural background can be used to build on their prior knowledge. Allow students to express their mathematical knowledge in their native language. For instance, Spanish-speaking students can answer "dos partes iguales" in response to the question about describing their shaded circle.

Guide students to rotate their circles to discover and discuss that halves are determined by equal parts not by the orientation of the line.

Pass out the shaded shapes template, and have students insert it into their personal white boards.

T: Look at the shapes on the page. Talk with your partner about all the reasons why each shape is or is not two equal shares, with one share shaded.

Circulate as students talk in order to listen for misconceptions or identify comments to share with the class.

S: Shape A looks like a card if you fold it over. The parts would be equal, and there are two of them, so they're halves.
T: What an interesting observation! We've said that the shapes need to be the same size, so if you can fold one side of the rectangle on top of the other side and they match, then they must be halves.
S: If Shape B were a pizza, it wouldn't be fair shares. The parts aren't equal, so it's not halves even though there are two parts. → Shape C is not halves because there are three parts not two, and it's not thirds because the parts aren't equal.
T: Ooh! I like your thinking! Halves means two equal parts make up the whole.

As students demonstrate proficiency, allow them to move on to the Problem Set.

Lesson 9: Partition circles and rectangles into equal parts, and describe those parts as halves, thirds, or fourths.

A STORY OF UNITS – TEKS EDITION
Lesson 9 2•8

Problem Set (10 minutes)

Students should do their personal best to complete the Problem Set within the allotted 10 minutes. For some classes, it may be appropriate to modify the assignment by specifying which problems they work on first. Some problems do not specify a method for solving. Students should solve these problems using the RDW approach used for Application Problems.

Student Debrief (10 minutes)

Lesson Objective: Partition circles and rectangles into equal parts, and describe those parts as halves, thirds, or fourths.

The Student Debrief is intended to invite reflection and active processing of the total lesson experience.

Invite students to review their solutions for the Problem Set. They should check work by comparing answers with a partner. Look for misconceptions or misunderstandings that can be addressed in the Debrief. Guide students in a conversation to debrief the Problem Set and process the lesson.

Any combination of the questions below may be used to lead the discussion.

- For Problem 2, are shapes (g) and (h) **partitioned** into two equal shares? How do you know?
- For Problems 2(c) and (h), why didn't you shade in one part?
- What similarities and differences do you notice among Problems 2(b), (e), and (k)?
- Can all the shapes in Problem 2 be split into two equal shares? How would Problem 2(d) change?
- Turn and talk. For Problem 3, what mental strategy did you use to split the shapes into halves? How does your work compare to your partner's work?
- For Problem 3, how many ways can you split the shapes into halves? Do you notice anything interesting about circles?
- For Problem 3(b), how many **right angles** does each of the shapes have?

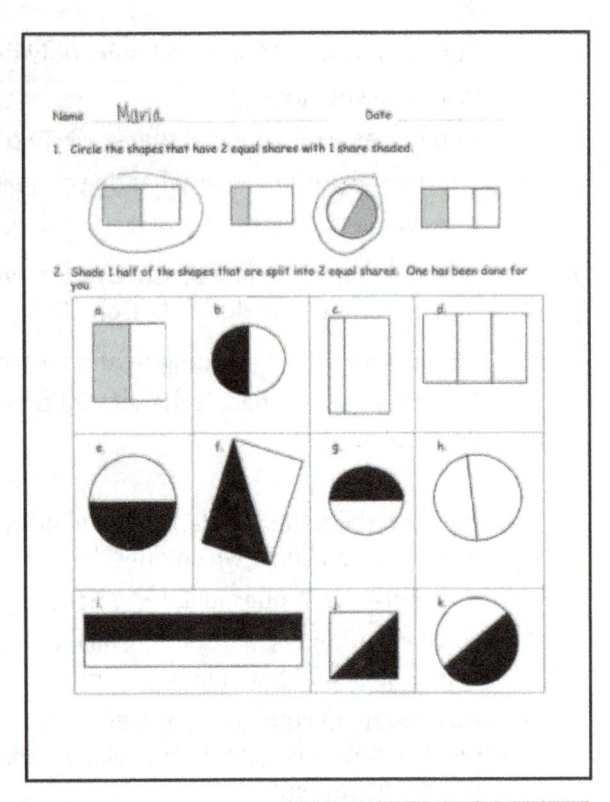

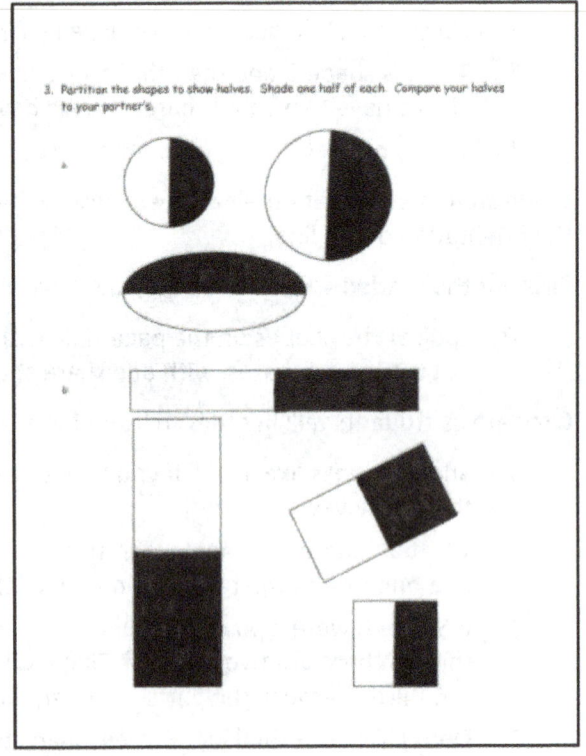

Lesson 9: Partition circles and rectangles into equal parts, and describe those parts as halves, thirds, or fourths.

Exit Ticket (3 minutes)

After the Student Debrief, instruct students to complete the Exit Ticket. A review of their work will help with assessing students' understanding of the concepts that were presented in today's lesson and planning more effectively for future lessons. The questions may be read aloud to the students.

A

Subtraction Patterns

Number Correct: _____

1.	5 − 1 =		23.	10 − 2 =	
2.	15 − 1 =		24.	11 − 2 =	
3.	25 − 1 =		25.	21 − 2 =	
4.	75 − 1 =		26.	31 − 2 =	
5.	5 − 2 =		27.	51 − 2 =	
6.	15 − 2 =		28.	51 − 12 =	
7.	25 − 2 =		29.	10 − 5 =	
8.	75 − 2 =		30.	11 − 5 =	
9.	4 − 1 =		31.	12 − 5 =	
10.	40 − 10 =		32.	22 − 5 =	
11.	43 − 10 =		33.	32 − 5 =	
12.	43 − 20 =		34.	62 − 5 =	
13.	43 − 21 =		35.	62 − 15 =	
14.	43 − 23 =		36.	72 − 15 =	
15.	12 − 2 =		37.	82 − 15 =	
16.	62 − 2 =		38.	32 − 15 =	
17.	62 − 12 =		39.	10 − 9 =	
18.	18 − 8 =		40.	11 − 9 =	
19.	78 − 8 =		41.	51 − 9 =	
20.	78 − 18 =		42.	51 − 10 =	
21.	41 − 11 =		43.	51 − 19 =	
22.	92 − 12 =		44.	65 − 46 =	

Lesson 9: Partition circles and rectangles into equal parts, and describe those parts as halves, thirds, or fourths.

B

Subtraction Patterns

Number Correct: _____
Improvement: _____

1.	4 – 1 =	
2.	14 – 1 =	
3.	24 – 1 =	
4.	74 – 1 =	
5.	5 – 3 =	
6.	15 – 3 =	
7.	25 – 3 =	
8.	75 – 3 =	
9.	3 – 1 =	
10.	30 – 10 =	
11.	32 – 10 =	
12.	32 – 20 =	
13.	32 – 21 =	
14.	32 – 22 =	
15.	15 – 5 =	
16.	65 – 5 =	
17.	65 – 15 =	
18.	16 – 6 =	
19.	76 – 6 =	
20.	76 – 16 =	
21.	51 – 11 =	
22.	82 – 12 =	

23.	10 – 5 =	
24.	11 – 5 =	
25.	21 – 5 =	
26.	31 – 5 =	
27.	51 – 5 =	
28.	51 – 15 =	
29.	10 – 9 =	
30.	11 – 9 =	
31.	12 – 9 =	
32.	22 – 9 =	
33.	32 – 9 =	
34.	62 – 9 =	
35.	62 – 19 =	
36.	72 – 19 =	
37.	82 – 19 =	
38.	32 – 19 =	
39.	10 – 2 =	
40.	11 – 2 =	
41.	51 – 2 =	
42.	51 – 10 =	
43.	51 – 12 =	
44.	95 – 76 =	

Lesson 9: Partition circles and rectangles into equal parts, and describe those parts as halves, thirds, or fourths.

A STORY OF UNITS – TEKS EDITION   Lesson 9 Problem Set 2•8

Name _____   Date _____

1. Circle the shapes that have 2 equal shares with 1 share shaded.

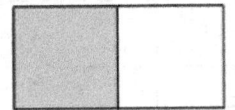

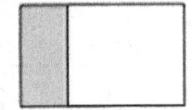

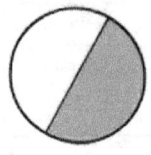

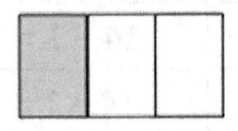

2. Shade 1 half of the shapes that are split into 2 equal shares. One has been done for you.

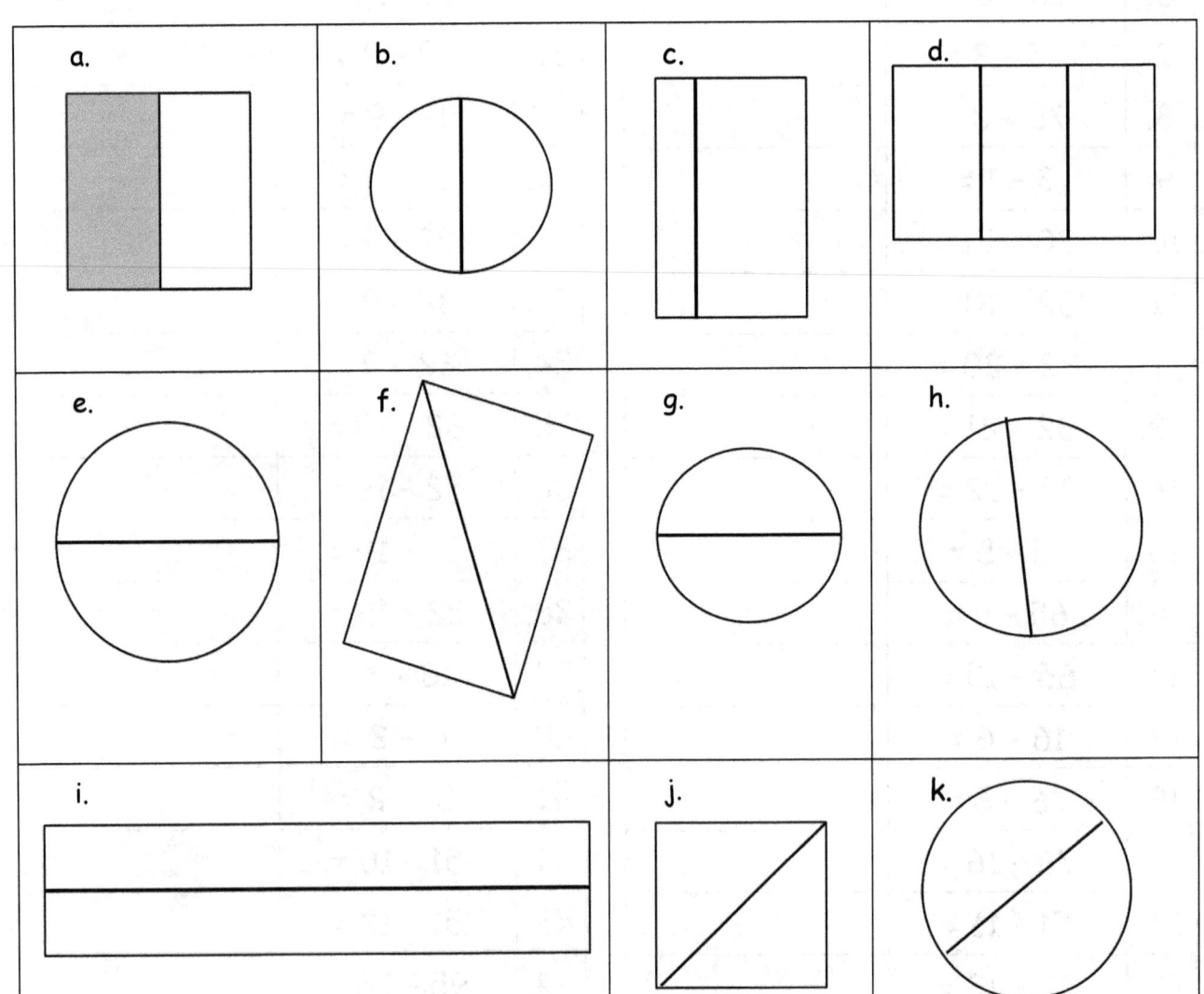

a.	b.	c.	d.
e.	f.	g.	h.
i.	j.	k.

136   Lesson 9:   Partition circles and rectangles into equal parts, and describe those parts as halves, thirds, or fourths.

3. Partition the shapes to show halves. Shade 1 half of each. Compare your halves to your partner's.

a.

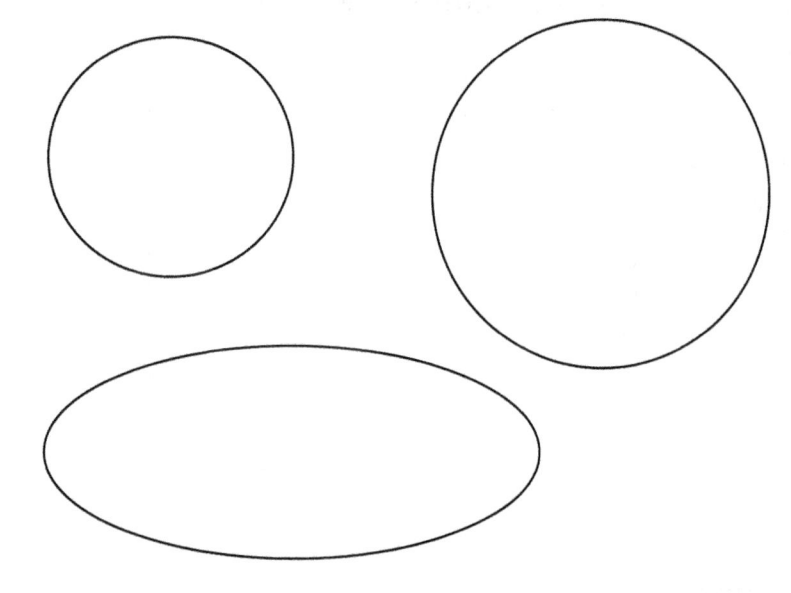

b.

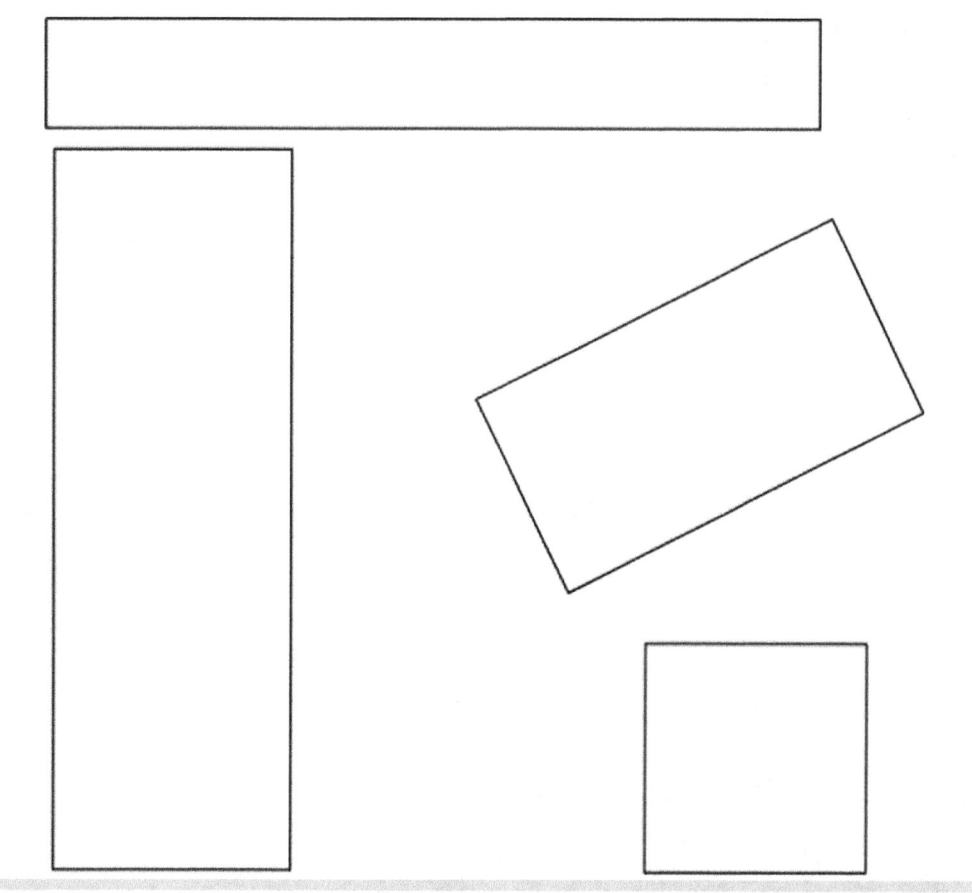

A STORY OF UNITS – TEKS EDITION

Lesson 9 Exit Ticket 2•8

Name _____ Date _____

Shade 1 half of the shapes that are split into 2 equal shares.

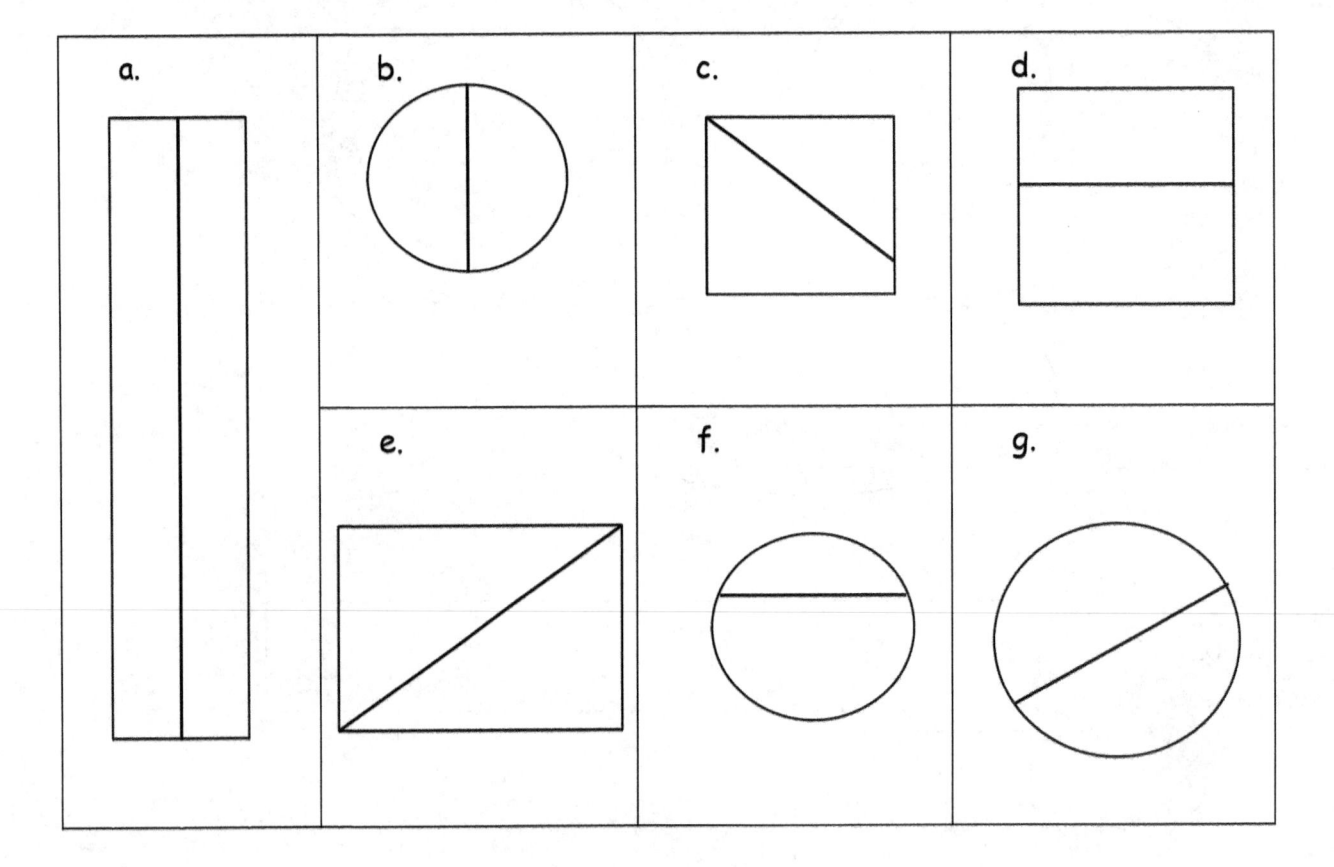

| a. | b. | c. | d. |
| e. | f. | g. |

Lesson 9: Partition circles and rectangles into equal parts, and describe those parts as halves, thirds, or fourths.

Name _____ Date _____

1. Circle the shapes that have 2 equal shares with 1 share shaded.

2. Shade 1 half of the shapes that are split into 2 equal shares. One has been done for you.

a.

b.

c.

d.

e.

f.

g.

h.

i.

3. Partition the shapes to show halves. Shade 1 half of each.

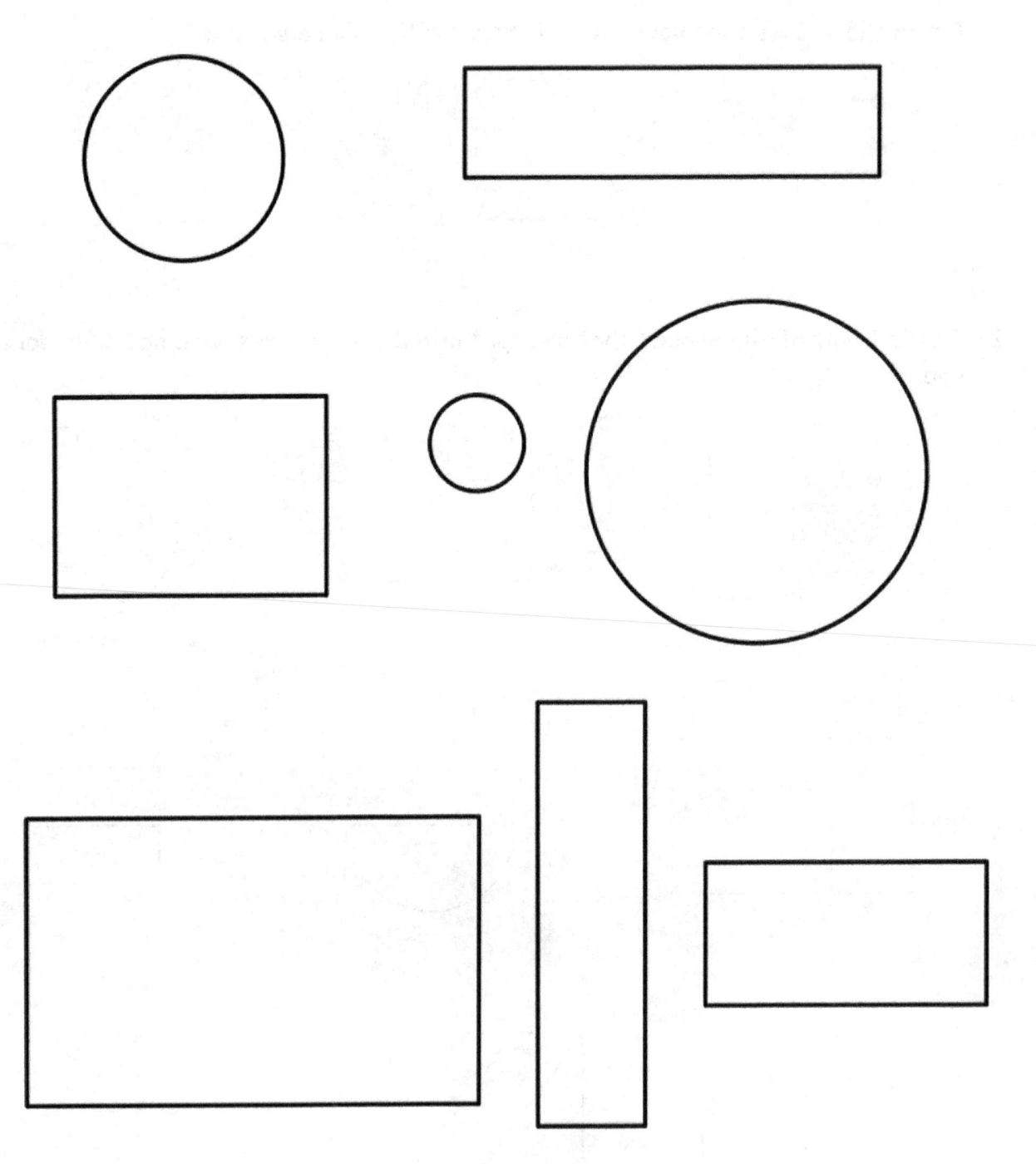

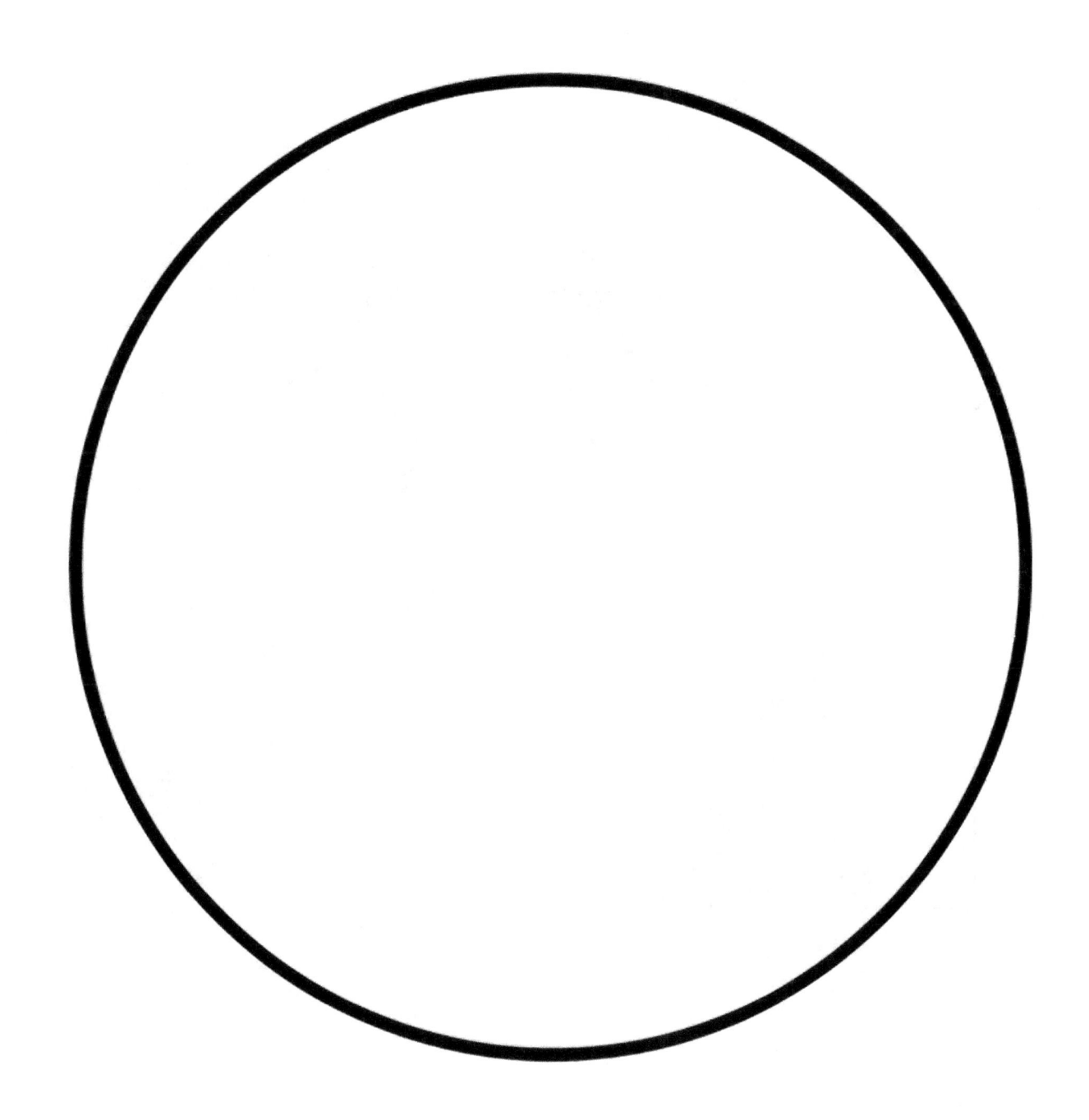

circle

Lesson 9: Partition circles and rectangles into equal parts, and describe those parts as halves, thirds, or fourths.

A STORY OF UNITS – TEKS EDITION

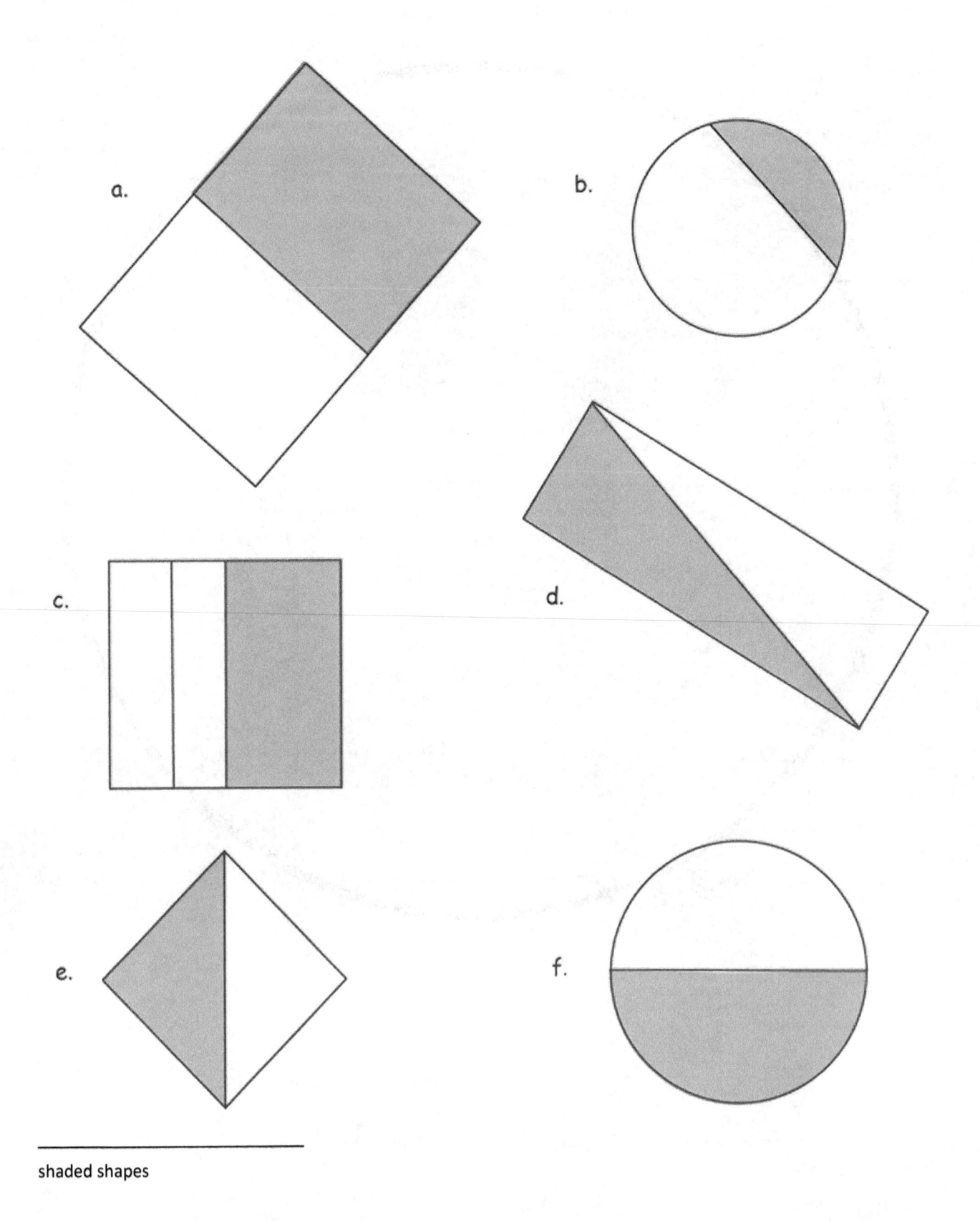

Lesson 9 Template 2   2•8

a.

b.

c.

d.

e.

f.

shaded shapes

Lesson 9: Partition circles and rectangles into equal parts, and describe those parts as halves, thirds, or fourths.

Lesson 10

Objective: Partition circles and rectangles into equal parts, and describe those parts as halves, fourths, and eighths.

Suggested Lesson Structure

- **Fluency Practice** (15 minutes)
- **Application Problem** (5 minutes)
- **Concept Development** (30 minutes)
- **Student Debrief** (10 minutes)

Total Time **(60 minutes)**

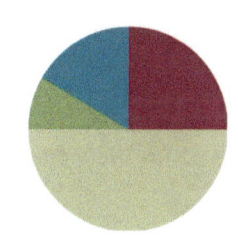

Fluency Practice (15 minutes)

- Rename for the Larger Unit **2.2A** (6 minutes)
- Sprint: Addition Patterns **2.4B** (9 minutes)

Rename for the Larger Unit (6 minutes)

Note: This fluency activity reviews place value foundations needed to bundle when adding multi-digit numbers.

T: I'm going to give you a number. I want you to bundle and rename the units. Ready?
T: (Write 13 tens = ____ hundred ____ tens.)
T: Say the number sentence. (Point to the board.)
S: 13 tens = 1 hundred 3 tens.
T: Say 13 tens in standard form.
S: 130.
T: (Write 26 tens 10 ones = ____ hundreds ____ tens.) Say the number sentence.
S: 26 tens 10 ones = 2 hundreds 7 tens.
T: Say the number in standard form.
S: 270.

Continue with the following possible sequence: 34 tens 10 ones, 56 tens 10 ones, 81 tens, 90 tens, 1 hundred 35 tens, 3 hundreds 44 tens, 7 hundreds 28 tens 10 ones, 5 hundreds 34 tens 13 ones, and 3 hundreds 44 tens 24 ones.

A STORY OF UNITS – TEKS EDITION   Lesson 10   2•8

Sprint: Addition Patterns (9 minutes)

Materials: (S) Addition Patterns Sprint

Note: Students practice adding in order to gain mastery of the sums and differences within 20 and relate those facts to larger numbers.

Application Problem (5 minutes)

Felix is passing out raffle tickets. He passes out 98 tickets and has 57 left. How many raffle tickets did he have to start?

Note: This is an *add to with start unknown* type problem that reviews two-digit addition with two compositions.

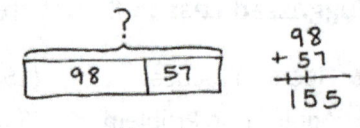

Felix had 155 tickets in the beginning.

Concept Development (30 minutes)

Materials: (T) 1 piece of 8½" × 11" paper, cut and colored circle (Lesson 9 Template 1) (S) Rectangles and circles (Template), personal white board, 1 piece of 8½" × 11" paper, crayons or colored pencils, cut and colored circle (Lesson 9 Template 1)

Part 1: Making Fourths

Have students take out their circle from yesterday's lesson.

T: Yesterday we worked with halves. Let's look at fourths. We already folded, colored, and labeled 1 half. Let's turn the circle over and make fourths, or quarters, on the other side. When something is divided into fourths, how many equal shares does it have?

S: Four!

T: Fold your circle to partition it into four equal parts. Make sure each part is equal in size. Fold so the ends of the first line come together at the edge. (Model as students do the same.)

T: Color and label 1 fourth of your circle. (Model as students do the same.)

T: Point and count the fourths with your partner.

S: 1 fourth, 2 fourths, 3 fourths, 4 fourths.

T: Now, use your personal white boards to partition the circles on your template into fourths. (Allow students time to work.) Tell your partner how you divided the circle into equal shares.

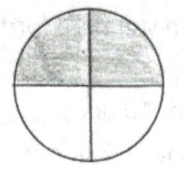

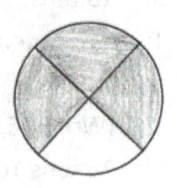

2 fourths   3 fourths

S: I made it look like my paper circle. → I drew a cross in the middle of the circle. → You can draw an X in the circle.

T: Choose the circle that shows the best fourths, and shade in 1 fourth. (Allow students time to work.)

144   Lesson 10:   Partition circles and rectangles into equal parts, and describe those parts as halves, fourths, and eighths.

A STORY OF UNITS – TEKS EDITION
Lesson 10 2•8

Have students continue to practice shading the following possible patterns: 2 fourths, 3 fourths, and 4 fourths.

- T: Now, let's partition our rectangles into fourths, or quarters. There are a few different ways we can do this. (Demonstrate and then allow students time to work.)

Have students continue to practice partitioning rectangles into fourths and then shading the following possible patterns: 3 fourths, 4 fourths, 1 quarter, and 2 quarters.

Part 2: Making Eighths

Provide students with another circle, the same size as the one just partitioned into fourths.

- T: Fold your circle to partition it into 2 equal parts. What is the name of each equal part?
- S: Half.
- T: How many halves are shown?
- S: 2 halves.
- T: Continue to fold this circle so that you have fourths. How many fourths do you have?
- S: 4 fourths.
- T: Continue to fold this circle so that you have eighths. (Demonstrate.) How many eighths do you have?
- S: 8 eighths.
- T: Point to and count the eighths.
- S: 1 eighth, 2 eighths, 3 eighths, 4 eighths, 5 eighths, 6 eighths, 7 eighths, 8 eighths.
- T: Compare the circle you used in Part 1 to this circle. How are they alike and how are they different? Turn and talk.
- S: The circles are the same size. → One circle shows fourths and one circle shows eighths.
- T: Which unit is larger? Fourths or eighths? Explain your thinking.
- S: Fourths are larger than eighths. → We started out with the same size circle, but made more parts with the eighths. → Eighths have to be smaller, because there are more of them than there are fourths.
- T: Use your personal white boards to partition the circles on your template into eighths.
- S: (Work.)
- T: Tell your partner how you partitioned your circle into eight equal parts.
- S: (Share.)

Have students partition the rectangle into eighths. Let them explore and then share their drawings.

Lesson 10: Partition circles and rectangles into equal parts, and describe those parts as halves, fourths, and eighths.

Part 3: Partitioning to Make Fourths and Eighths of a Sheet Cake and Pizza

- T: We're going to use your personal white boards and the template to show equal shares. Let's pretend that the rectangles are sheet cakes and the circle is a pizza.
- T: It's easy to think about food when we talk about equal shares because there are so many foods we cut up to share with friends and family, like cakes, pizza, quesadillas, and candy bars!
- T: You're going to draw lines to cut the pizza and sheet cakes into halves, thirds, and fourths. Please show two different ways of partitioning when slicing the two sheet cakes. Then, you'll color your share.
- T: For example, if I say, "You get 3 fourths of the cake," show me two different ways to partition the rectangles, and color 3 fourths on each cake.

Ask students to show a variety of partitions, for example, naming 1, 2, 3, and 4 fourths and 1, 2, 3, 4, 5, 6, 7, and 8 eighths, as students partition and color their share.

- T: Now, listen to my story, and show me how each shape should be divided. Mary, Colleen, and Saffron share a pizza equally. Show how to slice the pizza, and label each share with their name. (Allow students time to work.)
- T: Talk with your partner: What fraction of the pizza did the girls share in all?
- S: They shared the whole pizza. → That's 3 thirds!
- T: Correct! What if Mary also eats Colleen's share of the pizza? How much has she eaten?
- S: Mary has eaten 2 thirds of the pizza. → She has eaten double her share. → She has eaten two shares now.
- T: Here's another story. Hayley invited 7 friends to her birthday party. She shared the sheet cake equally with her friends. Show how to slice the cake.
- S: (Work.)
- T: How many equal pieces did you show?
- S: 8. → Hayley plus 7 friends makes 8.
- T: What fraction of the sheet cake will each friend get?
- S: 1 eighth.
- T: How many eighths in all?
- S: 8. → 8 eighths make one whole.

Allow students who have demonstrated proficiency to move on to the Problem Set.

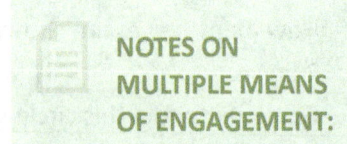

> **NOTES ON MULTIPLE MEANS OF ENGAGEMENT:**
>
> Support English language learners during partner shares by giving them sentence frames to assist them. For instance: "The four of them shared ___," or "They each got a ____ of the pizza."

A STORY OF UNITS – TEKS EDITION　　　　　　　　　　　　　Lesson 10 2•8

Problem Set (10 minutes)

Students should do their personal best to complete the Problem Set within the allotted 10 minutes. For some classes, it may be appropriate to modify the assignment by specifying which problems they work on first. Some problems do not specify a method for solving. Students should solve these problems using the RDW approach used for Application Problems.

Student Debrief (10 minutes)

Lesson Objective: Partition circles and rectangles into equal parts, and describe those parts as halves, fourths, and eighths.

The Student Debrief is intended to invite reflection and active processing of the total lesson experience.

Invite students to review their solutions for the Problem Set. They should check work by comparing answers with a partner. Look for misconceptions or misunderstandings that can be addressed in the Debrief. Guide students in a conversation to debrief the Problem Set and process the lesson.

Any combination of the questions below may be used to lead the discussion.

- For Problem 1(a), how did you determine where to draw another line to make fourths?
- For Problem 2, Jasmine looked at the shaded rectangles and exclaimed, "5 eighths equals 4 eighths plus 1 eighth" Do you agree with her? Why?
- For Problem 3, what is interesting about 2 fourths? Can you relate it to halves? When you shaded 3 fourths, what part was left unshaded? How about when you shaded 1 fourth?
- Look at Problems 4(d) and (g). How can 1 fourth be greater than 2 fourths?
- How are Problems 4(a), (d), and (g) alike? How are they different? When will the fourths be exactly the same?
- For Problem 5, what fraction of the pizza did Maria get? How do you know?
- Michael said that 1 eighth is more than 1 fourth because eight is more than 4. Explain his mistake.

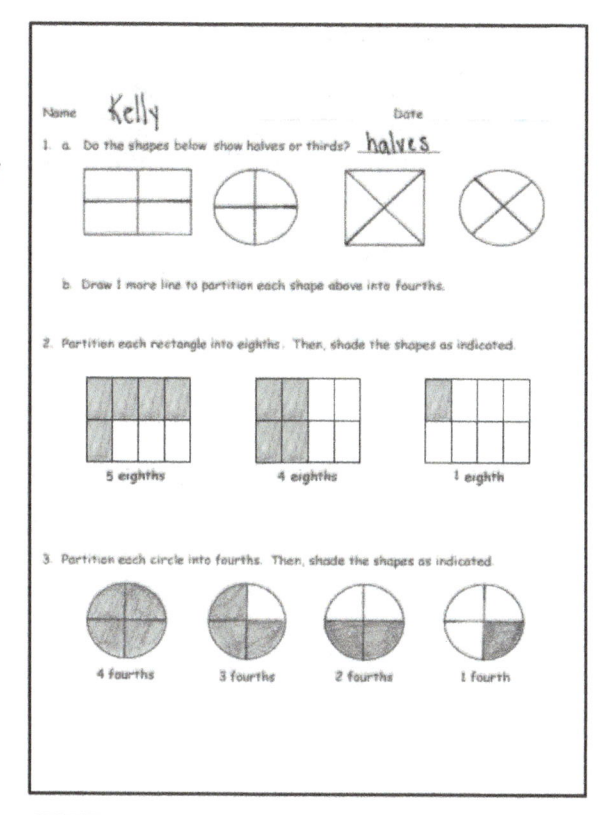

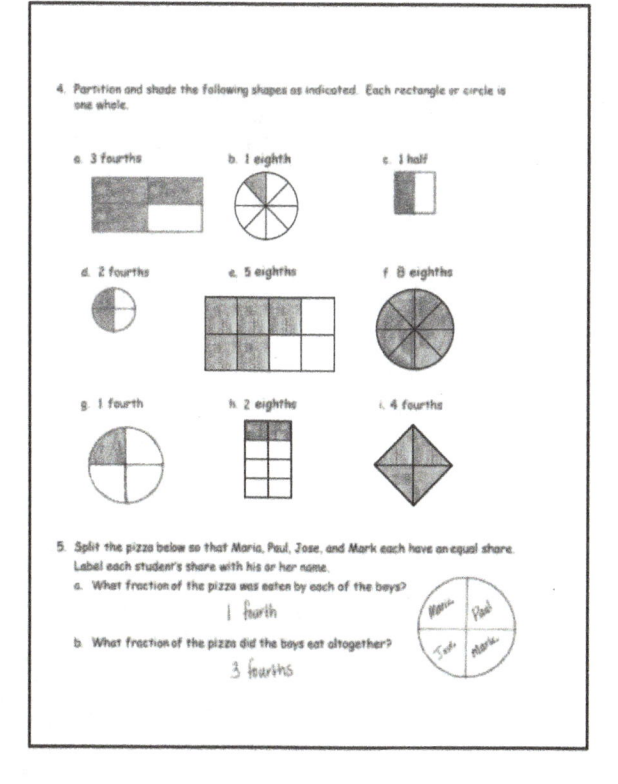

Lesson 10: Partition circles and rectangles into equal parts, and describe those parts as halves, fourths, and eighths.

147

Exit Ticket (3 minutes)

After the Student Debrief, instruct students to complete the Exit Ticket. A review of their work will help with assessing students' understanding of the concepts that were presented in today's lesson and planning more effectively for future lessons. The questions may be read aloud to the students.

A Number Correct: _____

Addition Patterns

1.	8 + 2 =		23.	18 + 6 =	
2.	18 + 2 =		24.	28 + 6 =	
3.	38 + 2 =		25.	16 + 8 =	
4.	7 + 3 =		26.	26 + 8 =	
5.	17 + 3 =		27.	18 + 7 =	
6.	37 + 3 =		28.	18 + 8 =	
7.	8 + 3 =		29.	28 + 7 =	
8.	18 + 3 =		30.	28 + 8 =	
9.	28 + 3 =		31.	15 + 9 =	
10.	6 + 5 =		32.	16 + 9 =	
11.	16 + 5 =		33.	25 + 9 =	
12.	26 + 5 =		34.	26 + 9 =	
13.	18 + 4 =		35.	14 + 7 =	
14.	28 + 4 =		36.	16 + 6 =	
15.	16 + 6 =		37.	15 + 8 =	
16.	26 + 6 =		38.	23 + 8 =	
17.	18 + 5 =		39.	25 + 7 =	
18.	28 + 5 =		40.	15 + 7 =	
19.	16 + 7 =		41.	24 + 7 =	
20.	26 + 7 =		42.	14 + 9 =	
21.	19 + 2 =		43.	19 + 8 =	
22.	17 + 4 =		44.	28 + 9 =	

Lesson 10: Partition circles and rectangles into equal parts, and describe those parts as halves, fourths, and eighths.

B

Addition Patterns

Number Correct: _____

Improvement: _____

1.	9 + 1 =		23.	19 + 5 =	
2.	19 + 1 =		24.	29 + 5 =	
3.	39 + 1 =		25.	17 + 7 =	
4.	6 + 4 =		26.	27 + 7 =	
5.	16 + 4 =		27.	19 + 6 =	
6.	36 + 4 =		28.	19 + 7 =	
7.	9 + 2 =		29.	29 + 6 =	
8.	19 + 2 =		30.	29 + 7 =	
9.	29 + 2 =		31.	17 + 8 =	
10.	7 + 4 =		32.	17 + 9 =	
11.	17 + 4 =		33.	27 + 8 =	
12.	27 + 4 =		34.	27 + 9 =	
13.	19 + 3 =		35.	12 + 9 =	
14.	29 + 3 =		36.	14 + 8 =	
15.	17 + 5 =		37.	16 + 7 =	
16.	27 + 5 =		38.	28 + 6 =	
17.	19 + 4 =		39.	26 + 8 =	
18.	29 + 4 =		40.	24 + 8 =	
19.	17 + 6 =		41.	13 + 8 =	
20.	27 + 6 =		42.	24 + 9 =	
21.	18 + 3 =		43.	29 + 8 =	
22.	26 + 5 =		44.	18 + 9 =	

Name _____ Date _____

1. a. Do the shapes below show halves or thirds? _____

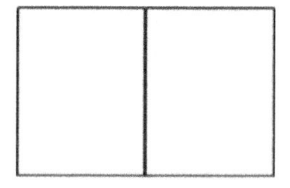

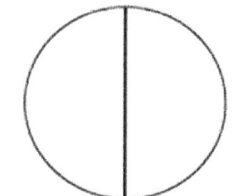

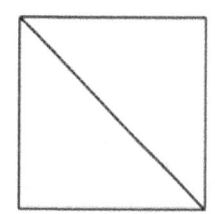

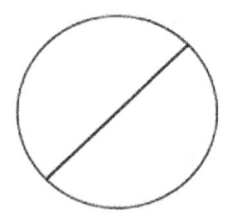

   [Four shapes: rectangle divided vertically, circle divided vertically, square divided diagonally, circle divided diagonally]

   b. Draw 1 more line to partition each shape above into fourths.

2. Partition each rectangle into eighths. Then, shade the shapes as indicated.

   [Three rectangles]

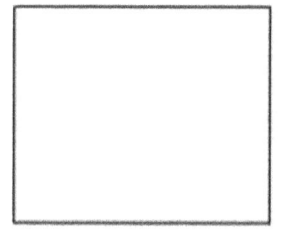

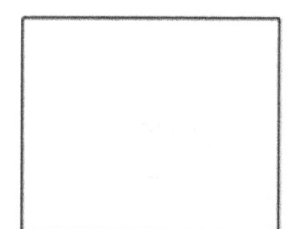

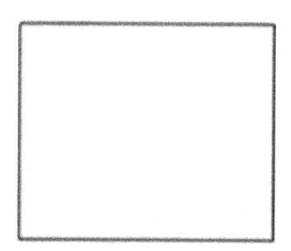

   5 eighths   4 eighths   1 eighth

3. Partition each circle into fourths. Then, shade the shapes as indicated.

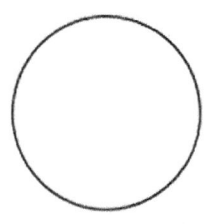

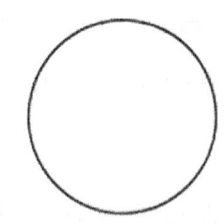

   [Four circles]

   4 fourths   3 fourths   2 fourths   1 fourth

Lesson 10: Partition circles and rectangles into equal parts, and describe those parts as halves, fourths, and eighths.

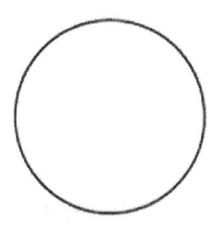

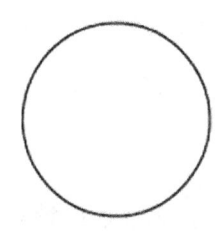

A STORY OF UNITS – TEKS EDITION
Lesson 10 Problem Set 2•8

4. Partition and shade the following shapes as indicated. Each rectangle or circle is one whole.

   a. 3 fourths

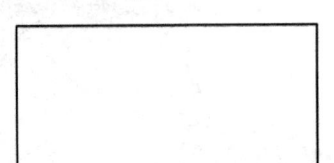

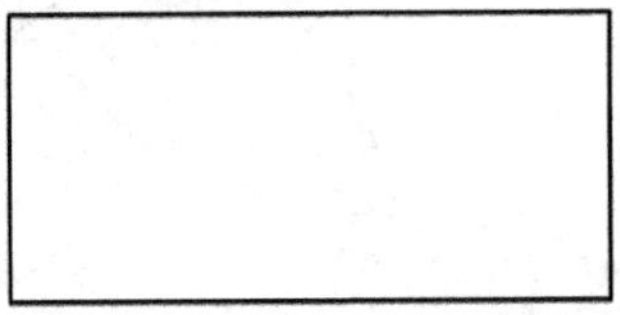

   b. 1 eighth

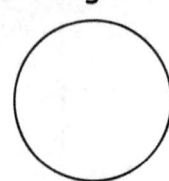

   c. 1 half

   d. 2 fourths

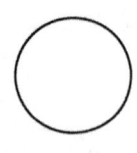

   e. 5 eighths

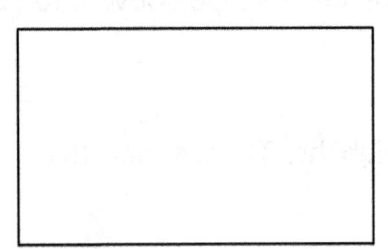

   f. 8 eighths

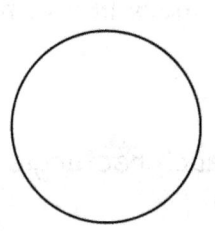

   g. 1 fourth

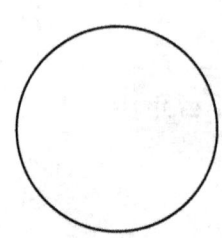

   h. 2 eighths

   i. 4 fourths

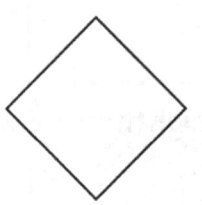

5. Split the pizza below so that Maria, Paul, Jose, and Mark each have an equal share. Label each student's share with his or her name.

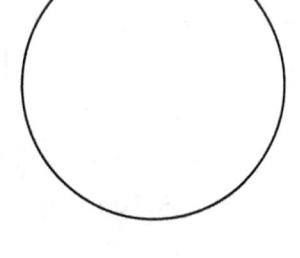

   a. What fraction of the pizza was eaten by each of the boys?

   b. What fraction of the pizza did the boys eat altogether?

Lesson 10: Partition circles and rectangles into equal parts, and describe those parts as halves, fourths, and eighths.

A STORY OF UNITS – TEKS EDITION

Lesson 10 Exit Ticket 2•8

Name _____ Date _____

Partition and shade the following shapes as indicated. Each rectangle or circle is one whole.

1. 2 halves

2. 1 eighth

3. 3 eighths

4. 1 half

5. 2 fourths

6. 1 fourth

Lesson 10: Partition circles and rectangles into equal parts, and describe those parts as halves, fourths, and eighths.

153

Name _____ Date _____

1. a. Do the shapes below show halves or thirds? _____

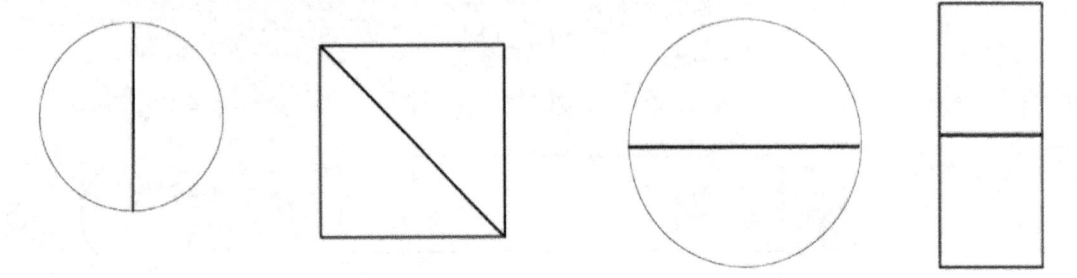

   b. Draw 1 more line to partition each shape above into fourths.

2. Partition each rectangle into eighths. Then, shade the shapes as indicated.

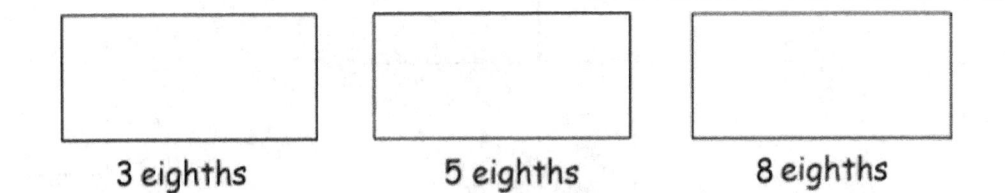

   3 eighths   5 eighths   8 eighths

3. Partition each circle into fourths. Then, shade the shapes as indicated.

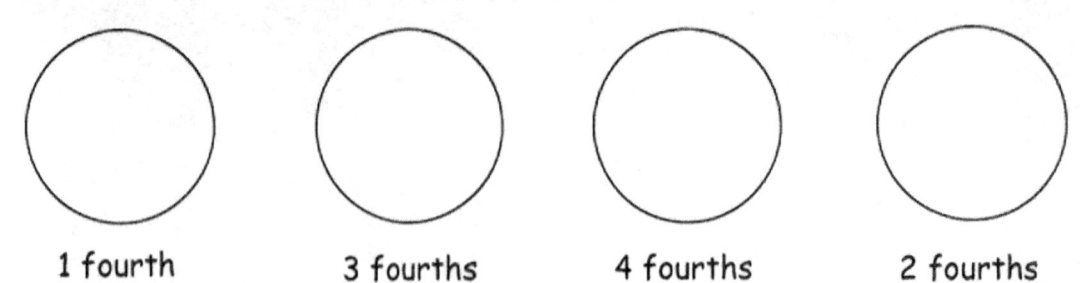

   1 fourth   3 fourths   4 fourths   2 fourths

4. Partition and shade the following shapes. Each rectangle or circle is one whole.

   a. 1 half

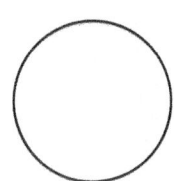

   b. 1 fourth

   c. 2 eighths

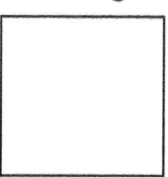

   d. 2 fourths

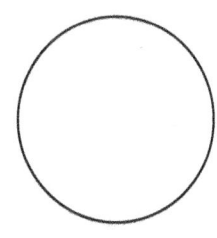

   e. 2 halves

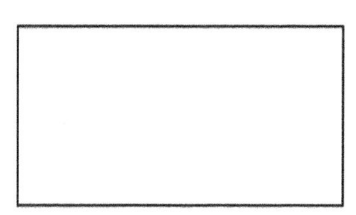

   f. 6 eighths

   g. 1 eighth

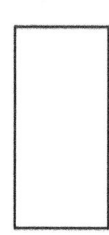

   h. 3 fourths

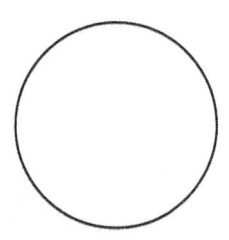

   i. 4 fourths

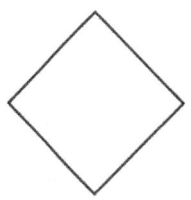

5. Split the pizza below so that Shane, Pedro, Raul, and John all have an equal share. Label each student's share with his name.

   What fraction of the pizza did the boys get in all?

rectangles and circles

Lesson 10: Partition circles and rectangles into equal parts, and describe those parts as halves, fourths, and eighths.

Lesson 11

Objective: Use concrete models to count fractional parts beyond one whole.

Suggested Lesson Structure

- Fluency Practice   (10 minutes)
- Application Problem   (5 minutes)
- Concept Development   (35 minutes)
- Student Debrief   (10 minutes)

Total Time   **(60 minutes)**

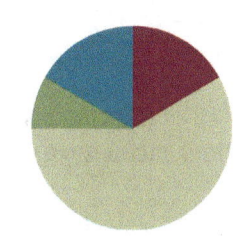

Fluency Practice (10 minutes)

- Addition with Renaming **2.4B**   (5 minutes)
- Grade 2 Fluency Differentiated Practice Sets **2.4A**   (5 minutes)

Addition with Renaming (5 minutes)

Materials: (S) Personal white board, hundreds place value chart (Lesson 4 Fluency Template)

Note: This fluency activity reviews the application of a chip model while recording with the algorithm. Allow students work time between each problem, and reinforce place value understandings by having students say their answer in both unit form and in standard form. Students use their personal white boards and a place value chart to solve.

- T: Slide the place value chart template into your personal white board.
- T: (Write 112 + 159 horizontally on the board.) Let's use a chip model to add. On your personal white board, record your work using the vertical method.
- S: (Solve.)
- T: 112 + 159 is…?
- S: 271.

Continue with the following possible sequence: 184 + 135, 385 + 108, 323 + 491, 263 + 178, 589 + 223, and 471 + 289.

A STORY OF UNITS – TEKS EDITION

Lesson 11 2•8

Grade 2 Fluency Differentiated Practice Sets (5 minutes)

Materials: (S) Fluency Practice Sets (Lesson 3)

Note: During Topic D and for the remainder of the year, each day's Fluency Practice includes an opportunity for review and mastery of the sums and differences with totals through 20 by means of the Fluency Practice Sets or Sprints. The process is detailed, with Practice Sets provided, in Lesson 3.

Application Problem (5 minutes)

Jacob collected 70 baseball cards. He gave half of them to his brother, Sammy. How many baseball cards does Jacob have left?

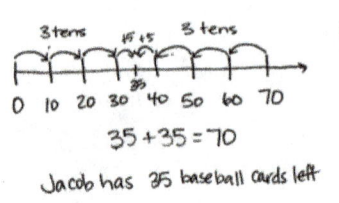

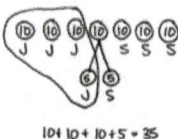

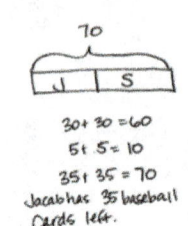

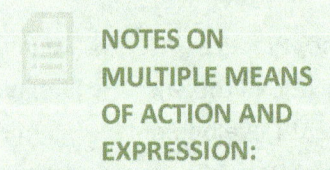

NOTES ON MULTIPLE MEANS OF ACTION AND EXPRESSION:

Offer students working below grade level the following version of the Application Problem: Jacob collected 70 baseball cards. He gave half of them to his brother, Sammy. Now Sammy has 35 baseball cards. How many baseball cards does Jacob have left?

Note: This Application Problem combines what students have learned about subtraction and their new knowledge of halves. It reinforces that halves are equal and a whole comprises equal parts. Three possible solutions are shown above.

Concept Development (35 minutes)

Materials: (T/S) Labeled fraction parts (Template), 1 piece of unlined paper, glue stick

Copy and cut out enough labeled fraction parts templates to have one piece for each student. Check to be sure that there are the right number of pieces to form complete circles.

Part 1: Counting Halves, Fourths, and Eighths Beyond One Whole

T: (Call on a volunteer, and give him one half of a circle from the labeled fraction parts template.) Look at the part that Student A is holding. Does he have a whole circle?

S: No.

T: What does he need to complete the circle?

S: Another half!

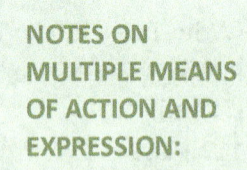

NOTES ON MULTIPLE MEANS OF ACTION AND EXPRESSION:

If the students have the four parts of a square oriented like a rectangle, have the discussion that four one-fourths of a rectangle still make the whole, but the question was asking for a square, a special kind of rectangle. Ask, "How could we change the orientation so that the four parts make a square?"

Lesson 11: Use concrete models to count fractional parts beyond one whole.

T: Good. Watch as I complete the whole. (Hold the other half of the circle next to Student A's part.) 1 half and 1 half make 1 whole; 2 halves make a whole! Say it with me.

S: 1 half and 1 half make a whole. 2 halves make a whole.

T: Good. (Give another volunteer another half.) Look at the part that Student B is holding. If he adds this to the halves I already have, how many halves are there? Count them all with me.

S: 1 half, 2 halves, 3 halves.

T: Is there another way to say 3 halves?

S: 1 whole and 1 half.

T: We can say one and 1 half.

Call on three volunteers and give them each a fourth of a rectangle from the labeled fraction parts template.

T: Look at the parts of the rectangle that these 3 students are holding. They each have 1 fourth. How many fourths do you see altogether?

S: 3 fourths.

T: What do they need to complete the whole rectangle?

S: 1 more fourth.

T: Yes. Watch as I complete the whole. (Hold 1 fourth of the rectangle next to the others.) 1 fourth and 1 fourth and 1 fourth and 1 fourth make a whole; 4 fourths make a whole! (Finish the shape to correctly form a square.) Say it with me.

S: 1 fourth and 1 fourth and 1 fourth and 1 fourth make a whole; 4 fourths make a whole.

T: Let's keep counting. (Ask 2 more students to contribute a fourth for the count.) 5 fourths, 6 fourths. How many fourths do we have now?

S: 6 fourths.

T: Is there another way we can this?

S: One and 2 fourths.

T: How many more fourths do I need to make the next whole?

S: 2 more fourths.

Count to make a whole using the labeled fraction parts template for eighths. Then count past 8 eighths to make fractions greater than 1. Rename these fractions as one and some more eighths.

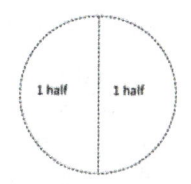

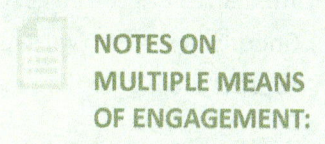

NOTES ON MULTIPLE MEANS OF ENGAGEMENT:

To help underscore for English language learners that fractional parts make a whole, get students to hold the two halves as you say, "One-half and one-half make a whole. Two halves make a whole." Then, have student volunteers join their halves to form a whole. Continue for thirds and fourths.

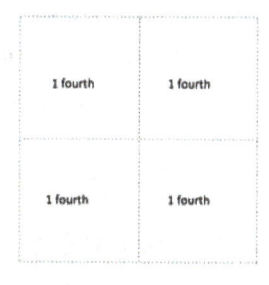

Lesson 11: Use concrete models to count fractional parts beyond one whole.

Part 2: Making a Whole Circle from Paper Cutouts

T: (From the previously cut labeled fraction parts templates, distribute one piece of a whole circle (halves, fourths or eighths) to 14 students.) Each of you has a piece of a whole circle. When I say, "Find your whole," walk around the room to complete your whole. Ready? Find your whole!

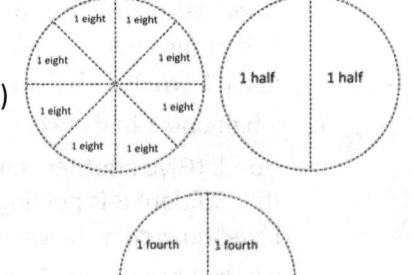

S: (Find the whole.)

T: (Assist students who need help making their whole group.)

T: Very good. Let's look at our whole groups. Do all of our groups have the same number of people?

S: No!

T: Which group has the most people? Which group has the fewest number of people?

S: The eighths have the most people because it takes 8 eighths to make the whole circle. → The halves have the fewest number of people because it only takes 2 halves to make a whole.

T: Which group has the biggest pieces? Which group has the smallest pieces?

S: The halves are the biggest. → The eighths are the smallest.

T: Good. So what can we say about eighths compared to halves and fourths?

S: Fourths are bigger than eighths but smaller than halves! → A shape can have more eighths than halves.

T: The circles was the same size. Explain why fourths are smaller than halves, even though 4 is more than 2.

S: The whole is broken up into more pieces. If there are more pieces, then each piece has to be smaller. The smaller the pieces, the more pieces we need to make the whole.

T: (Distribute additional halves, fourths, and eighths to remaining students. If no students remain, hand the additional fractional units to the groups.) Some more parts are joining! Find your group! (Students join the groups of halves, fourths, and eighths.) Now, count the parts in your group.

S: (Count.)

T: How many halves? How many fourths? How many eighths? (Answers will vary depending on how many additional halves, fourths, and eighths were distributed.)

Ask students to name the totals as fractions and then as mixed unit numbers. For example, a group might say they now have 6 fourths or 1 whole and 2 fourths. Continue to prompt students to notice that as the size of the fractional unit decreases, the number of that unit required to make 1 increases.

Problem Set (10 minutes)

Students should do their personal best to complete the Problem Set within the allotted 10 minutes. For some classes, it may be appropriate to modify the assignment by specifying which problems they work on first. Some problems do not specify a method for solving. Students should solve these problems using the RDW approach used for Application Problems.

A STORY OF UNITS – TEKS EDITION   Lesson 11   2•8

Student Debrief (10 minutes)

Lesson Objective: Use concrete models to count fractional parts beyond one whole.

The Student Debrief is intended to invite reflection and active processing of the total lesson experience.

Invite students to review their solutions for the Problem Set. They should check work by comparing answers with a partner. Look for misconceptions or misunderstandings that can be addressed in the Debrief. Guide students in a conversation to debrief the Problem Set and process the lesson.

Any combination of the questions below may be used to lead the discussion.

- For Problem 1(c), which is closer to one whole, 1 fourth or 5 fourths?
- What is the same and different about 2 halves, 4 fourths and 8 eighths?
- For Problem 2, how can you check to make sure your answer is correct?
- Sangeeta says that 2 halves cannot equal 4 fourths. Explain why you agree or disagree.
- Sangeeta counted sixteenths in Problem 1(c). What mistake did she make?

Exit Ticket (3 minutes)

After the Student Debrief, instruct students to complete the Exit Ticket. A review of their work will help with assessing students' understanding of the concepts that were presented in today's lesson and planning more effectively for future lessons. The questions may be read aloud to the students.

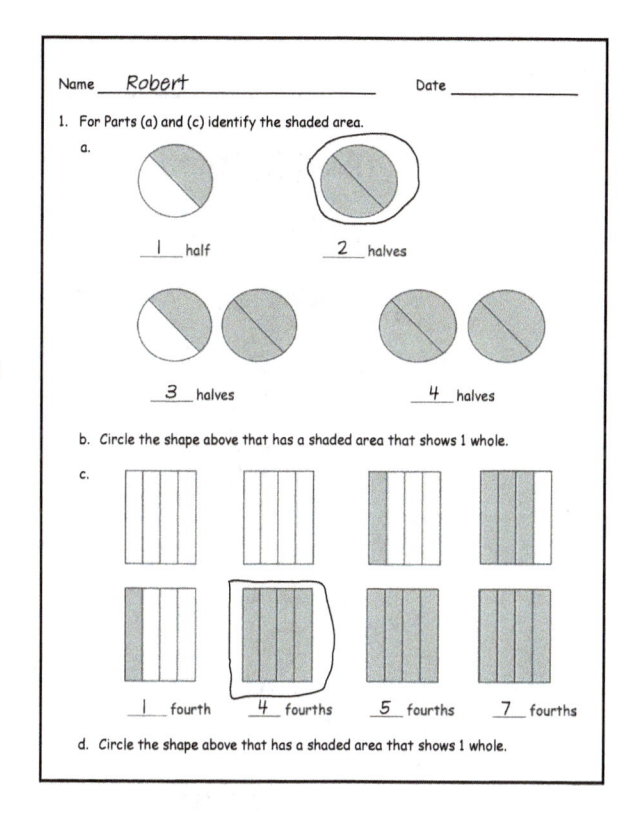

Name Robert   Date _____

1. For Parts (a) and (c) identify the shaded area.

   a.

   __1__ half   __2__ halves

   __3__ halves   __4__ halves

   b. Circle the shape above that has a shaded area that shows 1 whole.

   c.

   __1__ fourth   __4__ fourths   __5__ fourths   __7__ fourths

   d. Circle the shape above that has a shaded area that shows 1 whole.

2. What fraction do you need to color so that 1 whole is shaded?

   a. 7 eighths   b. 1 half

   c. 2 fourths   d. 6 eighths

   e. 1 half   f. 1 fourth

3. Complete the drawing to show 1 whole.

   a. This is 1 half.   b. This is 1 eighth.   c. This is 1 fourth.
      Draw 1 whole.   Draw 1 whole.   Draw 1 whole.

Lesson 11:   Use concrete models to count fractional parts beyond one whole.

A STORY OF UNITS – TEKS EDITION

Lesson 11 Problem Set 2•8

Name _____ Date _____

1. For Parts (a) and (c) identify the shaded area.

    a.

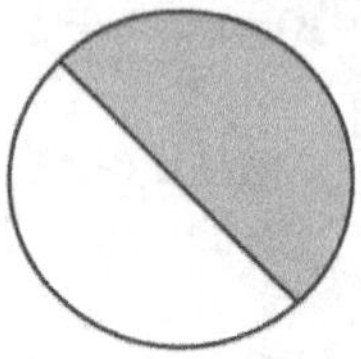

    _____ half 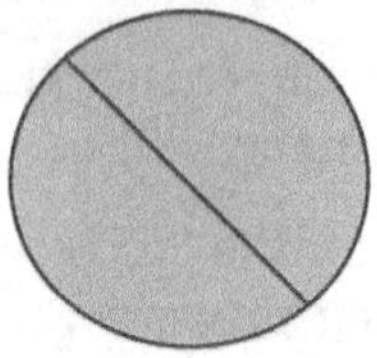   _____ halves

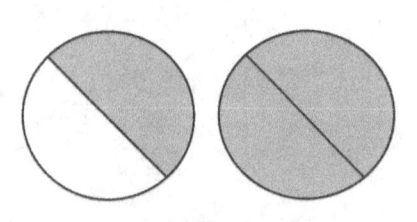

    _____ halves 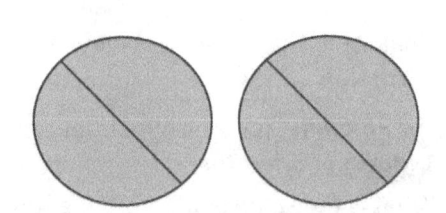   _____ halves

    b. Circle the shape above that has a shaded area that shows 1 whole.

    c.

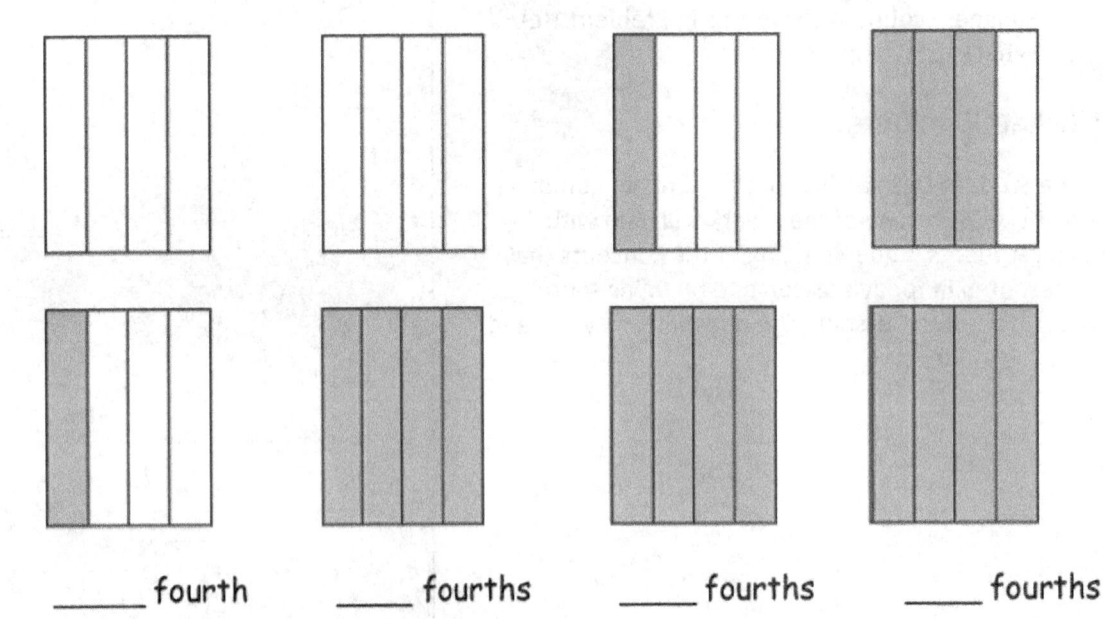

    _____ fourth   _____ fourths   _____ fourths   _____ fourths

    d. Circle the shape above that has a shaded area that shows 1 whole.

2. What fraction do you need to color so that 1 whole is shaded?

a.

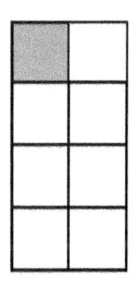

b.

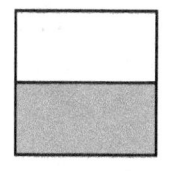

c.

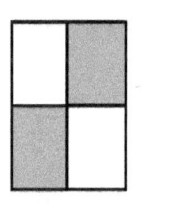

d.

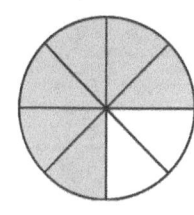

e.

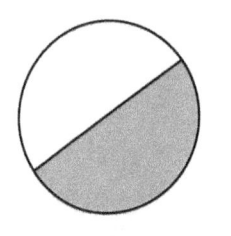

f.

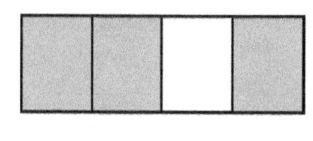

3. Complete the drawing to show 1 whole.

a. This is 1 half.
Draw 1 whole.

b. This is 1 eighth.
Draw 1 whole.

c. This is 1 fourth.
Draw 1 whole.

Name _____ Date _____

What fraction do you need to color so that 1 whole is shaded?

1.

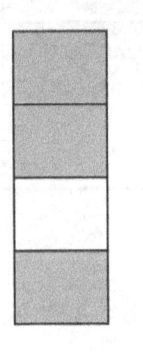

_____

2.

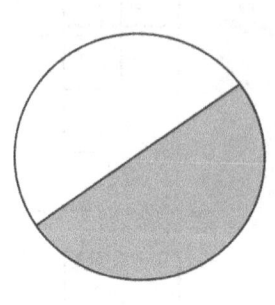

_____

3.

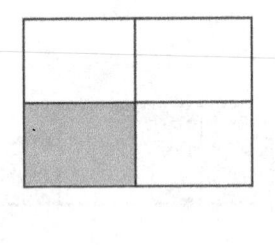

_____

4. What fraction is shaded?

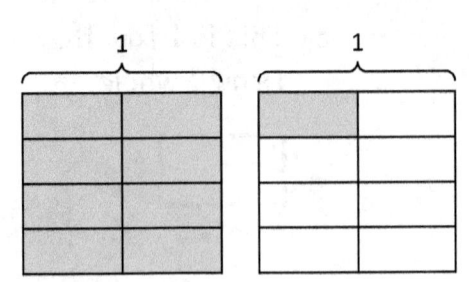

_____

A STORY OF UNITS – TEKS EDITION

Lesson 11 Homework 2•8

Name _____ Date _____

1. For Parts (a) and (c) identify the shaded area.

   a.

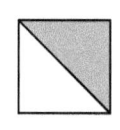

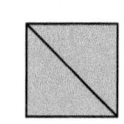

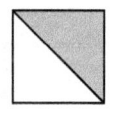

   _____ half   _____ halves

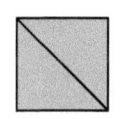

   _____ halves   _____ halves

   b. Circle the shape above that has a shaded area that shows 1 whole.

   c.

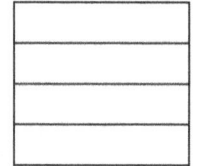

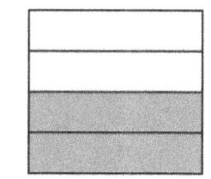

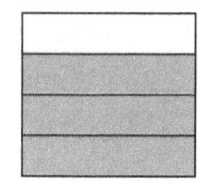

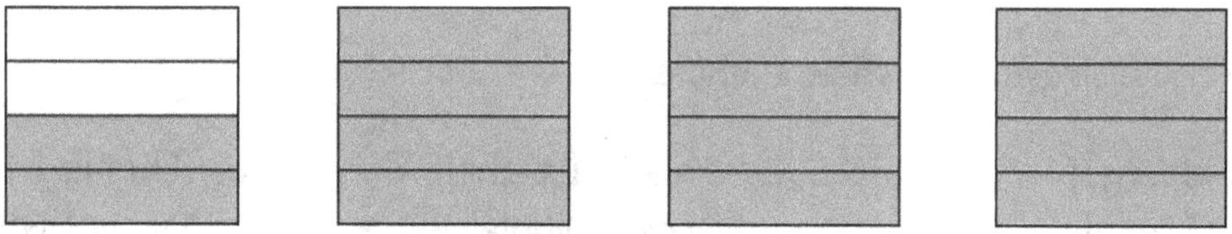

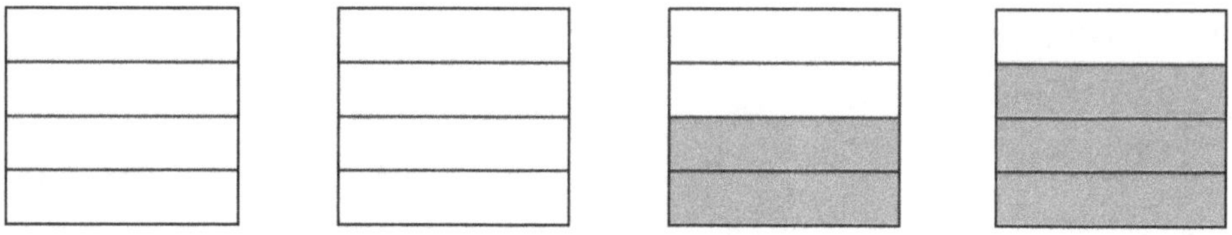

   ____ fourth   ____ fourths   ____ fourths   ____ fourths

   d. Circle the shape above that has a shaded area that shows 1 whole.

Lesson 11: Use concrete models to count fractional parts beyond one whole.

165

2. What fraction do you need to color so that 1 whole is shaded?

a.

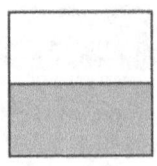

b.

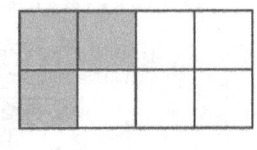

c.

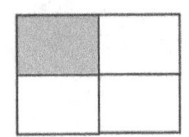

d.

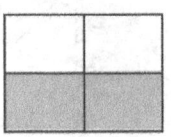

e.

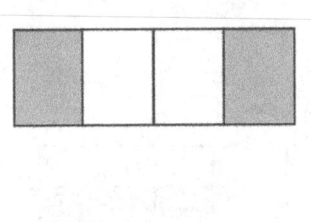

f.

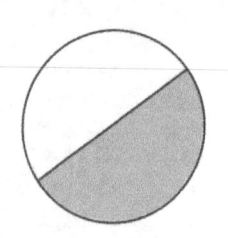

3. Complete the drawing to show 1 whole.

a. This is 1 half.
Draw 1 whole.

b. This is 1 eighth.
Draw 1 whole.

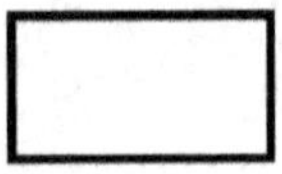

c. This is 1 fourth.
Draw 1 whole.

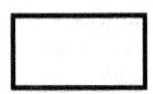

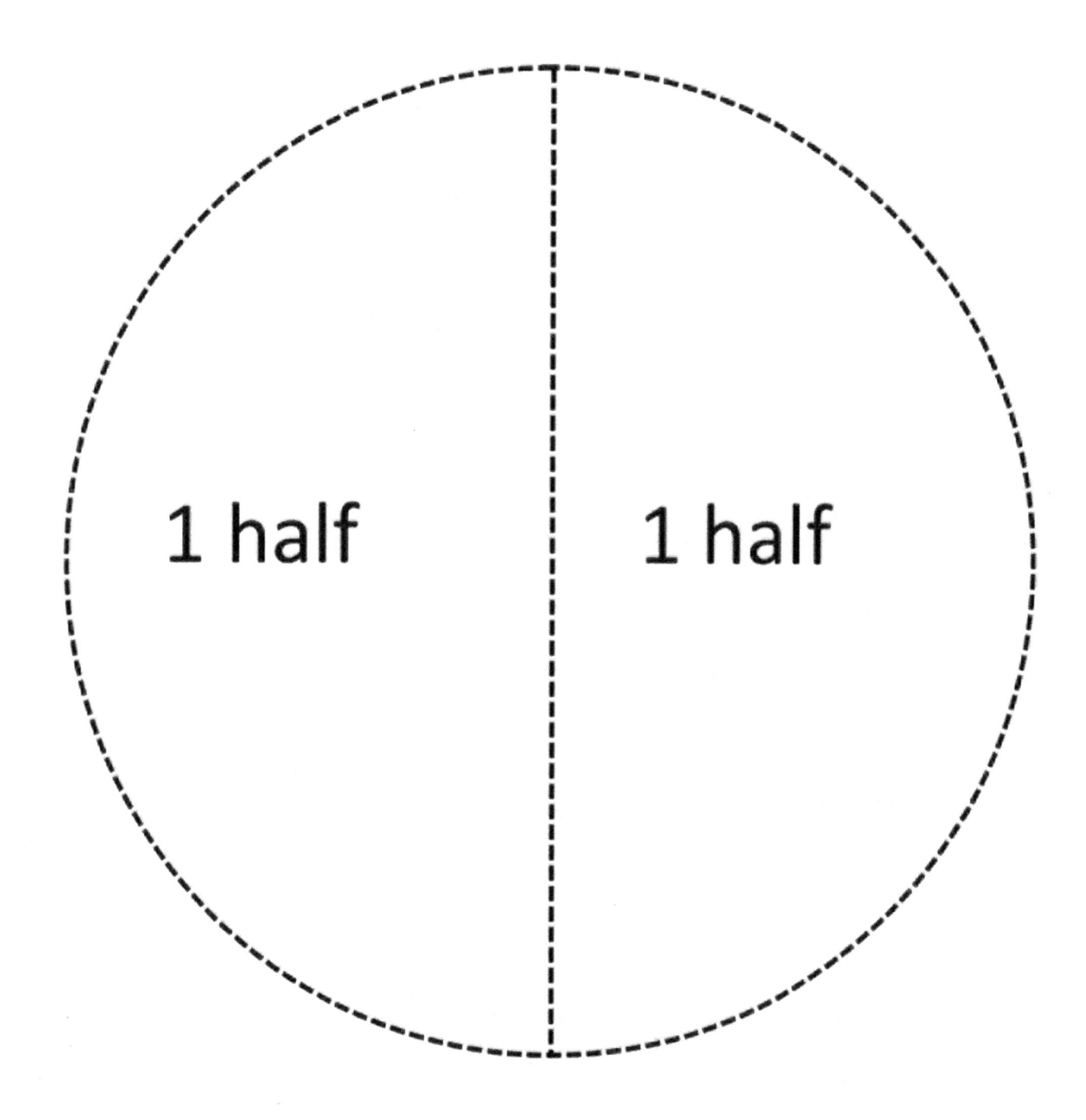

A circle divided vertically into two equal parts, each labeled "1 half".

labeled fraction parts

Lesson 11: Use concrete models to count fractional parts beyond one whole.

A STORY OF UNITS – TEKS EDITION

Lesson 11 Template 2•8

1 fourth	1 fourth
1 fourth	1 fourth

_____

labeled fraction parts

Lesson 11: Use concrete models to count fractional parts beyond one whole.

A STORY OF UNITS – TEKS EDITION

Lesson 11 Template 2•8

1 eighth	1 eighth
1 eighth	1 eighth
1 eighth	1 eighth
1 eighth	1 eighth

1 fourth	1 fourth
1 fourth	1 fourth

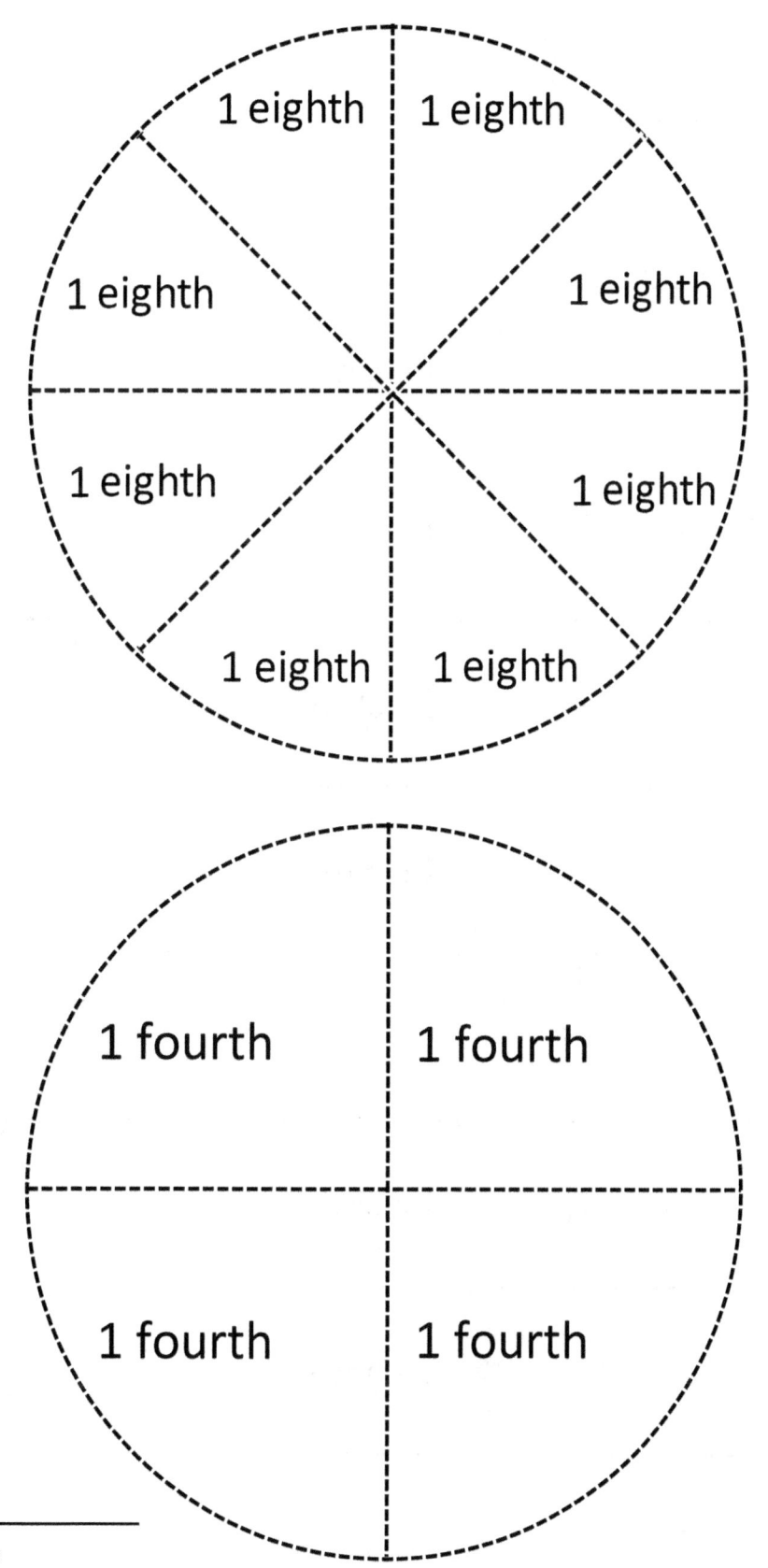

labeled fraction parts

Lesson 11: Use concrete models to count fractional parts beyond one whole.

A STORY OF UNITS – TEKS EDITION

Lesson 11 Template   2•8

1 eighth

1 eighth

1 eighth

1 eighth

1 eighth

1 eighth

1 eighth

1 eighth

labeled fractional parts

Lesson 11: Use concrete models to count fractional parts beyond one whole.

A STORY OF UNITS — TEKS EDITION

Mathematics Curriculum

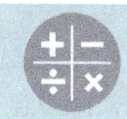

GRADE 2 • MODULE 8

Topic D
Application of Fractions to Tell Time

2.3A, 2.8E, 2.9G, 2.2C, 2.4A, 2.4B

Focus Standards:	2.3A	Partition objects into equal parts and name the parts, including halves, fourths, and eighths, using words.
	2.8E	Decompose two-dimensional shapes such as cutting out a square from a rectangle, dividing a shape in half, or partitioning a rectangle into identical triangles and identify the resulting geometric parts.
	2.9G	Read and write time to the nearest one-minute increment using analog and digital clocks and distinguish between a.m. and p.m.
Instructional Days:	5	
Coherence	-Links from: G1–M5	Identifying, Composing, and Partitioning Shapes
	-Links to: G3–M2	Place Value and Problem Solving with Units of Measure

In Topic D, students apply fraction and skip-counting skills to telling time. The topic starts with Lesson 12, in which students make paper clocks from templates. After a brief review of the clock using a geared instructional clock, students fold their paper clock face in half and trace along the fold line to delineate the 2 halves. They then mark the top of the fold with 12 and the bottom with 6. Students next fold the clock in half again so that the two fold points meet, creating quarters. Students trace along this second fold line and mark 3 and 9 at the new fold points. In the end, they label the remaining numbers and attach hands in order to use it as a practice clock.

Having constructed this tool, students then practice telling time to the nearest half and quarter hour. They relate 30 minutes to a half hour and 15 minutes to a quarter hour, associating, for example, "half past 7" with 7:30 or 2:45 with "a quarter to 3."

In Lesson 13, students start to relate each of the 12 numbers on the clock face to intervals of 5 minutes. They use skip-counting to count up to and down from 60 by fives in preparation for telling time to the nearest 5 minutes. Next, they learn to tell time by counting numbers on the clock face for the minute hand, as well as relating the position of the hour hand to the correct hour.

Lesson 14 continues the same process, now adding the complexity of telling time to the nearest minute and relating a.m. and p.m. to time of day. Students view pictures showing everyday activities along with the time represented in digital clock form. They determine whether the time shown in the picture would be a.m. or p.m.

A STORY OF UNITS – TEKS EDITION

Topic D 2•8

Lesson 15 builds students' understanding of time as a continuous unit of measurement. Students relate skip counting by fives and telling time to the number line. They learn to draw the model, labeling hours as endpoints and multiples of 5. Through this work, students recognize the analog clock as a portion of the number line shaped into a circle. From this point on, they use the number line as a tool for modeling and solving problems.

Lesson 16 increases students' level of precision as they read and write time to the nearest minute. Student use number line models that represent the minutes between multiples of 5 (number line model shown below). They apply the strategy of counting by fives and some ones to read time to the nearest minute on the clock (**2.9G**).

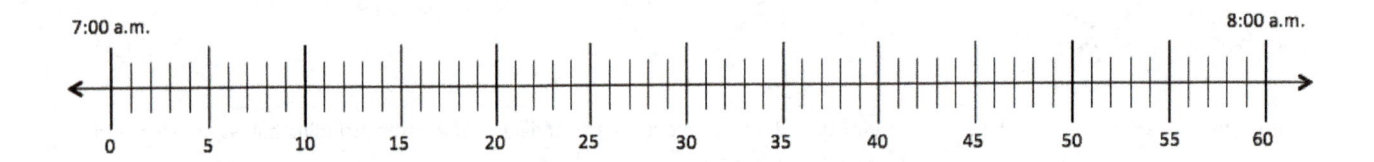

A Teaching Sequence Toward Mastery of Application of Fractions to Tell Time
Objective 1: Construct a paper clock by partitioning a circle into halves and quarters, and tell time to the half hour or quarter hour.   (Lesson 12)
Objective 2: Tell time to the nearest five minutes.   (Lesson 13)
Objective 3: Tell time to the nearest five minutes; relate *a.m.* and *p.m.* to time of day.   (Lesson 14)
Objective 4: Relate skip counting by fives on the clock and telling time to a continuous measurement model, the number line.   (Lesson 15)
Objective 5: Count by fives and ones on the number line as a strategy to tell time to the nearest minute on the clock.   (Lesson 16)

Lesson 12

Objective: Construct a paper clock by partitioning a circle into halves and quarters, and tell time to the half hour or quarter hour.

Suggested Lesson Structure

- Fluency Practice (10 minutes)
- Concept Development (10 minutes)
- Student Debrief (10 minutes)
- **Total Time** **(60 minutes)**

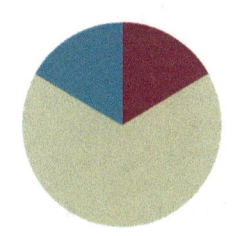

Fluency Practice (10 minutes)

- Rename for the Smaller Unit **2.2A** (1 minute)
- Subtraction with Renaming **2.4B** (9 minutes)

Rename for the Smaller Unit (1 minute)

Note: This fluency activity reviews using place value understanding to rename units in preparation for subtraction with chips and the algorithm during Fluency Practice in Lessons 13 and 14.

T: I'm going to give you a number of hundreds and tens. I want you to rename 1 of the hundreds for 10 tens and then tell me how many hundreds and tens. Ready?
T: (Write 1 hundred 1 ten = _____ tens.) Say the number sentence.
S: 1 hundred 1 ten = 11 tens.
T: (Write 2 hundreds = 1 hundred _____ tens.) Say the number sentence.
S: 2 hundreds = 1 hundred 10 tens.
T: (Write 2 hundreds = 1 hundred 9 tens _____ ones.) Say the number sentence.
S: 2 hundreds = 1 hundred 9 tens 10 ones.

Repeat the process for 3 hundreds 3 tens and 4 hundreds 4 tens.

Subtraction with Renaming (9 minutes)

Materials: (S) Personal white board, hundreds place value chart (Lesson 4 Fluency Template)

Note: This fluency activity reviews the application of a chip model while recording with the algorithm. Allow students work time between each problem, and reinforce place value understandings by having students say their answer in both unit form and in standard form. Students use their personal white boards and a place value chart to solve.

A STORY OF UNITS – TEKS EDITION Lesson 12 2•8

T: Slide the place value chart template into your personal white board.
T: (Write 132 – 118 horizontally on the board.) Let's use a chip model to subtract. On your board, record your work using the algorithm.
S: (Solve.)
T: 132 – 118 is...?
S: 14.

Continue with the following possible sequence: 183 – 129, 278 – 159, 347 – 183, 563 – 271, 646 – 295, and 438 – 239.

Concept Development (40 minutes)

Materials: (T) Large instructional clock with gears, clock (Template), document camera (if available), crayon, sentence strips to post vocabulary: *half past, a quarter past, a quarter to* (S) clock (Template) printed on cardstock, scissors, crayon, brad fastener, personal white board

Note: To allow ample time for the Concept Development, there is no Application Problem in this lesson.

Call students to the carpet. Use a geared demonstration clock to review the hour and minute hands and how they move in relation to each other, as well as the meaning of the numbers on the clock. Then, review telling time to the whole hour, starting at twelve o'clock.

Part 1: Brief Review Using a Geared Clock

T: (Show 12:00.) Where is the minute hand?
S: At the 12.
T: Where is the hour hand?
S: At the 12.
T: What time is it?
S: Twelve o'clock.
T: When the minute hand moves all the way around the clock, it has been 60 minutes, or 1 whole hour. When 1 hour passes, what time will it be? (Move the minute hand a full rotation.)
S: One o'clock.

Show various hours on the clock, and have students name them.

T: (Show 1:00 again.) When half an hour has passed, the minute hand is halfway around the circle. (Move the minute hand.) Tell me when to stop.
S: Stop!
T: At what number did the minute hand stop?
S: At the 6.
T: And the hour hand is halfway between the 1 and...?
S: 2.
T: What fraction of the whole hour has passed?
S: Half an hour.

Lesson 12: Construct a paper clock by partitioning a circle into halves and quarters, and tell time to the half hour or quarter hour.

T: Yes. This is why we call this time half past the hour. Let's read this time together as half past 1.
S: It is half past one.
T: Does anyone know another way to read this time?
S: One thirty.
T: Yes! What time is it one half hour later? (Move the minute hand.)
S: Two o'clock.

Repeat the process of showing a whole hour, having students name it, and then showing the half hour and having students name it both ways.

Part 2: Constructing a Paper Clock

Distribute the clock template and scissors to students seated at desks or tables.

T: Cut out the circle in front of you just outside the dark line along the dotted line. (Model as students do the same. Cutting on the dotted line leaves a small edge around the outline of the clock to write 15, 30, 45, and 60 in Part 4 of the lesson.)
T: Now, fold the circle in half along one set of dotted lines. (Model as students do the same.)
T: Unfold your circle, and look at it. How many equal parts do we have now?
S: 2.
T: What fraction is each equal part?
S: 1 half.
T: Yes! Let's trace along the folded line to clearly show the 2 halves. (Allow students time to trace.)
T: What number is at the top of the clock?
S: 12.
T: Let's write that in. (Write 12 on the top of the line as students do the same.)
T: How about at the bottom of the clock?
S: 6.
T: Let's fill that in. (Write 6 on the bottom of the line as students do the same.)
T: Now, let's take our circle and fold it in half again along the same line as before. And then let's fold it in half one more time. That means that we will fold along the flat part so the rounded parts are matching each other. (Demonstrate.)
T: Unfold the circle. (Pause for students to unfold.) What fraction is each part now?
S: Fourths!

> **NOTES ON MULTIPLE MEANS OF ENGAGEMENT:**
>
> Some students who struggle with fine motor cutting skills would benefit from using a pre-cut circle. Have some ready for the lesson for these students to use.

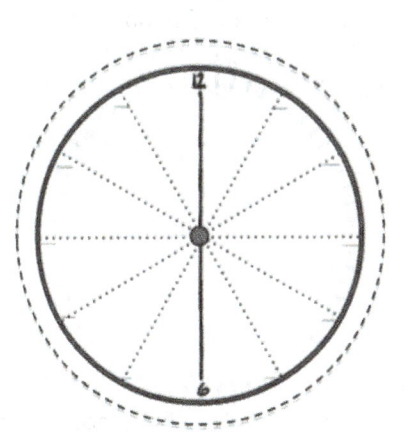

Lesson 12: Construct a paper clock by partitioning a circle into halves and quarters, and tell time to the half hour or quarter hour.

A STORY OF UNITS – TEKS EDITION · Lesson 12 · 2•8

T: Interesting. How did we get from halves to fourths? Turn and talk.

S: When we folded the half, we split it in half again. Now, we have 4 equal parts. → A half cut in half makes a fourth. → If you split 2 equal shares in half, then you'll have 4 equal shares.

T: That's right! We had 2 halves, and now we have 4 fourths! Let's trace along this second folded line. (Pause.)

T: Now that we can see the 4 quarters, let's use them to help us tell time.

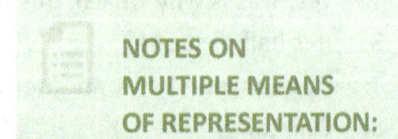

> **NOTES ON MULTIPLE MEANS OF REPRESENTATION:**
>
> Highlight the critical vocabulary for English language learners. For instance, show pictures for *circle*, *half*, and *fourth*. Posting the vocabulary with the pictures helps students follow the lesson and engage in partner talk.

Guide students through filling in the 3 and 9. Then, guide them through cutting out and attaching the clock hands with the brad fastener.

Part 3: Using a Paper Clock to Tell Time to the Half or Quarter Hour

T: Show me twelve o'clock. (Check as students do so.)

T: Now, move your minute hand to the 3. (Allow students time to move the hands.)

T: What fraction of an hour passes when the minute hand moves from the 12 to the 3? Turn and talk.

S: A quarter. → 1 fourth.

T: Yes! It moved 1 fourth, or a quarter, of an hour. So, when the minute hand points to 3, we say it's a **quarter past** the hour.

Practice telling a quarter past the hour by showing various hours on the geared clock. For each new hour, move the minute hand, and ask students to say "stop" at a quarter past the hour. This reinforces the 3 as the point on the clock that denotes the first quarter hour. Have students read each time as *a quarter past* ____. Also, have students note the movement of the hour hand in conjunction with the minute hand.

T: Your clocks should still show a quarter past twelve. Move the minute hand to show where the next quarter hour ends. (Check as students do so.)

T: At what number did the minute hand stop?

S: 6.

T: Think back to what we learned earlier. What fraction of the hour has passed when the minute hand is on 6? Turn and talk.

S: A half hour. → 2 quarters of an hour. → 30 minutes!

T: Yes! Let's keep going. Where does the next quarter hour end? Move the minute hand to show where the next quarter hour ends. (Check as students do so.)

T: At what number did the minute hand stop?

S: 9.

T: What fraction of the hour has passed when the minute hand is on 9? Turn and talk.

S: I see that it's 3 quarters past the 12. → I counted three equal parts, so 3 quarters.

T: Yes! 3 quarters past the hour. And how many quarters would be left until the next hour?

S: 1 quarter!

Lesson 12: Construct a paper clock by partitioning a circle into halves and quarters, and tell time to the half hour or quarter hour.

A STORY OF UNITS – TEKS EDITION Lesson 12 2•8

T: Correct! So, when we tell the time, we usually call it a **quarter to** the hour. For example, my clock shows one o'clock. (Show 1:00 on the geared clock. Then, move the hands to show 1:45.) Now, it shows a quarter to two.

Continue to practice telling a quarter to the hour using the geared clock. For each new hour, move the minute hand, and ask students to say "stop" at a quarter to the hour. This reinforces the 9 as the point on the clock that denotes the third quarter hour, or a quarter to the hour. Have students read each time as *a quarter to ___*. Also, have students note the movement of the hour hand in conjunction with the minute hand.

Part 4: Relating Minutes to a Half and a Quarter Hour

T: Let's fill in the missing numbers on our clocks. (Model with your clock as students do the same.)
T: Who remembers what each little mark on the side of the clock means?
S: One minute!
T: And how many minutes are between one number and the next? (Count with students.)
S: 5 minutes!
T: So, we can skip count by…?
S: Fives!
T: Let's count by fives to see how many minutes are in this quarter hour. (Move a finger along the edge of the clock, and count together.)
S: 5, 10, 15.
T: Write 15 on the outside of the circle next to the number 3. (Model as students do the same.)
T: How many minutes are in a quarter hour?
S: 15 minutes!
T: Let's keep counting by fives. (Move a finger from the 3 to the 6, and count together.)
S: 20, 25, 30.
T: Write 30 below the 6. (Model as students do the same.)
T: Keep going. (Move a finger from the 6 to the 9.)
S: 35, 40, 45.
T: Write 45 on the outside of the circle next to the 9. (Model as students do the same.)
T: Let's do the last quarter hour. (Move a finger from the 9 to the 12.)
S: 50, 55, 60.
T: Write 60 above the 12. (Model as students do the same.)

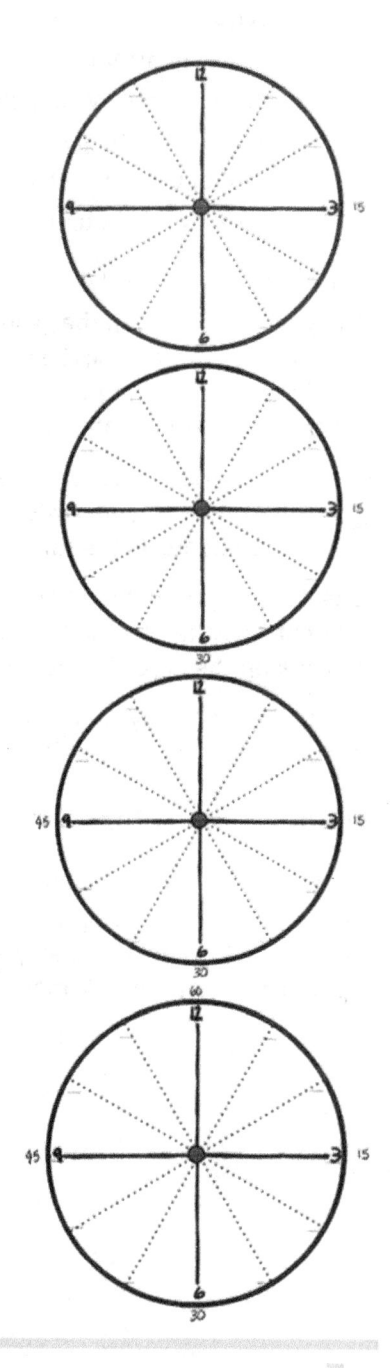

Lesson 12: Construct a paper clock by partitioning a circle into halves and quarters, and tell time to the half hour or quarter hour.

T: When the minute hand moves through all 4 quarters, we have completed what whole unit?

S: One hour!

T: (Show 6:15 on the geared clock.) How many minutes past the hour is it? Turn and talk.

S: It would be 5, 10, 15, so 15 minutes. → Three fives is 15, so 15 minutes. → It's 15 minutes past the hour.

T: Yes! The 3 represents 15 minutes past the hour, 3 groups of 5 minutes. And what fraction of the hour does it also represent?

S: A quarter. → A fourth.

T: Yes! A quarter of an hour is also 15 minutes.

T: Turn and talk. When the minute hand points to the 6, how many minutes past the hour is it?

S: It's another quarter, so 15 + 15 is 30, so 30 minutes. → An hour is 60 minutes, and 60 is 6 tens, and half of 6 is 3, so 30 minutes. → 5, 10, 15, 20, 25, 30. 30 minutes. → Half of 60 is 30, so 30 minutes.

T: Yes! Half an hour is 30 minutes. Great!

Repeat for the 9 as well.

Show various times on the geared clock, and have students name the time using both the posted vocabulary and the minutes (e.g., 4:15 and a quarter past four, 2:30 and half past two). Then, name times, alternating word form and number form, and have students show the time on their clocks and write it on their personal white boards, using both words and numbers.

T: On your personal white boards, write the time shown on your clocks in both words and numbers. Remember, we write the hour, then a colon, then the number of minutes. (Model the first few as students do the same.)

Check to ensure that the hour hands are positioned correctly, especially with *a quarter to two,* as some students may be confused by the language *to two.* As they demonstrate proficiency, instruct students to work on the Problem Set. Allow early finishers to shade each quarter of their clock a different color.

Note: Teachers may want to collect the clocks after students write their names on them because the clocks are used again in the next lesson.

Problem Set (10 minutes)

Students should do their personal best to complete the Problem Set within the allotted 10 minutes. For some classes, it may be appropriate to modify the assignment by specifying which problems they work on first. Some problems do not specify a method for solving. Students should solve these problems using the RDW approach used for Application Problems.

Student Debrief (10 minutes)

Lesson Objective: Construct a paper clock by partitioning a circle into halves and quarters, and tell time to the half hour or quarter hour.

The Student Debrief is intended to invite reflection and active processing of the total lesson experience.

Invite students to review their solutions for the Problem Set. They should check work by comparing answers with a partner. Look for misconceptions or misunderstandings that can be addressed in the Debrief. Guide students in a conversation to debrief the Problem Set and process the lesson.

Any combination of the questions below may be used to lead the discussion.

- For Problem 1, when telling time, what word(s) do you use to describe 1 fourth past the hour? What about 2 fourths past the hour? And 3 fourths past the hour?
- For Problem 2(b), how much time has passed? What fraction of the whole hour is 15 minutes? Explain why this is called **quarter past**. What fraction of the hour is left?
- For Problem 2(c), if it is 3:30, why isn't the hour hand pointed directly at the number 3?
- For Problem 3, explain how you know that 3:45 and a **quarter to** four represent the same time. Turn and talk.
- What is similar about describing these two times: 12:15 and 12:45?
- Using what you know about halves and quarters, how much time has passed from 1:15 to 1:45?

Exit Ticket (3 minutes)

After the Student Debrief, instruct students to complete the Exit Ticket. A review of their work will help with assessing students' understanding of the concepts that were presented in today's lesson and planning more effectively for future lessons. The questions may be read aloud to the students.

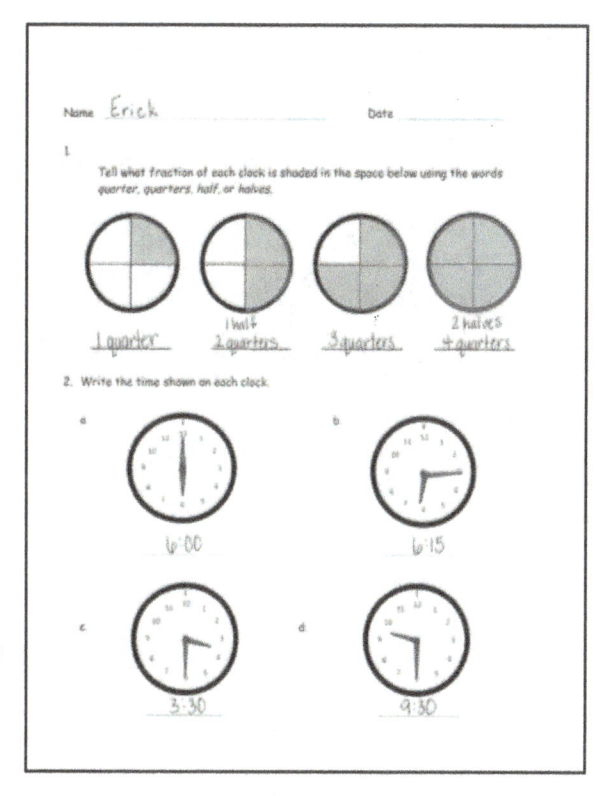

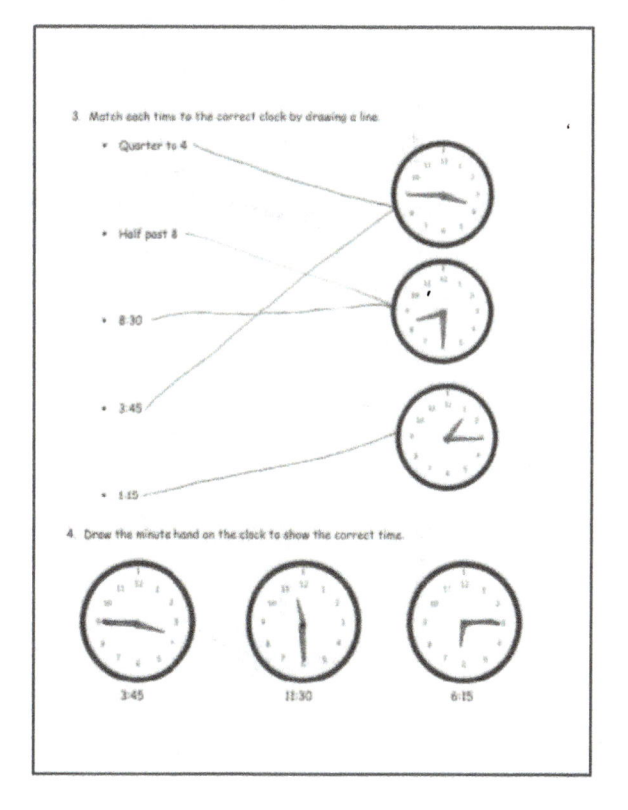

A STORY OF UNITS – TEKS EDITION   Lesson 12 Problem Set   2•8

Name _____   Date _____

1. Tell what fraction of each clock is shaded in the space below using the words *quarter, quarters, half,* or *halves*.

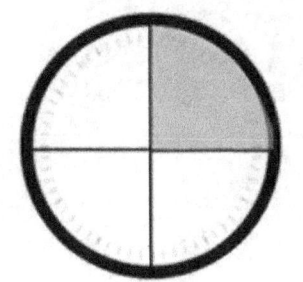

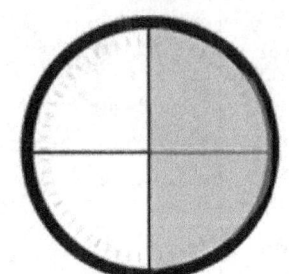

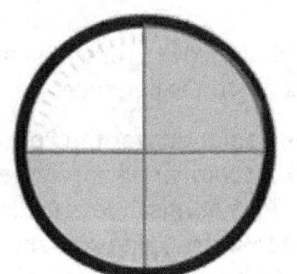

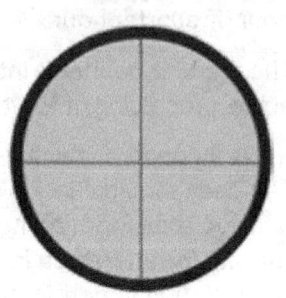

   _____   _____   _____   _____

2. Write the time shown on each clock.

   a.

   _____

   b.

   _____

   c.

   _____

   d.

   _____

180   Lesson 12:   Construct a paper clock by partitioning a circle into halves and quarters, and tell time to the half hour or quarter hour.

3. Match each time to the correct clock by drawing a line.
- Quarter to 4

- Half past 8

- 8:30

- 3:45

- 1:15

3. Draw the minute hand on the clock to show the correct time.

3:45   11:30   6:15

Name _____ Date _____

Draw the minute hand on the clock to show the correct time.

Half past 7   12:15   A quarter to 3

A STORY OF UNITS – TEKS EDITION

Lesson 12 Homework 2•8

Name _____ Date _____

1. Tell what fraction of each clock is shaded in the space below using the words *quarter, quarters, half,* or *halves*.

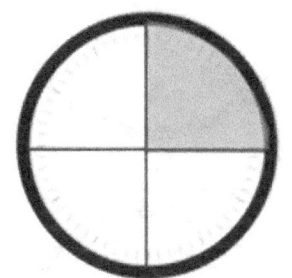

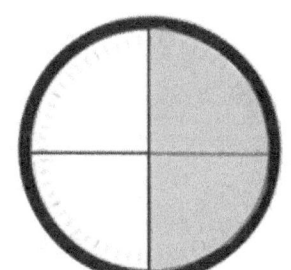

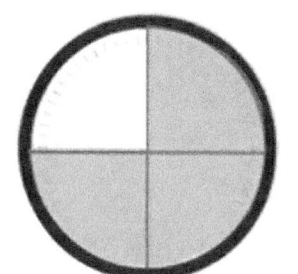

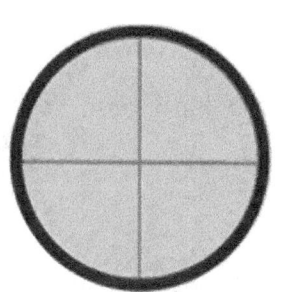

   _____   _____   _____   _____

2. Write the time shown on each clock.

   a. _____

   b. _____

   c. _____

   d. _____

Lesson 12: Construct a paper clock by partitioning a circle into halves and quarters, and tell time to the half hour or quarter hour.

3. Match each time to the correct clock by drawing a line.

- Quarter to 5

- Half past 5

- 5:15

- Quarter after 5

- 4:45

4. Draw the minute hand on the clock to show the correct time.

3:30   11:45   6:15

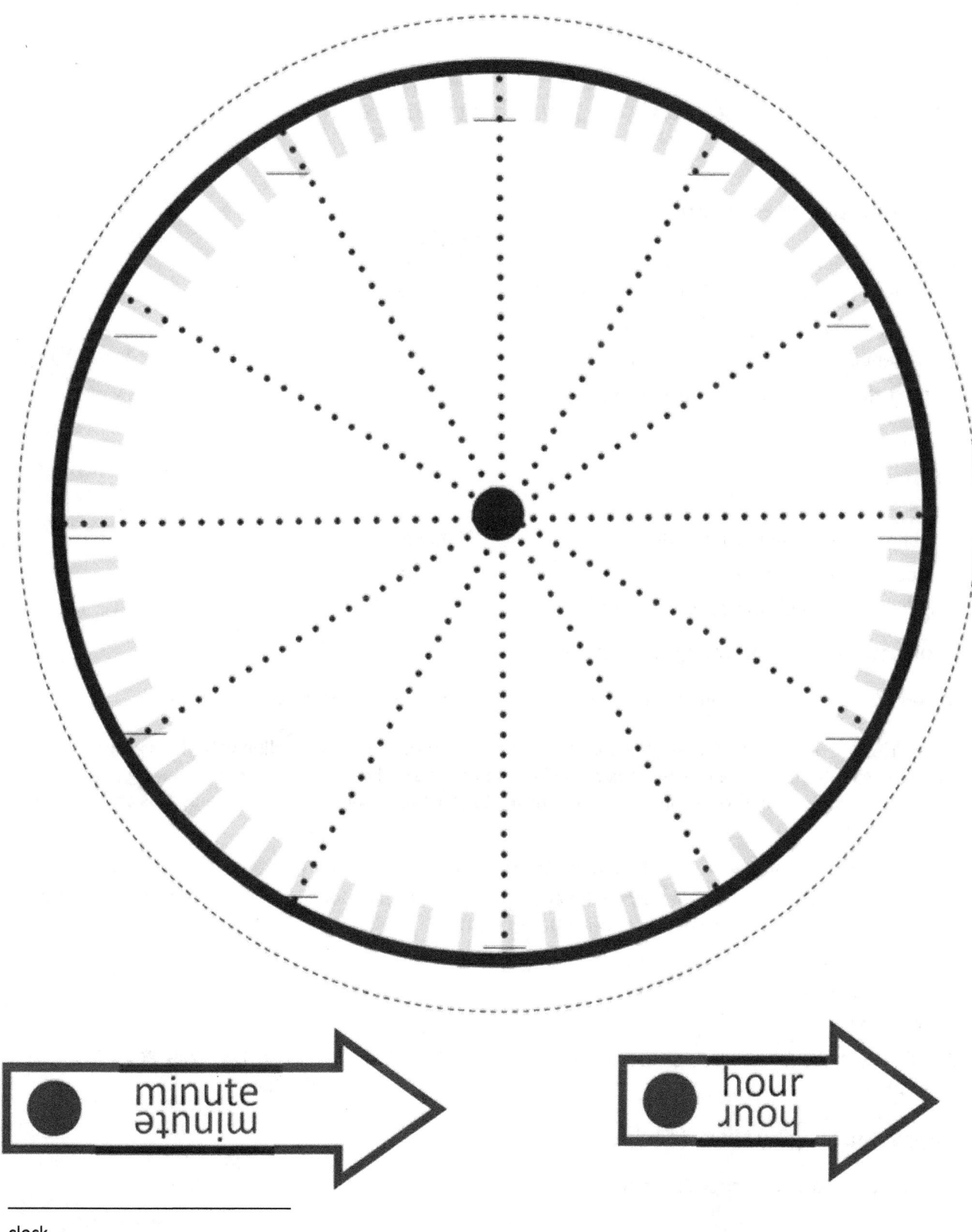

A STORY OF UNITS – TEKS EDITION

Lesson 12 Template 2•8

minute

hour

_____
clock

Lesson 12: Construct a paper clock by partitioning a circle into halves and quarters, and tell time to the half hour or quarter hour.

185

EUREKA MATH
TEKS EDITION

© Great Minds PBC
TEKS Edition | greatminds.org/texas

Lesson 13

Objective: Tell time to the nearest five minutes.

Suggested Lesson Structure

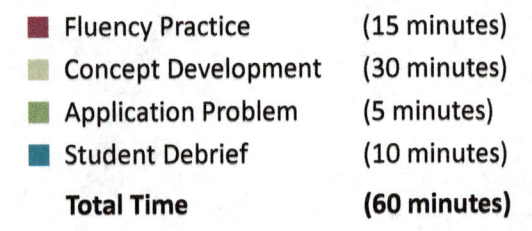

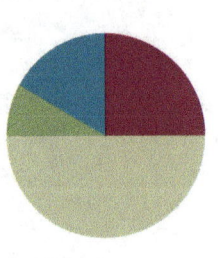

- **Fluency Practice**   (15 minutes)
- **Concept Development** (30 minutes)
- **Application Problem** (5 minutes)
- **Student Debrief**   (10 minutes)
- **Total Time**   **(60 minutes)**

Fluency Practice (15 minutes)

- Subtraction with Renaming **2.4B**   (5 minutes)
- Happy Counting by Fives **2.2C**   (1 minute)
- Sprint: Adding and Subtracting by 5 **2.4B** (9 minutes)

Subtraction with Renaming (5 minutes)

Materials: (S) Personal white board, hundreds place value chart (Lesson 4 Fluency Template)

Note: This fluency activity reviews the application of a chip model while recording with the algorithm. Allow students work time between each problem, and reinforce place value understandings by having students say their answer in both unit form and in standard form. Students use their personal white boards and a place value chart to solve.

- T: Slide the place value chart template into your personal white board.
- T: (Write 367 – 185 horizontally on the board.) Let's use a chip model to subtract. On your personal white board, record your work using the algorithm.
- S: (Solve.)
- T: 367 – 185 is...?
- S: 182.

Continue with the following possible sequence: 456 – 274, 625 – 295, 817 – 319, 528 – 229, 804 – 372, and 905 – 253.

Happy Counting by Fives (1 minute)

- T: Let's do some Happy Counting!

T: Let's count by fives, starting at 0. Ready? (Rhythmically point up until a change is desired. Show a closed hand, and then point down. Continue, mixing it up.)

S: 0, 5, 10, 15, 20. (Switch directions.) 15, 10. (Switch directions.) 15, 20, 25, 30, 35, 40. (Switch directions.) 35, 30, 25. (Switch directions.) 30, 35, 40, 45. (Switch directions.) 40, 35, 30. (Switch directions.) 35, 40, 45, 50, 55, 60. (Switch directions.) 55, 50, 45, 40, 35. (Switch directions.) 40, 45, 50. (Switch directions.) 45, 40, 35, 30, 25, 20, 15. (Switch directions.) 20, 25, 30, 35, 40, 45, 50, 55, 60.

Sprint: Adding and Subtracting by 5 (9 minutes)

Materials: (S) Adding and Subtracting by 5 Sprint

Note: Students add and subtract by 5 to gain automaticity counting by fives in preparation for counting minutes in the lesson.

Concept Development (30 minutes)

Materials: (T) Large instructional geared clock, clock made in Lesson 13, student clock (optional)
(S) Clock made in Lesson 13, student clocks (optional), personal white board

Distribute the clocks from Lesson 13.

T: Each number on the clock represents how many minutes?
S: 5 minutes!
T: How many fives does it take to get all the way around the clock? (Count together.)
S: 1 five, 2 fives, 3 fives, ..., 12 fives!
T: Let's count minutes around the clock by fives.
T: (Count with students by fives around the clock face, starting with the 12, with zero minutes.)
T: When we get to the 12, it's 60 minutes later. One hour equals 60 minutes, so we can say it's a new hour!
T: Now, let's show some times with our clocks.

Show 4:05 on the geared instructional clock.

T: Set your clocks to look like mine.
T: How many minutes have passed since four o'clock?
S: 5 minutes.
T: Yes. We say this time like this, four oh five, and we write it like this. (Write 4:05.)

Continue moving the minute hand around the clock, asking students to read the time at each five-minute interval. At each stop, draw students' attention to the position of the hour hand relative to the minute hand.

T: (Stop when students reach 4:55.) Notice how very close the hour hand is to the 5. But is it five o'clock yet?
S: No!

Lesson 13: Tell time to the nearest five minutes.

T: Turn and talk. What time is it now?
S: It's five minutes before five. → It's 4:55.
T: Yes! The hour hand takes a full hour to move from one number to the next, so it moves a little bit every minute.
T: How many more minutes are needed to complete the hour?
S: 5 minutes! (Move the minute hand ahead 5 minutes.)
T: What time is it now?
S: Five o'clock!

Repeat with more examples of hour-hand settings if students are unclear on the concept.

T: Now, let's read some times!

Show 7:35 on the geared instructional clock.

T: What time is this? Talk with a partner. You may use your student clock to figure it out.
S: The hour hand is after the 7, and the minute hand is on the 7. 5, 10, 15, 20, 25, 30, 35. It's 7:35. → The hour hand is past the 7, so 30, 35. 7:35.
T: Excellent! I noticed some people are using what they learned about fractions and the minutes to start at half past, or 30, and counting by 5 from there. Very clever!

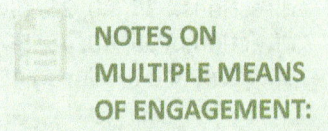

> **NOTES ON MULTIPLE MEANS OF ENGAGEMENT:**
>
> Provide students working below grade level with extra practice using an online animated clock such as that found at http://www.mathsisfun.com/time-clocks-analog-digital.html. English language learners would also benefit from using such a clock that not only gives the digital time along with the analog clock but writes the time out as well.

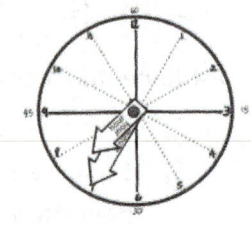

Continue to state times in number and word form (e.g., 8:10, a quarter to two) with the following sequence: 9:35, 1:10, a quarter after three, and 2:50, giving students ample practice reading time and setting time on their clocks. Have them record the times on their personal white boards as well. Let students suggest times to read until they demonstrate proficiency. Then, instruct them to work on the Problem Set and Application Problem.

Problem Set (10 minutes)

Students should do their personal best to complete the Problem Set within the allotted 10 minutes. For some classes, it may be appropriate to modify the assignment by specifying which problems they work on first. Some problems do not specify a method for solving. Students should solve these problems using the RDW approach used for Application Problems.

A STORY OF UNITS – TEKS EDITION   Lesson 13   2•8

Application Problem (5 minutes)

Brownies take 45 minutes to bake. Pizza takes half an hour less than brownies to warm up. How long does pizza take to warm up?

$45 \xrightarrow{-30} 15$

Pizza takes 15 minutes to warm up.

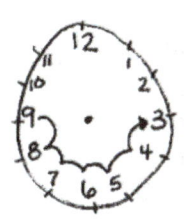

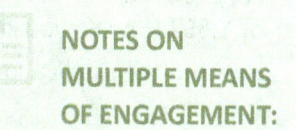

> **NOTES ON MULTIPLE MEANS OF ENGAGEMENT:**
>
> Challenge students working above grade level by extending the Application Problem. Ask them how long it takes to heat up a sandwich in the oven if it only takes one-third of the time it takes to bake brownies. Ask them to explain what strategy they used to find the answer.

Note: This problem offers students a chance to practice using the content from Lessons 13 and 14. Students may work together or independently to solve. They may draw a picture or use their clocks to help them solve the problem.

Student Debrief (10 minutes)

Lesson Objective: Tell time to the nearest five minutes.

The Student Debrief is intended to invite reflection and active processing of the total lesson experience.

Invite students to review their solutions for the Problem Set. They should check work by comparing answers with a partner. Look for misconceptions or misunderstandings that can be addressed in the Debrief. Guide students in a conversation to debrief the Problem Set and process the lesson.

Any combination of the questions below may be used to lead the discussion.

- For Problem 3, 3:35, how did you use the numbers on the face of the clock and skip-counting to draw the hands correctly?
- For Problem 3, 4:40, how could you use your knowledge of equal parts to figure out where to draw the minute hand?
- For Problem 3, what difference do you notice between the hour hands for 6:25 and 6:55? Why?

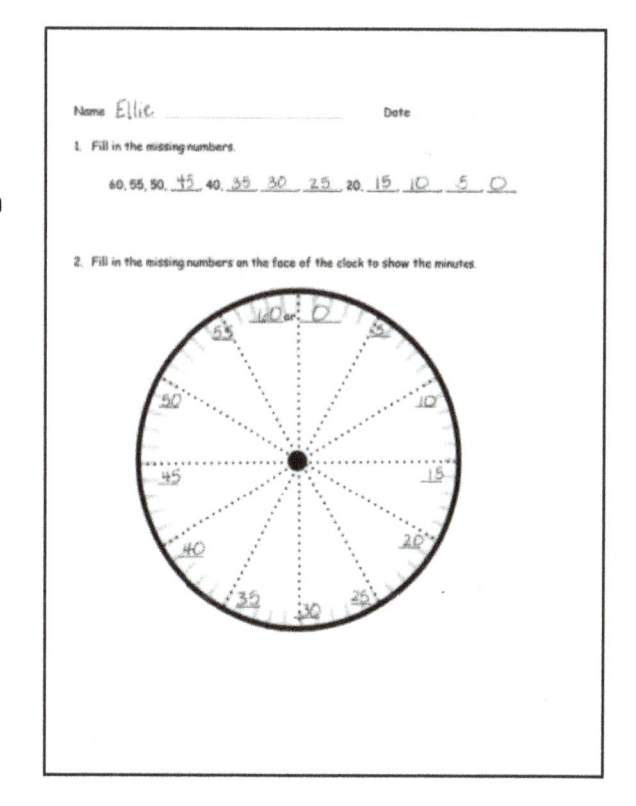

Lesson 13: Tell time to the nearest five minutes.

- For Problem 4, is the **analog clock** showing 12:55 or 1:55? How do you know?
- How did the Application Problem connect to today's lesson?

Exit Ticket (3 minutes)

After the Student Debrief, instruct students to complete the Exit Ticket. A review of their work will help with assessing students' understanding of the concepts that were presented in today's lesson and planning more effectively for future lessons. The questions may be read aloud to the students.

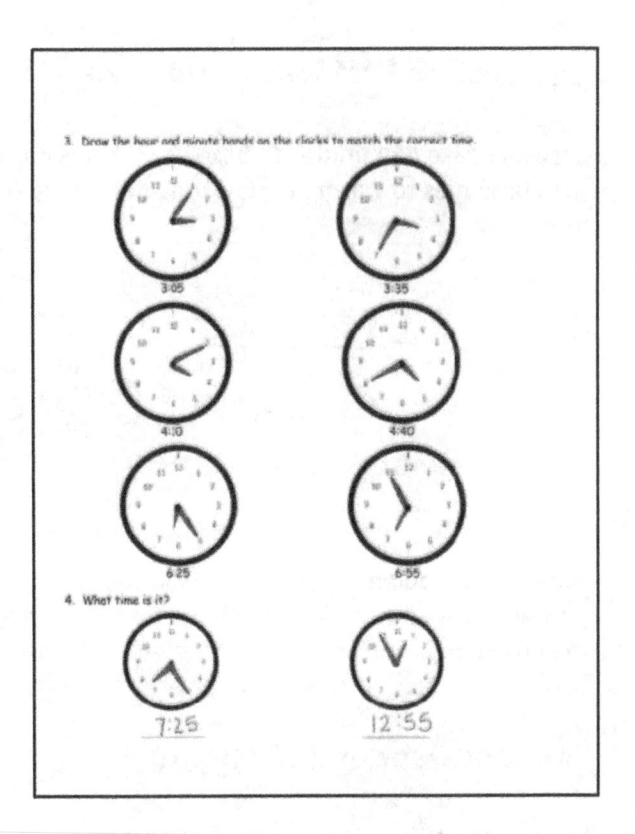

Lesson 13: Tell time to the nearest five minutes.

A

Number Correct: _____

Adding and Subtracting by 5

1.	0 + 5 =		23.	10 + 5 =	
2.	5 + 5 =		24.	15 + 5 =	
3.	10 + 5 =		25.	20 + 5 =	
4.	15 + 5 =		26.	25 + 5 =	
5.	20 + 5 =		27.	30 + 5 =	
6.	25 + 5 =		28.	35 + 5 =	
7.	30 + 5 =		29.	40 + 5 =	
8.	35 + 5 =		30.	45 + 5 =	
9.	40 + 5 =		31.	0 + 50 =	
10.	45 + 5 =		32.	50 + 50 =	
11.	50 - 5 =		33.	50 + 5 =	
12.	45 - 5 =		34.	55 + 5 =	
13.	40 - 5 =		35.	60 - 5 =	
14.	35 - 5 =		36.	55 - 5 =	
15.	30 - 5 =		37.	60 + 5 =	
16.	25 - 5 =		38.	65 + 5 =	
17.	20 - 5 =		39.	70 - 5 =	
18.	15 - 5 =		40.	65 - 5 =	
19.	10 - 5 =		41.	100 + 50 =	
20.	5 - 5 =		42.	150 + 50 =	
21.	5 + 0 =		43.	200 - 50 =	
22.	5 + 5 =		44.	150 - 50 =	

Lesson 13: Tell time to the nearest five minutes.

B

Adding and Subtracting by 5

Number Correct: _____

Improvement: _____

1.	5 + 0 =		23.	10 + 5 =	
2.	5 + 5 =		24.	15 + 5 =	
3.	5 + 10 =		25.	20 + 5 =	
4.	5 + 15 =		26.	25 + 5 =	
5.	5 + 20 =		27.	30 + 5 =	
6.	5 + 25 =		28.	35 + 5 =	
7.	5 + 30 =		29.	40 + 5 =	
8.	5 + 35 =		30.	45 + 5 =	
9.	5 + 40 =		31.	50 + 0 =	
10.	5 + 45 =		32.	50 + 50 =	
11.	50 - 5 =		33.	5 + 50 =	
12.	45 - 5 =		34.	5 + 55 =	
13.	40 - 5 =		35.	60 - 5 =	
14.	35 - 5 =		36.	55 - 5 =	
15.	30 - 5 =		37.	5 + 60 =	
16.	25 - 5 =		38.	5 + 65 =	
17.	20 - 5 =		39.	70 - 5 =	
18.	15 - 5 =		40.	65 - 5 =	
19.	10 - 5 =		41.	50 + 100 =	
20.	5 - 5 =		42.	50 + 150 =	
21.	0 + 5 =		43.	200 - 50 =	
22.	5 + 5 =		44.	150 - 50 =	

Lesson 13: Tell time to the nearest five minutes.

Name _____ Date _____

1. Fill in the missing numbers.

   60, 55, 50, _____, 40, _____, _____, _____, 20, _____, _____, _____, _____

2. Fill in the missing numbers on the face of the clock to show the minutes.

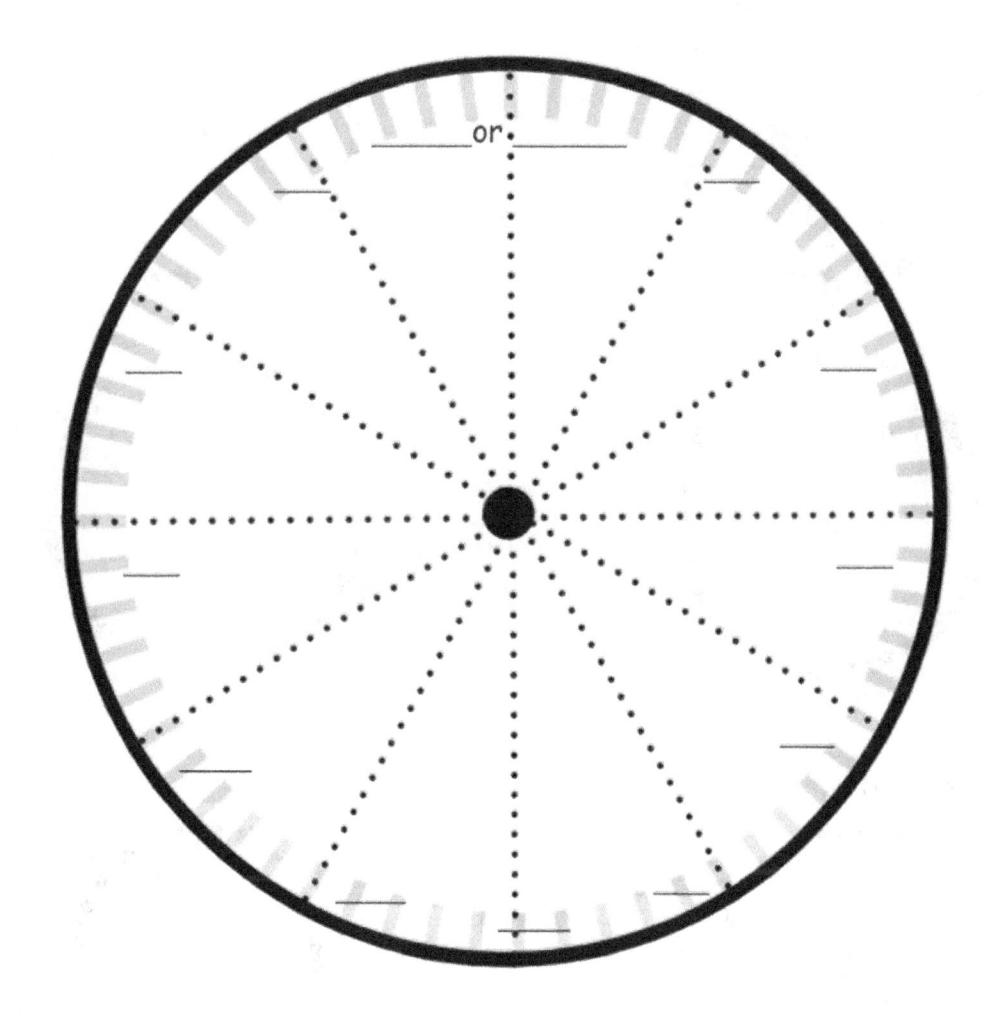

3. Draw the hour and minute hands on the clocks to match the correct time.

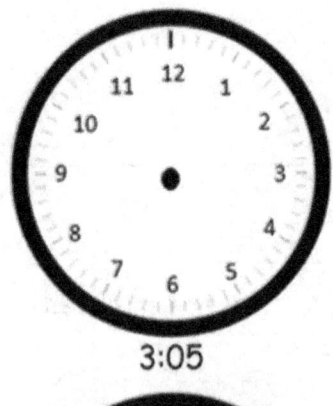

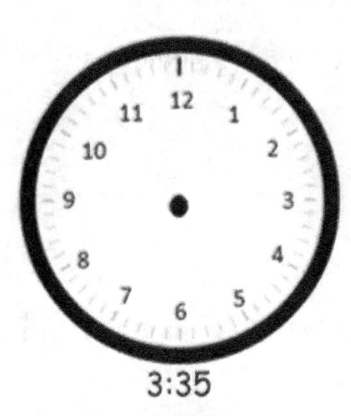

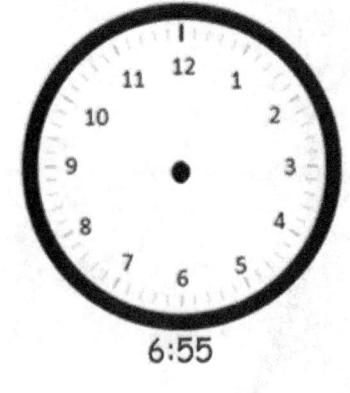

3:05

3:35

4:10

4:40

6:25

6:55

4. What time is it?

_____   _____

Name _____ Date _____

Draw the hour and minute hands on the clocks to match the correct time.

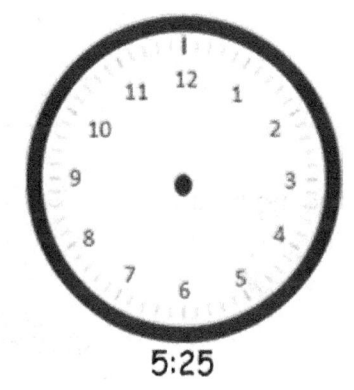

12:55

5:25

Name _____ Date _____

1. Fill in the missing numbers.

   0, 5, 10, _____, _____, _____, _____, 35, _____, _____, _____, _____, _____

   _____, _____, _____, 45, 40, _____, _____, _____, 20, 15, _____, _____, _____

2. Fill in the missing minutes on the face of the clock.

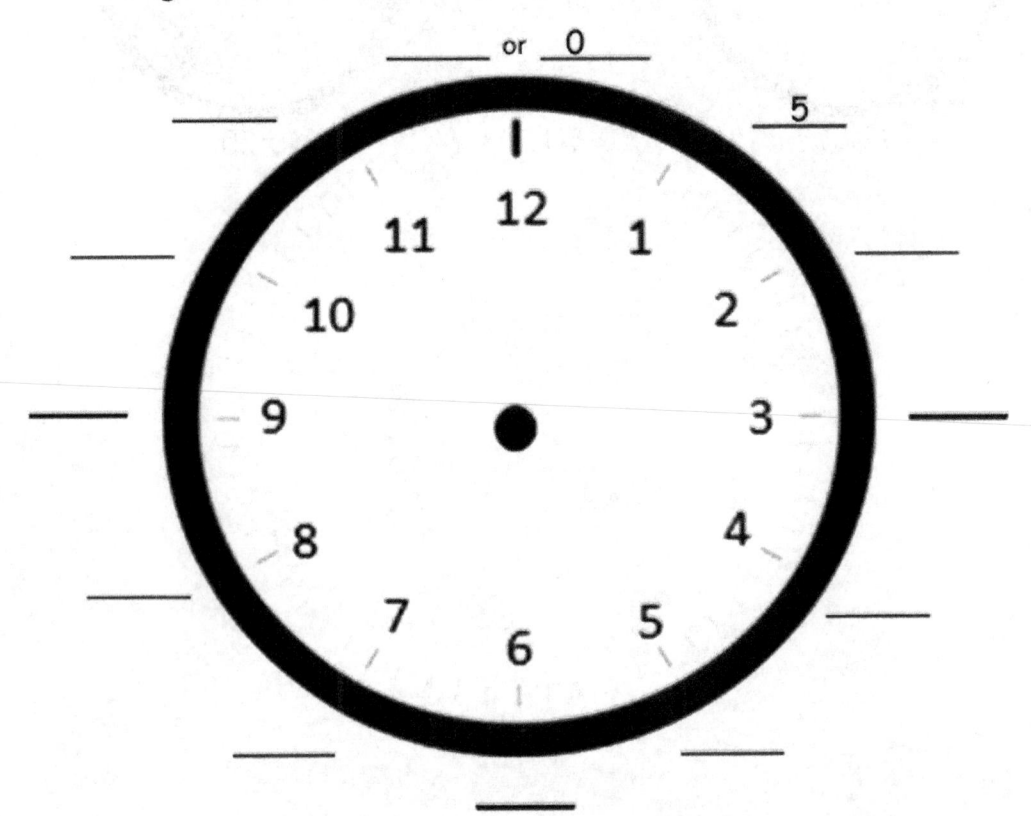

   _____ or 0

   _____   5

   _____   _____

   _____   _____

   _____   _____

   _____   _____

   _____

3. Draw the minute hands on the clocks to match the correct time.

   3:25   7:15   9:55

Lesson 13: Tell time to the nearest five minutes.

4. Draw the hour hands on the clocks to match the correct time.

   12:30    10:10    3:45

5. Draw the hour and minute hands on the clocks to match the correct time.

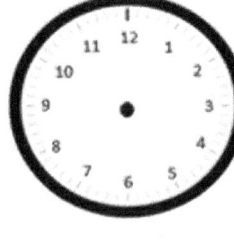

   6:55 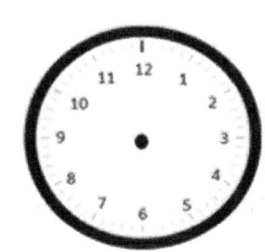   1:50 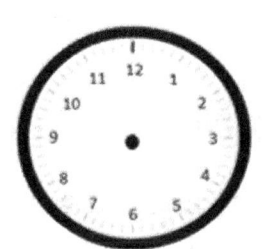   8:25

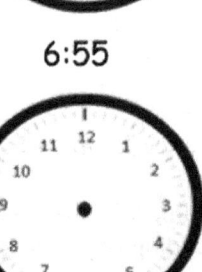

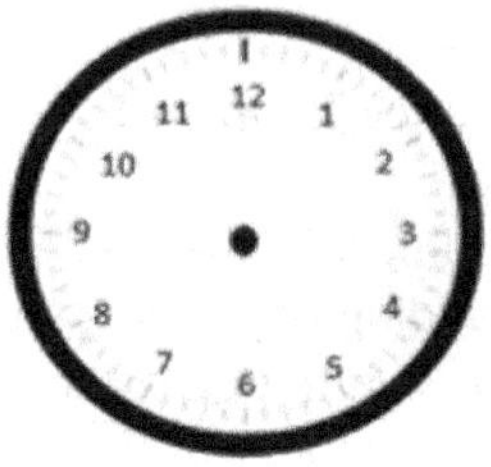

   4:40 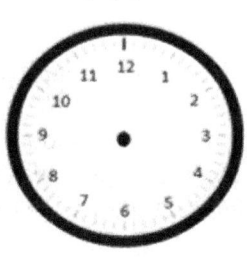   7:45 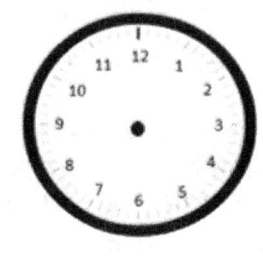   2:05

6. What time is it?

   _____   _____

Lesson 13: Tell time to the nearest five minutes.

Lesson 14

Objective: Tell time to the nearest five minutes; relate *a.m.* and *p.m.* to time of day.

Suggested Lesson Structure

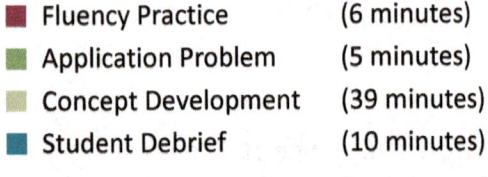

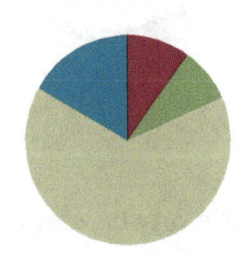

- Fluency Practice   (6 minutes)
- Application Problem   (5 minutes)
- Concept Development   (39 minutes)
- Student Debrief   (10 minutes)

Total Time   **(60 minutes)**

Fluency Practice (6 minutes)

- Subtraction with Renaming **2.4B**   (5 minutes)
- Happy Counting by Fives **2.2C**   (1 minute)

Subtraction with Renaming (5 minutes)

Materials: (S) Personal white board, hundreds place value chart (Lesson 4 Fluency Template)

Note: This fluency activity reviews the application of a chip model while recording with the algorithm. Allow students work time between each problem, and reinforce place value understandings by having students say their answer in both unit form and in standard form. Students use their personal white boards and a place value chart to solve.

  T: Slide the place value chart template into your personal white board.
  T: (Write 300 – 118 horizontally on the board.) Let's use a chip model to subtract. On your personal white board, record your work using the algorithm.
  S: (Solve.)
  T: 300 – 118 is…?
  S: 182.

Continue with the following possible sequence: 500 – 276, 700 – 347, 803 – 239, 506 – 271, 800 – 108, and 900 – 507.

Happy Counting by Fives (1 minute)

T: Let's do some Happy Counting!

T: Let's count by fives, starting at 0. Ready? (Rhythmically point up until a change is desired. Show a closed hand, and then point down. Continue, mixing it up.)

S: 0, 5, 10, 15, 20. (Switch directions.) 15, 10. (Switch directions.) 15, 20, 25, 30, 35, 40. (Switch directions.) 35, 30, 25. (Switch directions.) 30, 35, 40, 45. (Switch directions.) 40, 35, 30. (Switch directions.) 35, 40, 45, 50. (Switch directions.) 45, 40, 35. (Switch directions.) 40, 45, 50. (Switch directions.) 45, 40, 35, 30, 25, 20, 15.

Application Problem (5 minutes)

At Memorial School, students have a quarter hour for morning recess and 33 minutes for a lunch break. How much free time do they have in all? How much more time for lunch than recess do they have?

Note: Students have the opportunity to solve another two-step problem involving addition and subtraction with time. At this stage, some do not need to draw a strip diagram, but for those who struggle, encourage them to do so.

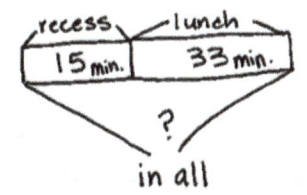

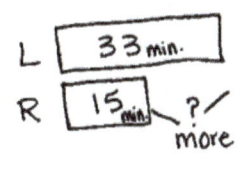

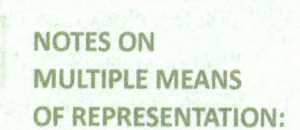

NOTES ON MULTIPLE MEANS OF REPRESENTATION:

For students who are working below grade level, scaffold the Application Problem by guiding them through the problem-solving process through questioning. Give them a number bond template and ask, "Are we looking for a part or the whole when we want to know how much free time students have in all? What do they have more time for: recess or lunch? How can we find out how much more time they have for lunch?"

Lesson 14: Tell time to the nearest five minutes; relate *a.m.* and *p.m.* to time of day.

Concept Development (39 minutes)

Materials: (T) Telling time story (Template) as a display or booklet, document camera (if available)
(S) Telling time story (Template) as a booklet, crayons (optional)

Note: Students are asked to tell the current time of day. The vignette uses an example of a morning class. Adjust the questions to fit if math is scheduled for the afternoon.

Images are provided in a format that can either be printed as a full-size book to be read to the whole class, as a booklet to be distributed, or as images to project. The four-on-a-page template appears before the full-page version in this document. Copies of either version may be given to students if resources are available, and they can color them in school or at home to make a home connection. The pictures can also be either cut out and ordered by students or left in chronological order as they appear.

If the teacher is showing the book to the group, gather students in the center of the room.

T: Look at the classroom clock. What time is it now?
S: (Tell time to the nearest five minutes.)
T: Where does the clock tell us if it is morning or night?
S: The clock doesn't tell that. → The sun is shining, so it is morning. → We know it is morning because we just got to school. → We haven't had lunch yet, so it must be morning.
T: Will the clock look exactly like this again today?
S: I'm not sure. → Yes! It will show [insert time] again tonight.
T: That's right. The clock will look just like it does now at [insert time] tonight.
T: (Hold up the analog clock showing the time that school starts.) What time does this clock show?
S: (Tell time.)
T: What do we do at [time] each morning?
S: That's the beginning of school!
T: What do you do around this time each evening?
S: Get ready for bed. → Finish my homework. → Take a shower.

Repeat using a few other important times in the class schedule, and include both morning and afternoon times.

T: Which comes first in the alphabet, A or P?
S: A!
T: Yes! Which comes first in a day, the morning or the afternoon?
S: The morning!
T: Yes! That's an easy way to remember **a.m.** and **p.m.** (Write a.m. and p.m. on the board.)
T: We use a.m. as a short way to talk about the time between 12:00 midnight and 12:00 noon, or morning.

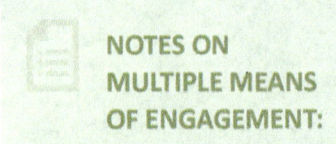

NOTES ON MULTIPLE MEANS OF ENGAGEMENT:

Support English language learners' oral language by providing them with sentence starters to aid them in sharing their ideas with a partner. "The sky would be _____ if it were 10 p.m." and "When it is 5 a.m., I am _____."

Lesson 14: Tell time to the nearest five minutes; relate *a.m.* and *p.m.* to time of day.

T: We use p.m. as a way to talk about the time between 12:00 noon and midnight.

T: Remember that a digital clock shows the time like we are used to writing it. Turn and talk. Why do you think it's called a digital clock?

S: Because it's electronic, like a digital camera. → Because it shows the digits of the hour and minutes.

T: Yes! It shows the time using digits instead of hands pointing to a number.

T: Let's read our story now.

Distribute booklets or images to sort if you are using them; otherwise, show images using a book or document camera. Have students look at the pictures and put them in order to tell the story. This can be done as a whole class or in small groups.

Relate the time of day shown to a.m. and p.m. throughout. Students need to recognize and fill in the time and a.m. or p.m. on the line for each picture. Encourage them to discuss how they know whether it is a.m. or p.m. Ask questions like, "What would the sky look like outside if this were p.m. instead of a.m. (or vice versa)?"

If there is time, have students color the pictures, or send the booklet home to be colored and shared with family.

When students have completed this activity, instruct them to work on the Problem Set.

Problem Set (10 minutes)

Students should do their personal best to complete the Problem Set within the allotted 10 minutes. For some classes, it may be appropriate to modify the assignment by specifying which problems they work on first. Some problems do not specify a method for solving. Students should solve these problems using the RDW approach used for Application Problems.

Student Debrief (10 minutes)

Lesson Objective: Tell time to the nearest five minutes; relate *a.m.* and *p.m.* to time of day.

The Student Debrief is intended to invite reflection and active processing of the total lesson experience.

Invite students to review their solutions for the Problem Set. They should check work by comparing answers with a partner. Look for misconceptions or misunderstandings that can be addressed in the Debrief. Guide students in a conversation to debrief the Problem Set and process the lesson.

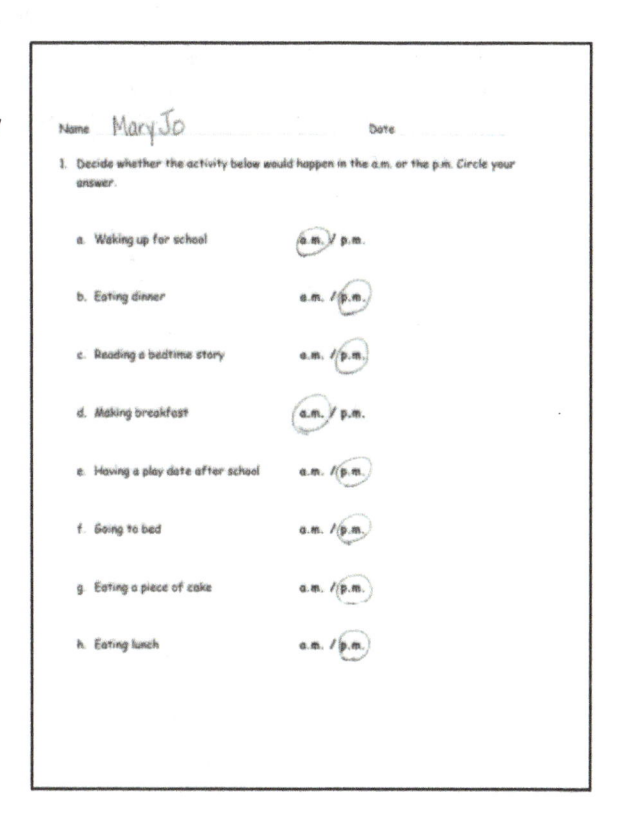

A STORY OF UNITS – TEKS EDITION
Lesson 14   2•8

Any combination of the questions below may be used to lead the discussion.

- For Problem 2(a), how did you determine where to place the minute hand?
- For Problem 2(b), where did you draw the hour hand? Why?
- Explain to your partner the difference between **a.m.** and **p.m.**
- What is the difference between 12 a.m. and 12 p.m.? What might you be doing at those times?
- When you are sleeping at night, are you sleeping during the a.m. or p.m.? Explain your thinking.

Exit Ticket (3 minutes)

After the Student Debrief, instruct students to complete the Exit Ticket. A review of their work will help with assessing students' understanding of the concepts that were presented in today's lesson and planning more effectively for future lessons. The questions may be read aloud to the students.

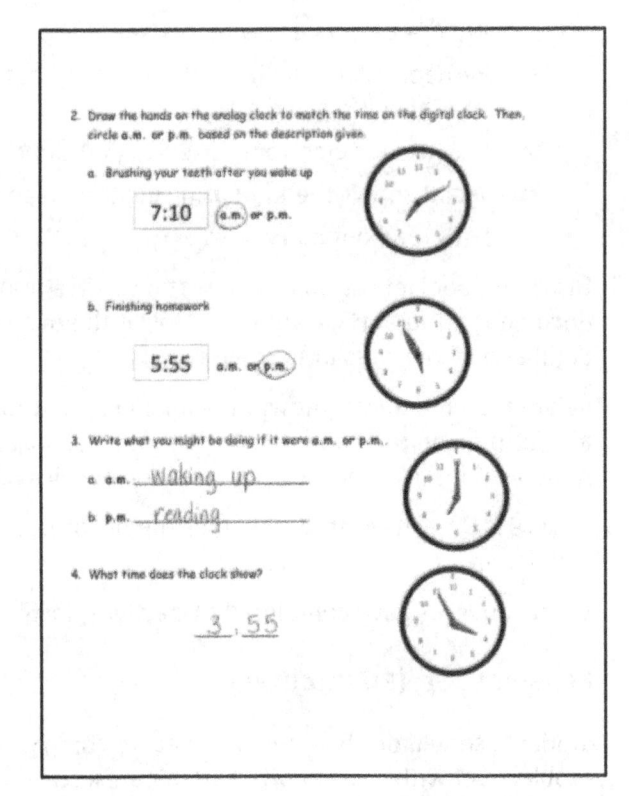

Lesson 14: Tell time to the nearest five minutes; relate *a.m.* and *p.m.* to time of day.

Name _____   Date _____

1. Decide whether the activity below would happen in the a.m. or the p.m. Circle your answer.

   a. Waking up for school   a.m. / p.m.

   b. Eating dinner   a.m. / p.m.

   c. Reading a bedtime story   a.m. / p.m.

   d. Making breakfast   a.m. / p.m.

   e. Having a play date after school   a.m. / p.m.

   f. Going to bed   a.m. / p.m.

   g. Eating a piece of cake   a.m. / p.m.

   h. Eating lunch   a.m. / p.m.

2. Draw the hands on the analog clock to match the time on the digital clock. Then, circle **a.m. or p.m.** based on the description given.

   a. Brushing your teeth after you wake up

   7:10   a.m. or p.m.

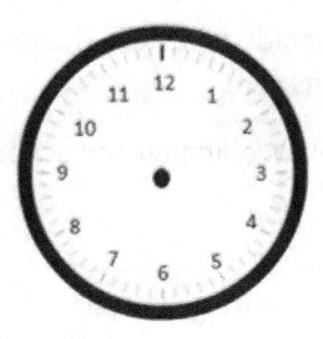

   b. Finishing homework

   5:55   a.m. or p.m.

3. Write what you might be doing if it were **a.m. or p.m.**

   a. a.m. _____

   b. p.m. _____

4. What time does the clock show?

   _____ : _____

A STORY OF UNITS – TEKS EDITION

Lesson 14 Exit Ticket 2•8

Name _____ Date _____

Draw the hands on the analog clock to match the time on the digital clock. Then, circle **a.m. or p.m.** based on the description given.

1. The sun is rising.

   6:10   a.m. or p.m.

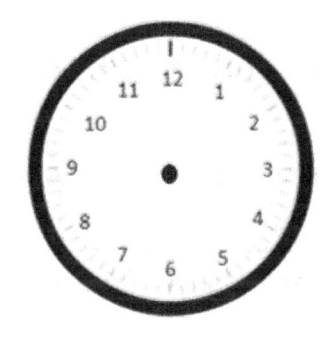

2. Walking the dog

   3:40   a.m. or p.m.

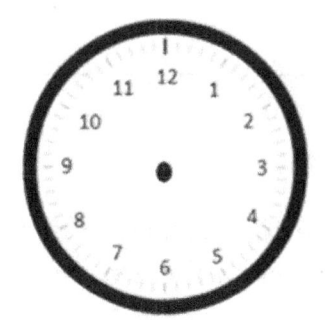

Lesson 14: Tell time to the nearest five minutes; relate *a.m.* and *p.m.* to time of day.

205

A STORY OF UNITS – TEKS EDITION   Lesson 14 Homework 2•8

Name _____   Date _____

1. Decide whether the activity below would happen in the a.m. or the p.m. Circle your answer.

a. Eating breakfast	a.m. / p.m.	b. Doing homework	a.m. / p.m.
c. Setting the table for dinner	a.m. / p.m.	d. Waking up in the morning	a.m. / p.m.
e. After-school dance class	a.m. / p.m.	f. Eating lunch	a.m. / p.m.
g. Going to bed	a.m. / p.m.	h. Heating up dinner	a.m. / p.m.

2. Write the time displayed on the clock. Then, choose whether the activity below would happen in the a.m. or the p.m.

a. Brushing your teeth before school

____:____ a.m. / p.m.

b. Eating dessert after dinner

____:____ a.m. / p.m.

Lesson 14: Tell time to the nearest five minutes; relate *a.m.* and *p.m.* to time of day.

3. Draw the hands on the analog clock to match the time on the digital clock. Then, circle **a.m.** or **p.m.** based on the description given.

   a. Brushing your teeth before bedtime

   8:15   a.m. or p.m.

   b. Recess after lunch

   12:30   a.m. or p.m.

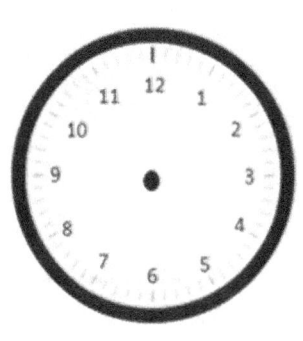

4. Write what you might be doing if it were **a.m.** or **p.m.**

   a. a.m. _____

   b. p.m. _____

   c. a.m. _____

   d. p.m. _____

Lesson 14: Tell time to the nearest five minutes; relate *a.m.* and *p.m.* to time of day.

A STORY OF UNITS – TEKS EDITION

Lesson 14 Template 2•8

Write the time. Circle a.m. or p.m.

_____ a.m./p.m.

_____ a.m./p.m.

_____ a.m./p.m.

_____ a.m./p.m.

telling time story (small)

Lesson 14: Tell time to the nearest five minutes; relate *a.m.* and *p.m.* to time of day.

A STORY OF UNITS – TEKS EDITION

Lesson 14 Template 2•8

Write the time. Circle a.m. or p.m.

_____
a.m./p.m.

_____
a.m./p.m.

_____
a.m./p.m

_____
a.m./p.m.

telling time story (small)

Lesson 14: Tell time to the nearest five minutes; relate *a.m.* and *p.m.* to time of day.

209

A STORY OF UNITS – TEKS EDITION — Lesson 14 Template — 2•8

Write the time. Circle a.m. or p.m.

_____ a.m./p.m.

_____
telling time story (large)

Lesson 14: Tell time to the nearest five minutes; relate *a.m.* and *p.m.* to time of day.

Write the time. Circle a.m. or p.m.

_____
a.m./p.m.

telling time story (large)

Lesson 14: Tell time to the nearest five minutes; relate *a.m.* and *p.m.* to time of day.

A STORY OF UNITS – TEKS EDITION

Lesson 14 Template 2•8

Write the time. Circle a.m. or p.m.

_____
a.m. / p.m.

telling time story (large)

Lesson 14: Tell time to the nearest five minutes; relate *a.m.* and *p.m.* to time of day.

Write the time. Circle a.m. or p.m.

_____ a.m./p.m.

telling time story (large)

Write the time. Circle a.m. or p.m.

_____
a.m./p.m.

telling time story (large)

A STORY OF UNITS – TEKS EDITION

Lesson 14 Template 2•8

Write the time. Circle a.m. or p.m.

_____
a.m./p.m.

telling time story (large)

Lesson 14: Tell time to the nearest five minutes; relate *a.m.* and *p.m.* to time of day.

A STORY OF UNITS – TEKS EDITION · Lesson 14 Template · 2•8

Write the time. Circle a.m. or p.m.

_____ a.m./p.m.

telling time story (large)

Lesson 14: Tell time to the nearest five minutes; relate *a.m.* and *p.m.* to time of day.

Write the time. Circle a.m. or p.m.

_____
a.m./p.m.

telling time story (large)

Lesson 14: Tell time to the nearest five minutes; relate *a.m.* and *p.m.* to time of day.

Lesson 15

Objective: Relate skip-counting by fives on the clock and telling time to a continuous measurement model, the number line.

Suggested Lesson Structure

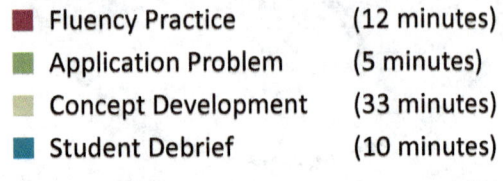

- **Fluency Practice** (12 minutes)
- **Application Problem** (5 minutes)
- **Concept Development** (33 minutes)
- **Student Debrief** (10 minutes)
- **Total Time** **(60 minutes)**

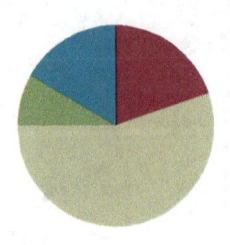

Fluency Practice (12 minutes)

- Tell Time on the Clock **2.9G**   (3 minutes)
- Skip Count by Fives on the Clock **2.9G**   (9 minutes)

Tell Time on the Clock (3 minutes)

Materials: (T) Analog clock for demonstration (S) Personal white board

Note: This activity reviews the Grade 2 standard of telling and writing time to the nearest 5 minutes. It prepares students to use the number line and clock to tell time to the nearest 5 minutes in the Concept Development.

T: (Show an analog demonstration clock.) Start at 12 and count by 5 minutes on the clock. (Move finger from 12 to 1, 2, 3, 4, etc., as students count.)

S: 5, 10, 15, 20, 25, 30, 35, 40, 45, 50, 55, 60.

T: I'll show a time on the clock. Write the time on your personal white board. (Show 3:05.)

S: (Write 3:05.)

T: (Show 2:35.)

S: (Write 2:35.)

Repeat process, varying the hour and 5-minute interval so that students read and write a variety of times to the nearest 5 minutes.

Skip Count by Fives on the Clock (9 minutes)

Materials: (T) A "clock" made from a 24-inch ribbon marked off at every 2 inches

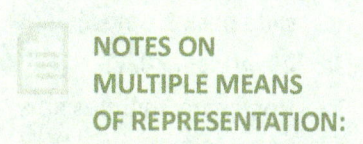

NOTES ON MULTIPLE MEANS OF REPRESENTATION:

Students have just finished working with meter strips, which are concrete number lines. In this activity, they move to working with an abstract number line: the clock. A clock is a circular number line. Visually demonstrate this for students by making the clock from a 24-inch ribbon marked off every 2 inches, similar to the one pictured with this activity.

Consider measuring the intervals in advance, making the marks very lightly so that they are hard for others to see. Then, begin the activity by making the marks dark enough for all to see as students count along by ones to notice that there are 12 marks.

T: (Display the ribbon as a horizontal number line—example pictured above.) Count by fives as I touch each mark on the ribbon.
S: (Starting with 0, count by fives to 60.)
T: (Make the ribbon into a circle resembling a clock.) Now I've shaped my ribbon to look like a …
S: Circle! Clock!
T: Let's call it a clock. Again, count by fives as I touch each mark on the clock.
S: (Starting with 0, skip-count by fives to 60.)
T: This time, the direction my finger moves on the clock will show you whether to count up or down. (While explaining, demonstrate sliding a finger forward and backward around the clock.)
T: As I slide to the marks, you count them by fives.

Starting at 12, slide forward to 4 as students count on. On a clock, 12 represents both 0 and 60. We are not stating 0 so that students count on effectively.

S: 5, 10, 15, 20.
T: How many minutes is that?
S: 20 minutes!
T: (Starting from 4, slide a finger forward to 9. Do not restate 20. Count on.)
S: 25, 30, 35, 40, 45.
T: How many minutes is that?
S: 45 minutes!
T: (Keep a finger at 9.) What if I slide back one mark, then how many minutes?
S: 40 minutes!
T: Good. What if I slide forward one mark, then how many minutes?
S: 45 minutes!

Lesson 15: Relate skip-counting by fives on the clock and telling time to a continuous measurement model, the number line.

A STORY OF UNITS – TEKS EDITION   Lesson 15   2•8

T: Nice job. Let's count back from 50. (Start from 50 and slide back 5 times.)
S: 45, 40, 35, 30, 25.
T: How many minutes now?
S: 25 minutes!

Continue. Notice which switches or numbers students find most difficult, and use their cues to guide the practice provided.

Application Problem (5 minutes)

Christine has 12 math problems for homework. It takes her 5 minutes to complete each problem. How many minutes does it take Christine to finish all 12 problems?

?minutes
|5|5|5|5|5|5|5|5|5|5|5|5|

5, 10, 15, 20, 25, 30, 35, 40, 45, 50, 55, 60
It takes Christine 60 minutes to finish her homework.

Note: This problem anticipates the Concept Development. It activates prior knowledge from Lesson 14 about math with minutes. Encourage them to solve by skip-counting. Students use the solution to this problem as a springboard for modeling 12 intervals of 5 minutes on the number line in the Concept Development.

Concept Development (33 minutes)

Materials: (T) Analog clock for demonstration (S) Personal white board, strip diagram (Template 1), two clocks (Template 2), centimeter ruler

Part 1: Draw a number line and relate skip-counting by fives to skip-counting intervals of 5 minutes.

Students place the strip diagram template in personal white boards.

T: Model the Application Problem using the strip diagram on the template.
S: (Model.)

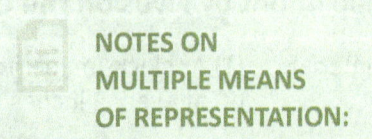

> **NOTES ON MULTIPLE MEANS OF REPRESENTATION:**
>
> **Partner Talk**
> Partner talk provides an opportunity for English language learners to rehearse language in a smaller, safer setting. It also provides an opportunity to pair children who can support one another with a shared first language. Balance pairings so that students feel supported but also benefit from the peer modeling and individualized practice with English provided by structured partner talk. Partner talk serves struggling and advanced students by allowing them to work at their own levels. It's wise to consider students' strengths when assigning who will talk first. It can work well for Partner A to model strong language when partnered with English language learners or less verbally advanced students.
>
> **Questioning**
> If students have difficulty growing ideas or sustaining conversation, consider asking an advancing question: "Yes, you can count on both of them. What do you measure with each?" This scaffold is especially relevant for students who have difficulty staying focused and students working below grade level. It also provides scaffolding for English language learners who, in order to respond, may rely on the vocabulary used in the question that is asked.

Lesson 15: Relate skip-counting by fives on the clock and telling time to a continuous measurement model, the number line.

Guide discussion so that students articulate the following: the strip diagram is divided into 12 parts, with each part representing the time it takes Christine to do one math problem; the whole strip diagram represents a total of 60 minutes.

- T: A different way to model this problem is to use a number line. Let's use our strip diagram to help us draw a number line that represents a total of 60 minutes.
- T: Draw a line a few centimeters below the strip diagram. Make it the same length as the strip diagram. Make tick marks on the number line where units are divided on the strip diagram. (Model each step as students follow along.)
- T: What do you notice about the relationship between the strip diagram and the number line?
- S: The lines are in the same place. → They have the same number of parts.
- T: What part of the strip diagram do the spaces between tick marks represent?
- S: The units. → The time it takes to do each math problem. → They each represent 5 minutes.
- T: We know that time doesn't stop. It was happening before Christine started her homework, and it keeps going after she's finished. To show that time is continuous, we'll extend our number line on both sides and add arrows to it. (Model.)
- S: (Extend number lines and add arrows.)
- T: Let's label our number lines. The space between 2 tick marks represents a 5-minute **interval**. Write 0 under the first tick mark on the left. Then, skip-count by fives. As you count, write each number under the next tick mark. Stop when you've labeled 60. (Model as students follow along.)
- T: The space between 2 marks represents one 5-minute interval. How many minutes are in the interval from 0 to 10? From 0 to 60? From 15 to 30?
- S: From 0 to 10 is 10 minutes, from 0 to 60 is 60 minutes, and from 15 to 30 is 15 minutes.
- T: Let's use the number line to find how many minutes it takes Christine to do 4 math problems. (Place finger at 0. Move to 5, 10, 15, and 20 as you count 1 problem, 2 problems, 3 problems, 4 problems.) It takes Christine 20 minutes to do 4 math problems. Use the word *interval* to explain to your partner how we used the number line to figure that out.
- S: (Discuss.)

Use guided practice to find how long it takes Christine to solve 7, 9, and 11 problems.

Part 2: Use a number line to tell time to the nearest 5 minutes within 1 hour.

- T: Use your ruler to draw a 12-centimeter number line. (Model as students follow along.)
- T: How many 5-minute intervals will the number line need to represent a total of 60 minutes?
- S: Twelve!
- T: Marking 12 equally spaced intervals is difficult! How can the ruler help do that?

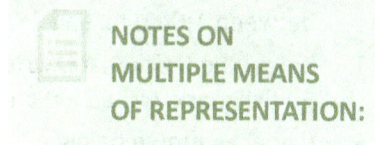

> **NOTES ON MULTIPLE MEANS OF REPRESENTATION:**
>
> Support English language learners and other students with the term *interval* by creating and posting a reference chart. Include a visual of a number line with the space between 2 tick marks labeled as 5-minute interval.

S: It has 12 centimeters. → The centimeters show us where to draw tick marks.

T: Use the centimeters on your ruler to draw tick marks for the number line. (Model.)

S: (Use rulers to draw tick marks.)

T: Just like on the first number line, we'll need to show that time is continuous. Extend each side of your number line and make arrows. Then skip-count to label each 5-minute interval starting with 0 and ending with 60. (Model while students follow along.)

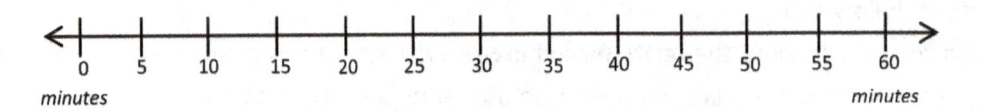

T: How many minutes are labeled on our number line?

S: 60 minutes.

T: There are 60 minutes between 1:00 p.m. and 2:00 p.m. Let's use the number line to model exactly when we will do the activities on our class schedule that happen between 1:00 p.m. and 2:00 p.m.

T: Below the 0 tick mark, write 1:00 p.m. Below the 60 tick mark, write 2:00 p.m. (Model.)

S: (Label as shown below.)

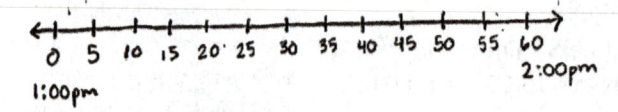

> **NOTES ON MULTIPLE MEANS OF ACTION AND EXPRESSION:**
>
> You need not use 1 p.m. to 2 p.m. as the interval; pick an hour that is relevant to today's class. As students determine the number of 5-minute intervals on the number line, some may count tick marks instead of spaces and get an answer of 13. Watch for this misconception and guide students to make a distinction between tick marks and intervals if necessary.

T: Now this number line shows the hour between 1:00 p.m. and 2:00 p.m.

T: We start recess at 1:10 p.m. Is that time between 1:00 p.m. and 2:00 p.m.?

S: (Agree.)

T: To find that spot on the number line, I'll put my finger on 1:00 and move it to the right as I skip-count intervals until I reach 1:10. Remind me, what are we counting by?

S: Fives!

T: (Model, with students chorally counting along.)

T: I'll draw a dot on the spot where the tick mark and number line cross and label it *R* for recess. (Draw and label as shown on the right.) That dot shows the location of a **point**. Finding and drawing a point is called **plotting** a position on the number line.

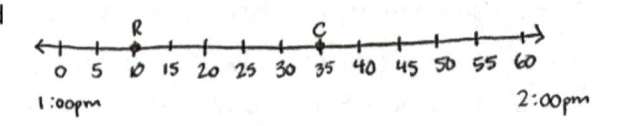

T: At 1:35 p.m., we'll start science. Is 1:35 p.m. between 1:00 p.m. and 2:00 p.m.?

S: (Agree.)

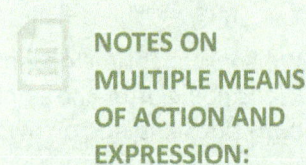

Lesson 15: Relate skip-counting by fives on the clock and telling time to a continuous measurement model, the number line.

> T: Plot 1:35 p.m. as a point on your number line. Label it C.
> S: (Plot a point on the number line at 1:35.)

Continue guided practice using the following suggested sequence: 1:45 p.m. and 2:00 p.m.

> T: How does the number line you've labeled compare to the analog clock on the wall?
> S: We count the minutes by fives on both. → The clock is like the number line wrapped in a circle.

Part 3: Relate the number line to the clock and tell time to the nearest 5 minutes.

Students have Template 2 (two clocks) ready. Display a clock face without hands.

> **NOTES ON MULTIPLE MEANS OF ACTION AND EXPRESSION:**
>
> Extend the discussion by inviting students to discuss whether or not 12:55 p.m. and 2:15 p.m. can be plotted on this number line. Help them reason about their answer and think about where the times might be plotted, given the continuity of time.

> T: We counted by fives to plot minutes on a number line, and we'll do the same on a clock.
> T: How many 5-minute intervals show 15 minutes on a clock?
> S: 3 intervals.
> T: We started at 0 on the number line, but a clock has no 0. Where is the starting point on a clock?
> S: The 12.
> T: Let's count each 5-minute interval and plot a point on the clock to show 15 minutes. (Model.)

Options for further practice:

- Plot 30 minutes, 45 minutes, and 55 minutes using the process above.
- Write 9:15 a.m., 3:30 p.m., and 7:50 a.m. on the board as they would appear on a digital clock, or say the time rather than write it. Students copy each time, plot points, and draw hands to show that time. (Model drawing hands with 10:20 a.m.)

Template 2

Problem Set (10 minutes)

Students should do their personal best to complete the Problem Set within the allotted 10 minutes. For some classes, it may be appropriate to modify the assignment by specifying which problems they work on first. Some problems do not specify a method for solving. Students should solve these problems using the RDW approach used for Application Problems.

Student Debrief (10 minutes)

Lesson Objective: Relate skip-counting by fives on the clock and telling time to a continuous measurement model, the number line.

A STORY OF UNITS – TEKS EDITION   Lesson 15   2•8

The Student Debrief is intended to invite reflection and active processing of the total lesson experience.

Invite students to review their solutions for the Problem Set. They should check work by comparing answers with a partner. Look for misconceptions or misunderstandings that can be addressed in the Debrief. Guide students in a conversation to debrief the Problem Set and process the lesson.

Any combination of the questions below may be used to lead the discussion.

- In Problem 2, what information was important for **plotting** the **point** on the number line that matched the time shown on each clock?
- Each **interval** on the analog clock is labeled with the numbers 1–12. Compare those with our labels from 0 to 60 on the number line. What do the labels represent on both tools?
- How does multiplication using units of 5 help you read or measure time?
- Students may have different answers for Problem 4 (11:25 p.m. may come before or after 11:20 a.m.). Allow students with either answer a chance to explain their thinking.
- How did our minute counting and time telling activities in today's Fluency Practice help you with the rest of the lesson?
- Look at the number line used for Problem 2. Where do you think 5:38 would be? (This anticipates Lesson 3 by counting by fives and then ones on a number line.)

Exit Ticket (3 minutes)

After the Student Debrief, instruct students to complete the Exit Ticket. A review of their work will help with assessing students' understanding of the concepts that were presented in today's lesson and planning more effectively for future lessons. The questions may be read aloud to the students.

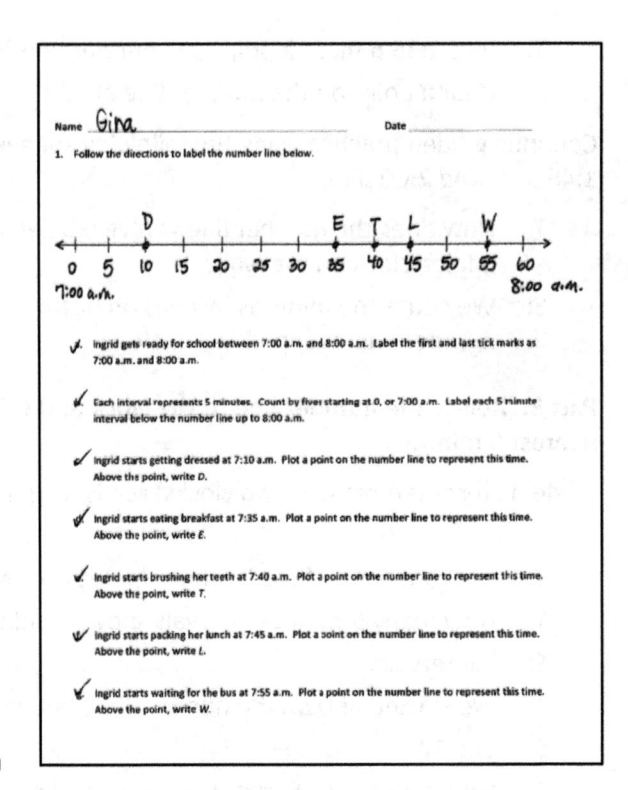

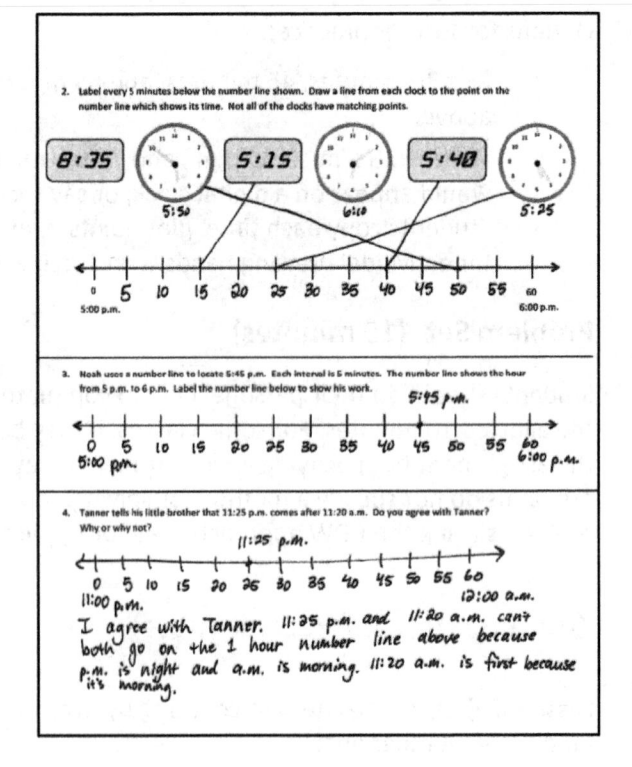

224   Lesson 15: Relate skip-counting by fives on the clock and telling time to a continuous measurement model, the number line.

Name _____ Date _____

1. Follow the directions to label the number line below.

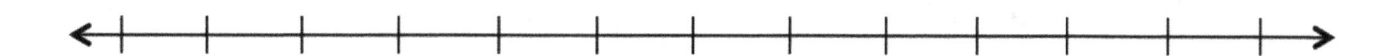

←—+—+—+—+—+—+—+—+—+—+—+—+—+—→

a. Ingrid gets ready for school between 7:00 a.m. and 8:00 a.m. Label the first and last tick marks as 7:00 a.m. and 8:00 a.m.

b. Each interval represents 5 minutes. Count by fives starting at 0, or 7:00 a.m. Label each 5-minute interval below the number line up to 8:00 a.m.

c. Ingrid starts getting dressed at 7:10 a.m. Plot a point on the number line to represent this time. Above the point, write D.

d. Ingrid starts eating breakfast at 7:35 a.m. Plot a point on the number line to represent this time. Above the point, write E.

e. Ingrid starts brushing her teeth at 7:40 a.m. Plot a point on the number line to represent this time. Above the point, write T.

f. Ingrid starts packing her lunch at 7:45 a.m. Plot a point on the number line to represent this time. Above the point, write L.

g. Ingrid starts waiting for the bus at 7:55 a.m. Plot a point on the number line to represent this time. Above the point, write W.

Lesson 15: Relate skip-counting by fives on the clock and telling time to a continuous measurement model, the number line.

2. Label every 5 minutes below the number line shown. Draw a line from each clock to the point on the number line which shows its time. Not all of the clocks have matching points.

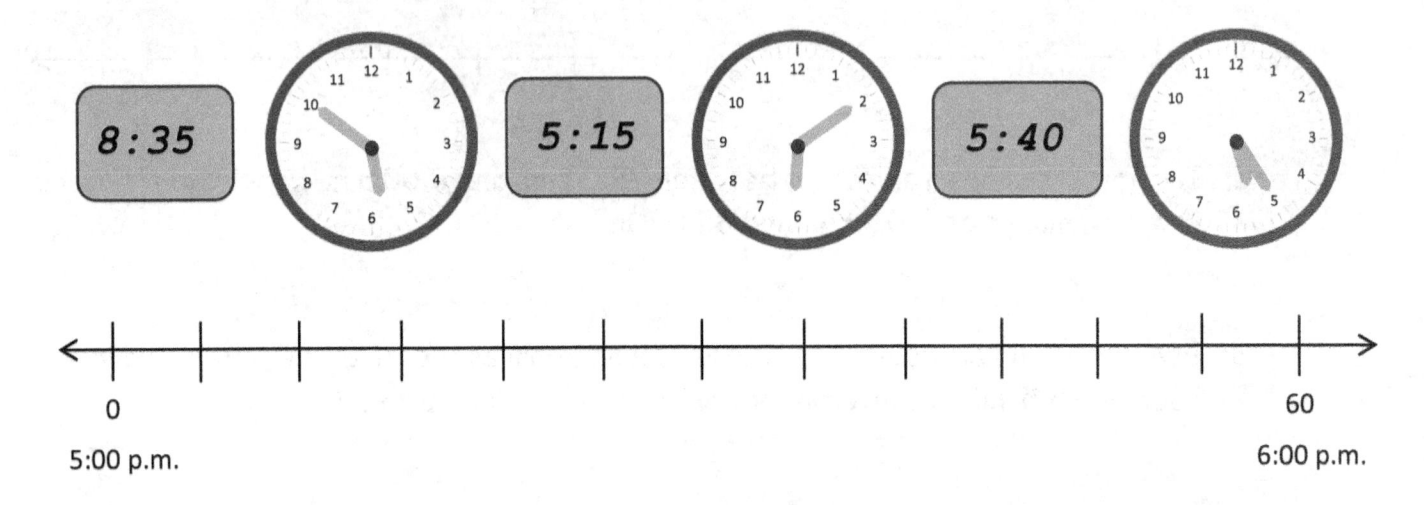

8:35   5:15   5:40

←|—|—|—|—|—|—|—|—|—|—|—|—|→
0   60
5:00 p.m.   6:00 p.m.

3. Noah uses a number line to locate 5:45 p.m. Each interval is 5 minutes. The number line shows the hour from 5 p.m. to 6 p.m. Label the number line below to show his work.

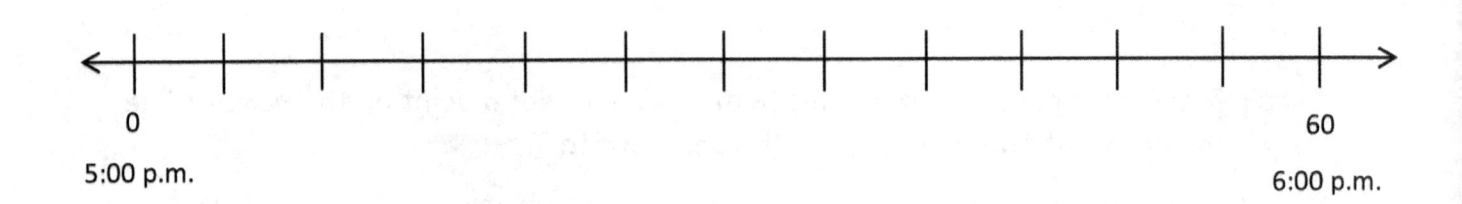

←|—|—|—|—|—|—|—|—|—|—|—|—|→
0   60
5:00 p.m.   6:00 p.m.

4. Tanner tells his little brother that 11:25 p.m. comes after 11:20 a.m. Do you agree with Tanner? Why or why not?

Name _____ Date _____

The number line below shows a math class that begins at 10:00 a.m. and ends at 11:00 a.m. Use the number line to answer the following questions.

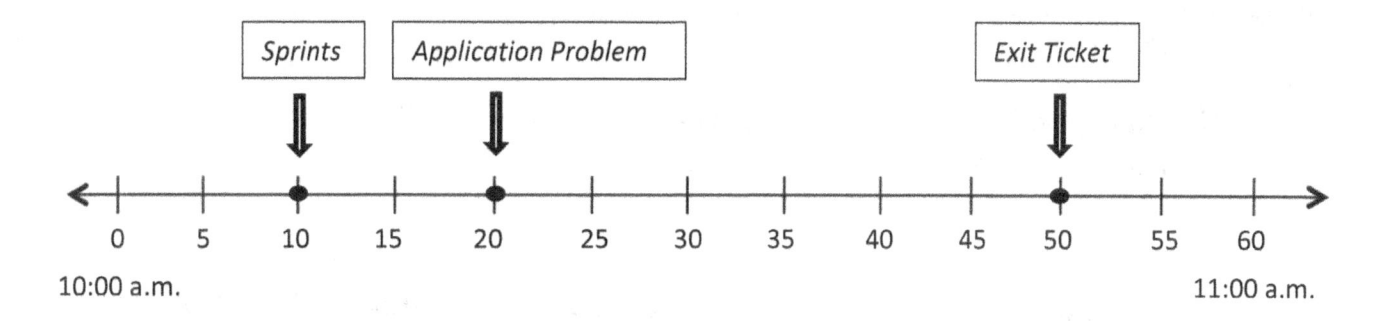

a. What time do Sprints begin?

b. What time do students begin the Application Problem?

c. What time do students work on the Exit Ticket?

d. How long is math class?

Name _____   Date _____

Follow the directions to label the number line below.

←—|———|———|———|———|———|———|———|———|———|———|———|———|→

a. The basketball team practices between 4:00 p.m. and 5:00 p.m. Label the first and last tick marks as 4:00 p.m. and 5:00 p.m.

b. Each interval represents 5 minutes. Count by fives starting at 0, or 4:00 p.m. Label each 5-minute interval below the number line up to 5:00 p.m.

c. The team warms up at 4:05 p.m. Plot a point on the number line to represent this time. Above the point, write W.

d. The team shoots free throws at 4:15 p.m. Plot a point on the number line to represent this time. Above the point, write F.

e. The team plays a practice game at 4:25 p.m. Plot a point on the number line to represent this time. Above the point, write G.

f. The team has a water break at 4:50 p.m. Plot a point on the number line to represent this time. Above the point, write B.

g. The team reviews their plays at 4:55 p.m. Plot a point on the number line to represent this time. Above the point, write P.

Lesson 15: Relate skip-counting by fives on the clock and telling time to a continuous measurement model, the number line.

strip diagram

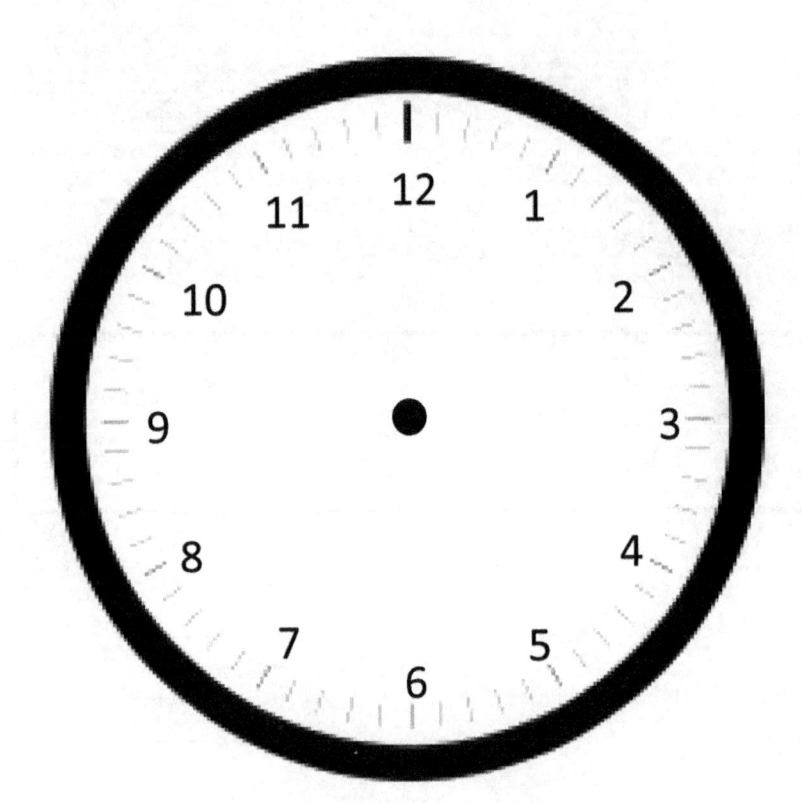

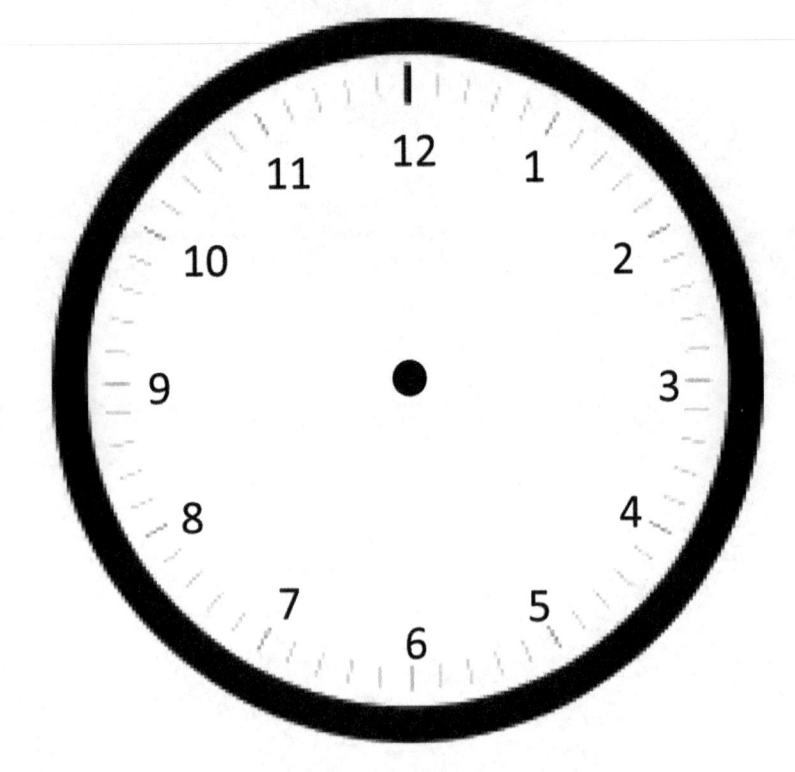

A STORY OF UNITS – TEKS EDITION

Lesson 15 Template 2   2•8

two clocks

Lesson 15: Relate skip-counting by fives on the clock and telling time to a continuous measurement model, the number line.

Lesson 16

Objective: Count by fives and ones on the number line as a strategy to tell time to the nearest minute on the clock.

Suggested Lesson Structure

- Fluency Practice   (10 minutes)
- Application Problem   (7 minutes)
- Concept Development   (33 minutes)
- Student Debrief   (10 minutes)

Total Time   **(60 minutes)**

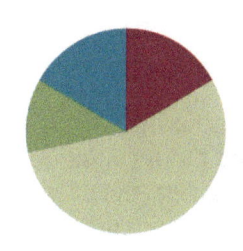

Fluency Practice (10 minutes)

- Subtraction with Renaming **2.4B**   (5 minutes)
- Grade 2 Fluency Differentiated Practice Sets **2.4A**   (5 minutes)

Subtraction with Renaming (5 minutes)

Materials: (S) Personal white board, hundreds place value chart (Lesson 4 Fluency Template)

Note: This fluency activity reviews the application of a chip model while recording with the algorithm. Allow students work time between each problem, and reinforce place value understandings by having students say their answer in both unit form and in standard form. Students use their personal white boards and a place value chart to solve.

- T: Slide the place value chart template into your personal white board.
- T: (Write 600 – 356 horizontally on the board.) Let's use a chip model to subtract. On your personal white board, record your work using the algorithm.
- S: (Solve.)
- T: 600 – 356 is…?
- S: 244.

Continue with the following possible sequence: 406 – 218, 507 – 269, 314 – 185, 672 – 274, and 842 – 296.

A STORY OF UNITS – TEKS EDITION Lesson 16 2•8

Grade 2 Fluency Differentiated Practice Sets (5 minutes)

Materials: (S) Fluency Practice Sets from Lesson 3

Note: During Topic D and for the remainder of the year, each day's Fluency Practice includes an opportunity for review and mastery of the sums and differences with totals through 20 by means of the Fluency Practice Sets or Sprints. The process is detailed, with Practice Sets provided, in Lesson 3.

Application Problem (7 minutes)

On Saturdays, Jean may only watch cartoons for one hour. Her first cartoon lasts 14 minutes, and the second lasts 28 minutes. After a 5-minute break, Jean watches a 15-minute cartoon. How much time does Jean spend watching cartoons? Did she break her time limit?

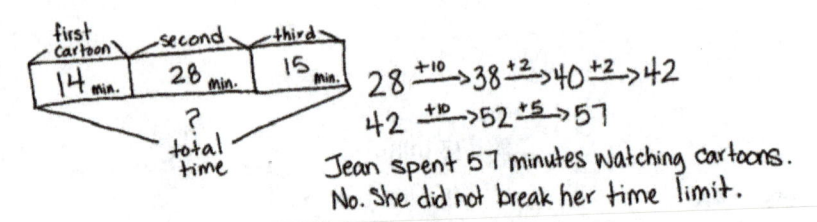

$$28 \xrightarrow{+10} 38 \xrightarrow{+2} 40 \xrightarrow{+2} 42$$
$$42 \xrightarrow{+10} 52 \xrightarrow{+5} 57$$

Jean spent 57 minutes watching cartoons. No. She did not break her time limit.

NOTES ON MULTIPLE MEANS OF REPRESENTATION:

Scaffold the Application Problem for students working below grade level by encouraging them to draw what they know or by providing them with a blank number bond to use. Help them make sense of the 5-minute break in the problem: "When Jean took a break, was she watching cartoons? Should we count those 5 minutes?"

Note: This Application Problem provides an opportunity to practice mental addition and double-digit addition within 100. Students must pay careful attention not to add in the 5-minute break. If they do, they will think Jean has broken the time limit.

Concept Development (33 minutes)

Template

Materials: (T) Analog clock for demonstration (S) Personal white board, centimeter ruler, clock (Template) (pictured to the right)

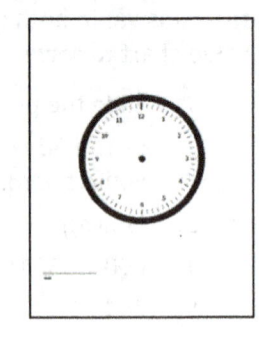

Problem 1: Count minutes by fives and ones on a number line.

T: Use your ruler to draw a 12-centimeter line on your personal white board. Start at the 0 mark, and make a tick mark at each centimeter up to the number 12. Label the first tick mark 0 and the last tick mark 60. Then, count by fives from 0 to 60 to label each interval, like we did in the last lesson.

S: (Draw and label a number line as shown.)

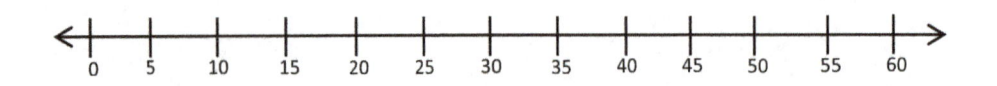

Lesson 16: Count by fives and ones on the number line as a strategy to tell time to the nearest minute on the clock.

T: Put your finger on 0. Count by ones from 0 to 5. What numbers did you count between 0 and 5?
S: 1, 2, 3, and 4.
T: We could draw tick marks, but let's instead imagine they are there. Can you see them?
S: Yes!
T: Put your finger on 5. Count on by ones from 5 to 10. What numbers did you count between 5 and 10?
S: 6, 7, 8, and 9.
T: Can you imagine those tick marks, too?
S: Yes!
T: Let's find 58 minutes on the number line. Put your finger on 0. Count by five to 55.
S: (Count 11 fives.)
T: Let's draw the tick marks from 55 to 60. Count with me as I draw the tick marks from 55 to 60. Start at 55, which is already there.
S: 55, (begin drawing) 56, 57, 58, 59, (stop drawing) 60.
T: How many ticks did I draw?
S: 4.
T: Go ahead and draw yours. (Allow students time to draw.)
T: Count on by ones to find 58 using the tick marks we made in the interval between 55 and 60.

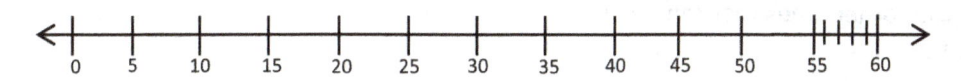

S: (Count on by ones and say numbers aloud.) 56, 57, 58.
T: How many fives did we count?
S: 11.
T: How many ones did we count?
S: 3.
T: 11 fives + 3. How can we write that as multiplication? Discuss with your partner.
S: $(11 \times 5) + 3$.
T: Discuss with a partner how our modeling with the number line relates to the Application Problem.
S: (Discuss.)

> **NOTES ON MULTIPLE MEANS OF REPRESENTATION:**
>
> Consider preparing in advance a flexible number line to show how the clock is like a circular number line. For example, use a strip of paper to create a number line that can be wrapped around the clock. As you describe twisting the number line into a circle, model using the strip of paper. Pass the flexible number line around, allowing students to do the same. English language learners and other students may benefit from this concrete experience.

> **NOTES ON MULTIPLE MEANS OF ACTION AND EXPRESSION:**
>
> Use preprinted number lines for students with fine motor or perception difficulties. You can also have students actually draw all the tick marks, but be aware this may encourage counting all when the objective is to count by fives and ones.

Lesson 16: Count by fives and ones on the number line as a strategy to tell time to the nearest minute on the clock.

Repeat the process with other combinations of fives and ones, such as (4 × 5) + 2 and (0 × 5) + 4.

T: Which units did we count by on the number line to solve these problems?
S: Fives and ones.
T: Whisper to your partner. What steps did we take to solve these problems on the number line?
S: (Discuss.)

Problem 2: Count by fives and ones on a number line to tell time to the nearest minute.

T: I arrived at school this morning at 7:37 a.m. Let's find that time on our number line. Label 7:00 a.m. above the 0 mark and 8:00 a.m. above the 60 mark.
S: (Label 7:00 a.m. and 8:00 a.m.)
T: Which units should we count by to get to 7:37?
S: Count by fives to 7:35 and then by ones to 7:37.
T: How many fives?
S: 7 fives.
T: How many ones?
S: 2 ones.
T: Let's move our fingers over 7 fives and 2 ones on the number line.
S: (Move fingers and count.)
T: Give me a number sentence.
S: (7 × 5) + 2 = 37.
T: Plot the point on your number line.

Repeat the process with other times that can be plotted on this same number line, such as 7:13 a.m., 7:49 a.m., and 7:02 a.m.

Problem 3: Count by fives and ones on a clock to tell time to the nearest minute.

T: Insert the clock template in your personal white board. How is the clock similar to our number line?
S: There are 4 tick marks between the numbers on both. → They both have intervals of 5 with 4 marks in between.
T: What do the small tick marks represent on the clock?
S: Ones. → 1 minute!
T: We can use a clock just like we use a number line to tell time because a clock is a circular number line. Imagine twisting our number line into a circle. In your mind's eye, at what number do the ends of your number line connect?
S: At the 12.
T: The 12 on the clock represents the end of one hour and the beginning of another.
T: (Project the analog clock and draw the hands as shown.) This clock shows what time I woke up this morning. Draw the minute hand on your clock to look like mine.

S: (Draw the hand on the clock template.)
T: Let's find the minutes by counting by fives and ones. Put your finger on the 12—the zero—and count by fives with me.
S: (Move finger along the clock and count by fives to 45.)
T: (Stop at 45.) How many minutes?
S: 45.
T: Let's count on by ones until we get to the minute hand. Move your finger and count on with me.
S: 46, 47, 48. (Move finger and count on by ones.)
T: How many minutes?
S: 48.
T: Draw the hour hand. How many hours?
S: 5.
T: What is the time?
S: 5:48 a.m.
T: Write the time on your personal white boards.
S: (Write 5:48 a.m.)

Repeat the process of telling time to the nearest minute, providing a small context for each example. Use the following suggested sequence: 12:14 a.m. and 2:28 p.m.

T: Can anyone share another strategy they used to tell the time on the clock for 2:28 p.m. other than counting by fives and ones from the 0 minute mark?
S: I started at 2:30 p.m. and counted back 2 minutes to get to 2:28 p.m.

Problem Set (10 minutes)

Students should do their personal best to complete the Problem Set within the allotted 10 minutes. For some classes, it may be appropriate to modify the assignment by specifying which problems they work on first. Some problems do not specify a method for solving. Students should solve these problems using the RDW approach used for Application Problems.

Student Debrief (10 minutes)

Lesson Objective: Count by fives and ones on the number line as a strategy to tell time to the nearest minute on the clock.

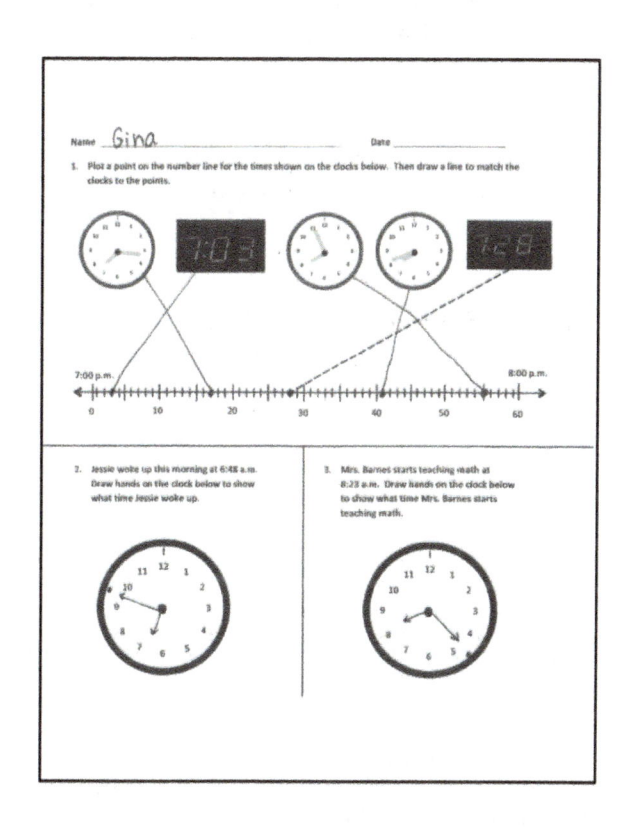

A STORY OF UNITS – TEKS EDITION   Lesson 16   2•8

The Student Debrief is intended to invite reflection and active processing of the total lesson experience.

Invite students to review their solutions for the Problem Set. They should check work by comparing answers with a partner. Look for misconceptions or misunderstandings that can be addressed in the Debrief. Guide students in a conversation to debrief the Problem Set and process the lesson.

Any combination of the questions below may be used to lead the discussion.

- Look at Problem 1. Talk to a partner: How is the number line similar to the analog clock? How is it different?
- What strategy did you use to draw the hands on the clock in Problem 3?
- Look at Problem 4. How many fives did you count by? Write a multiplication equation to show that. How many ones did you count on by? Write a multiplication equation to show that. How many minutes altogether?
- How does the strip diagram that many of us drew to solve the Application Problem relate to the first number line we drew in the Concept Development?
- Look at Problem 5. Can you share another strategy you used to tell the time on the clock other than counting by fives and ones from the 0 minute mark?
- How is Problem 5(b) different from the rest of the problems? How can you solve Problem 5(b)?

Exit Ticket (3 minutes)

After the Student Debrief, instruct students to complete the Exit Ticket. A review of their work will help with assessing students' understanding of the concepts that were presented in today's lesson and planning more effectively for future lessons. The questions may be read aloud to the students.

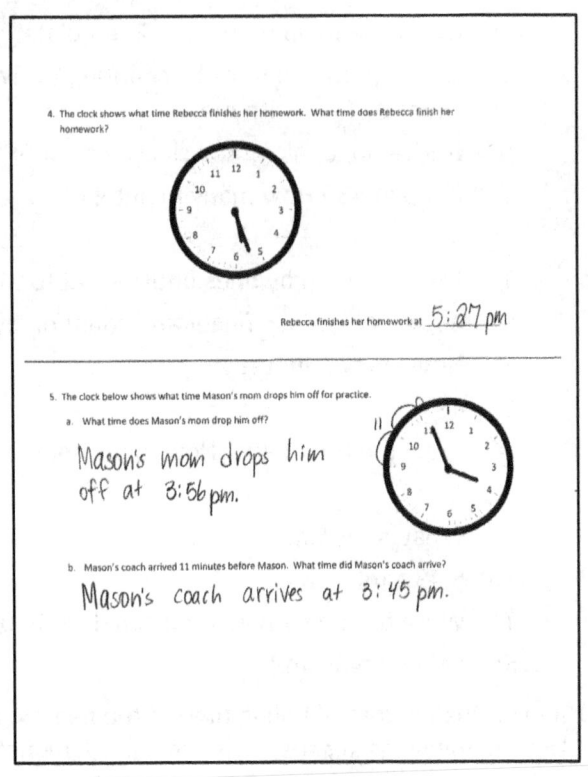

Lesson 16: Count by fives and ones on the number line as a strategy to tell time to the nearest minute on the clock.

A STORY OF UNITS – TEKS EDITION

Lesson 16 Problem Set 2•8

Name _____ Date _____

1. Plot a point on the number line for the times shown on the clocks below. Then, draw a line to match the clocks to the points.

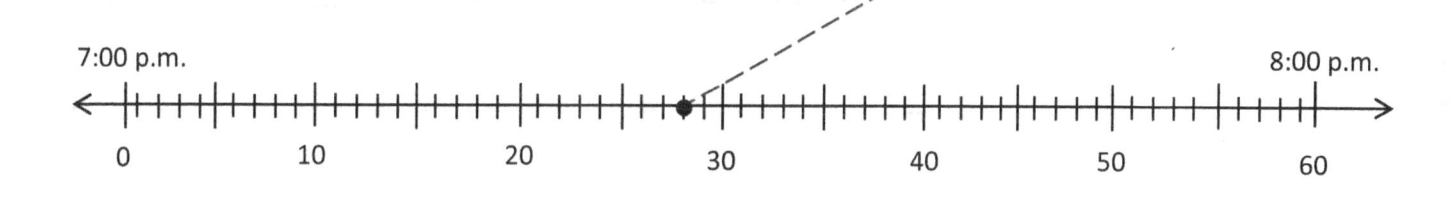

7:00 p.m. ←|||||||||||||||||||||||||||||||||||||||||||||||||||||||||||→ 8:00 p.m.
0   10   20   30   40   50   60

2. Jessie woke up this morning at 6:48 a.m. Draw hands on the clock below to show what time Jessie woke up.

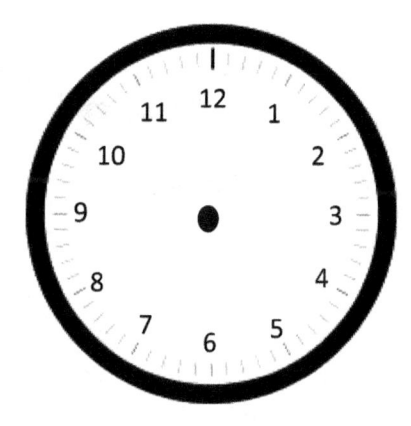

3. Mrs. Barnes starts teaching math at 8:23 a.m. Draw hands on the clock below to show what time Mrs. Barnes starts teaching math.

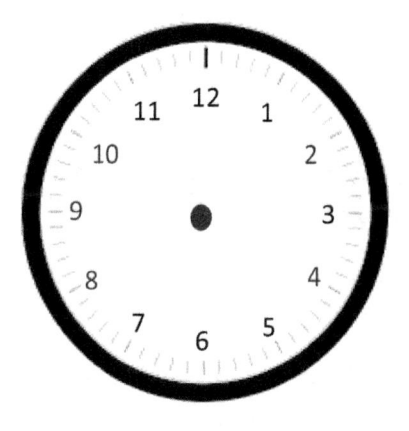

Lesson 16: Count by fives and ones on the number line as a strategy to tell time to the nearest minute on the clock.

4. The clock shows what time Rebecca finishes her homework. What time does Rebecca finish her homework?

Rebecca finishes her homework at _____.

5. The clock below shows what time Mason's mom drops him off for practice.

   a. What time does Mason's mom drop him off?

   b. Mason's coach arrived 11 minutes before Mason. What time did Mason's coach arrive?

A STORY OF UNITS – TEKS EDITION   Lesson 16 Exit Ticket   2•8

Name _____   Date _____

The clock shows what time Jason gets to school in the morning.

Arrival at School

a. What time does Jason get to school?

b. The first bell rings at 8:23 a.m. Draw hands on the clock to show when the first bell rings.

First Bell Rings

c. Label the first and last tick marks 8:00 a.m. and 9:00 a.m. Plot a point to show when Jason arrives at school. Label it A. Plot a point on the line when the first bell rings and label it B.

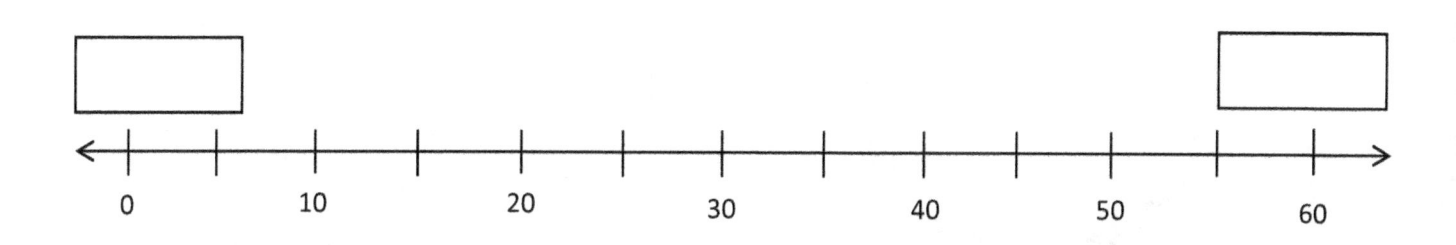

0   10   20   30   40   50   60

Lesson 16: Count by fives and ones on the number line as a strategy to tell time to the nearest minute on the clock.

239

Name _____ Date _____

1. Plot points on the number line for each time shown on a clock below. Then, draw lines to match the clocks to the points.

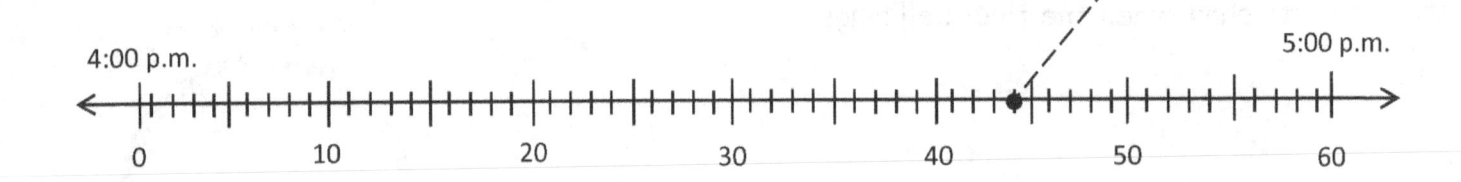

4:00 p.m.   5:00 p.m.

2. Julie eats dinner at 6:07 p.m. Draw hands on the clock below to show what time Julie eats dinner.

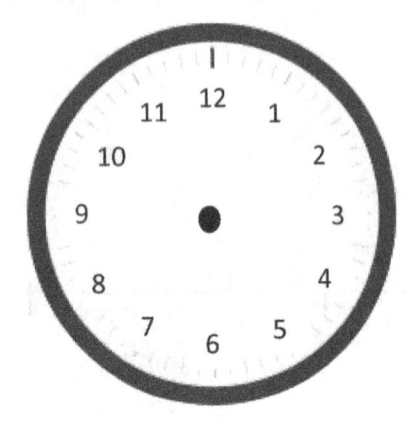

3. P.E. starts at 1:32 p.m. Draw hands on the clock below to show what time P.E. starts.

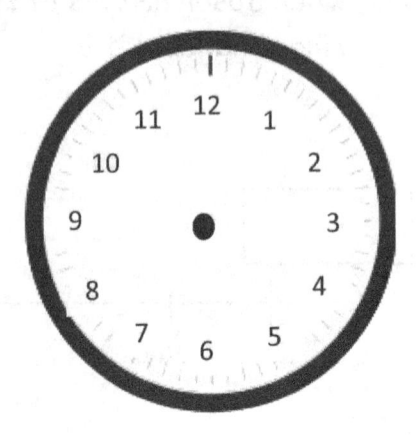

Lesson 16: Count by fives and ones on the number line as a strategy to tell time to the nearest minute on the clock.

4. The clock shows what time Zachary starts playing with his action figures.

   a. What time does he start playing with his action figures?

   b. He plays with his action figures for 23 minutes. What time does he finish playing?

   c. Draw hands on the clock to the right to show what time Zachary finishes playing.

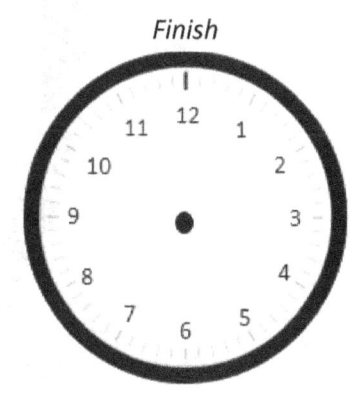

   d. Label the first and last tick marks with 2:00 p.m. and 3:00 p.m. Then, plot Zachary's start and finish times. Label his start time with a B and his finish time with an F.

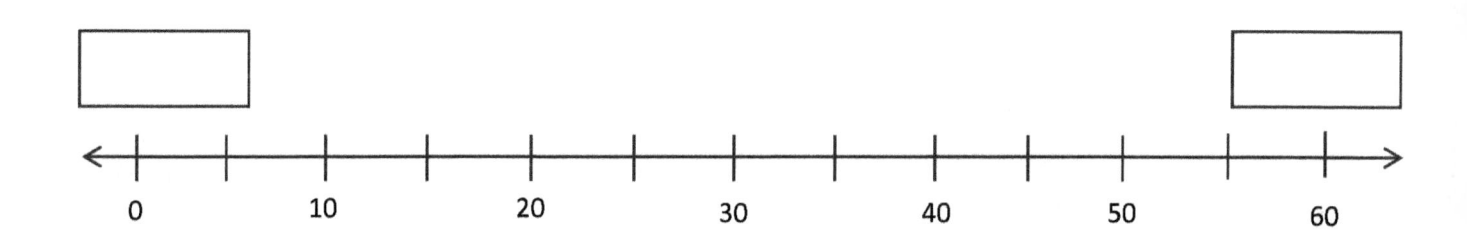

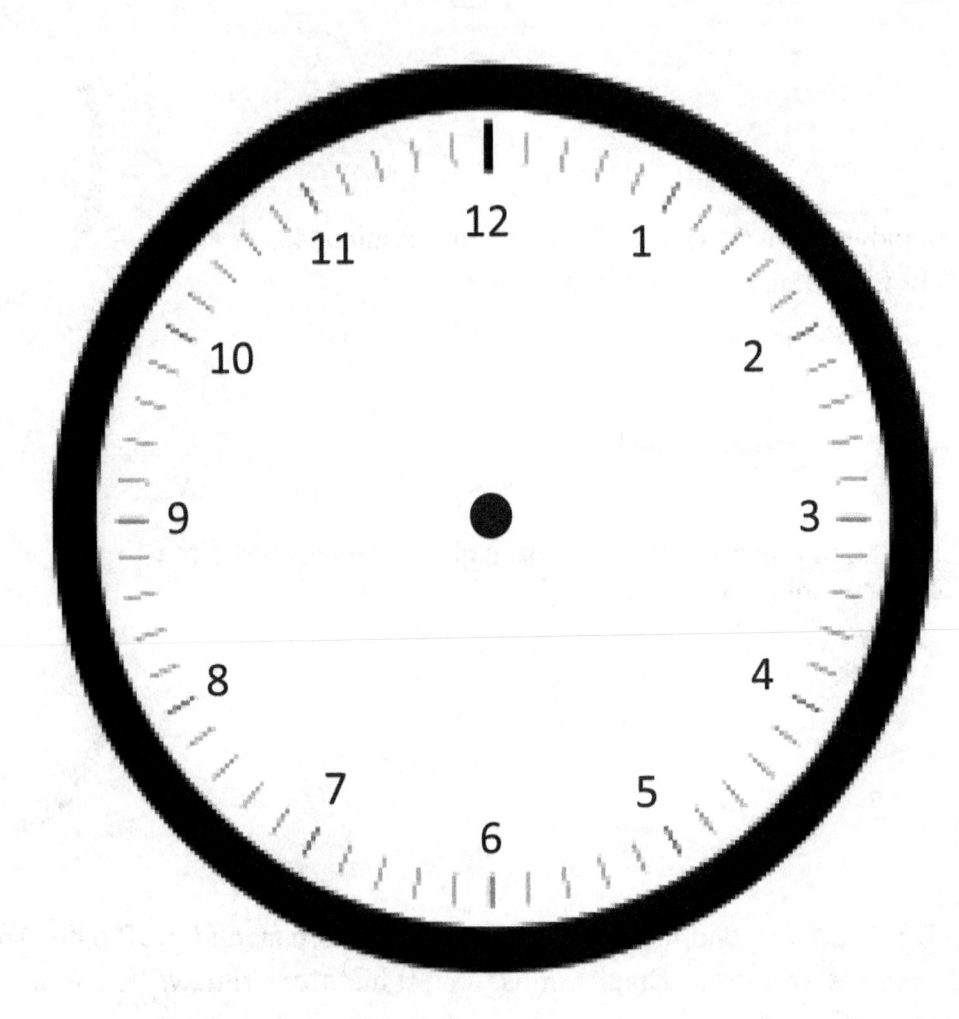

clock

Lesson 16: Count by fives and ones on the number line as a strategy to tell time to the nearest minute on the clock.

Name _____   Date _____

1. Match each description to the correct shape name by drawing a line. Draw an example for each shape to the right.

   five angles   **triangle**

   three sides   **octagon**

   eight vertices   **hexagon**

   six square faces   **pentagon**

   six sides   **cube**

2. Partition each whole circle into equal shares of 2 halves, 4 fourths, and 8 eighths.

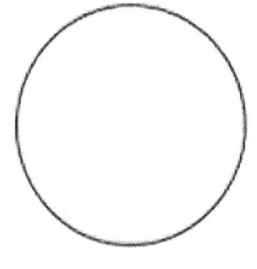

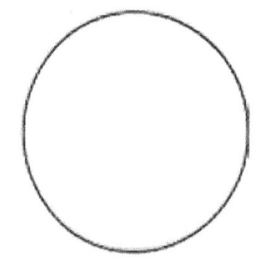

   2 halves   4 fourths   8 eighths

Module 8: Time, Shapes, and Fractions as Equal Parts of Shapes

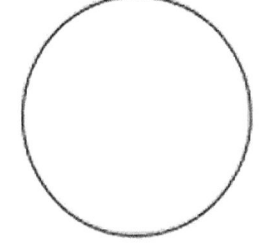

3. Solve.

   a. 1 whole = _____ halves   1 whole = _____ fourths   1 whole = _____ eighths

   b. Use vertical lines to partition rectangle:

   A into halves.

   B into fourths.

   C into eighths.

   c. Use horizontal lines to partition rectangle:

   D into halves.

   E into fourths.

   F into eighths.

d. Circle all of the rectangles that are partitioned into fourths, and cross out any rectangle that is not partitioned into fourths.

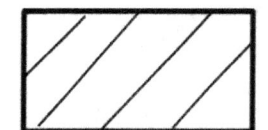

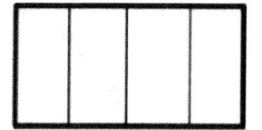

4. Draw the hands on the analog clock to match the time shown on the digital clock. Then, circle a.m. or p.m. based on the description given.

   a. Time to go to school.

   8:10   a.m. or p.m.

   b. Time for lunch.

   12:25   a.m. or p.m.

   c. Time for dinner.

   5:45   a.m. or p.m.

Module 8: Time, Shapes, and Fractions as Equal Parts of Shapes

5. Write the time shown on each analog clock.

a. _____

b. _____

c. _____

End-of-Module Assessment Task
Standards Addressed — Topics A–D

Number and Operations

The student is expected to:

- **2.3A**   partition objects into equal parts and name the parts, including halves, fourths, and eighths, using words;
- **2.3C**   use concrete models to count fractional parts beyond one whole using words and recognize how many parts it takes to equal one whole;
- **2.3D**   identify examples and non-examples of halves, fourths, and eighths.

Geometry and Measurement

The student is expected to:

- **2.8C**   classify and sort polygons with 12 or fewer sides according to attributes, including identifying the number of sides and number of vertices;
- **2.8E**   decompose two-dimensional shapes such as cutting out a square from a rectangle, dividing a shape in half, or partitioning a rectangle into identical triangles and identify the resulting geometric parts;
- **2.9G**[1]   read and write time to the nearest one-minute increment using analog and digital clocks and distinguish between a.m. and p.m.

Evaluating Student Learning Outcomes

A Progression Toward Mastery is provided to describe steps that illuminate the gradually increasing understandings that students develop *on their way to proficiency*. In this chart, this progress is presented from left (Step 1) to right (Step 4). The learning goal for students is to achieve Step 4 mastery. These steps are meant to help teachers and students identify and celebrate what the students CAN do now and what they need to work on next.

---

[1] Time is revisited using an analog clock as part of the work with 2.9G. Clock faces provide an excellent application of partitioning the whole into halves, etc., and to the corresponding angle sizes.

Module 8: Time, Shapes, and Fractions as Equal Parts of Shapes

A STORY OF UNITS – TEKS EDITION
End-of-Module Assessment Task 2•8

A Progression Toward Mastery				
Assessment Task Item and Standards Assessed	STEP 1 Little evidence of reasoning without a correct answer. (1 Point)	STEP 2 Evidence of some reasoning without a correct answer. (2 Points)	STEP 3 Evidence of some reasoning with a correct answer or evidence of solid reasoning with an incorrect answer. (3 Points)	STEP 4 Evidence of solid reasoning with a correct answer. (4 Points)
1 2.8C	The student answers one out of five parts correctly.	The student answers two out of five parts correctly.	The student answers three to four out of five parts correctly.	The student correctly: • Matches *triangle* to *three sides* and draws a triangle. • Matches *hexagon* to *six sides* and draws a hexagon. • Matches *pentagon* to *five angles* and draws a pentagon. • Matches *cube* to *six square faces* and draws a cube. • Matches *octagon* to *eight vertices* and draws a octagon.
2 2.3A 2.8E	The student is unable to answer any parts correctly.	The student answers one out of three parts correctly.	The student answers two out of three parts correctly.	The student correctly: • Partitions the first circle into halves. • Partitions the middle circle into fourths. • Partitions the last circle into eighths.

Module 8: Time, Shapes, and Fractions as Equal Parts of Shapes

A STORY OF UNITS – TEKS EDITION
End-of-Module Assessment Task 2•8

A Progression Toward Mastery				
3 **2.3A** **2.3C** **2.3D** **2.8E**	The student answers one out of four parts correctly.	The student answers two out of four parts correctly.	The student answers three out of four parts correctly.	The student correctly: a. Solves 2, 4, 8. b. Using vertical lines, partitions rectangle A into halves, B into fourths, and C into eighths. c. Using horizontal lines, partitions rectangle D into halves, E into fourths, and F into eighths. d. Circles the first, second, and fourth rectangles and crosses out the third rectangle.
4 **2.9G**	The student is unable to answer any of the parts correctly.	The student answers one out of three parts correctly.	The student answers two out of three parts correctly.	The student correctly draws clock hands and circles: a.m. p.m. p.m.
5 **2.9G**	The student is unable to answer any of the parts correctly.	The student answers one out of three parts correctly.	The student answers two out of three parts correctly.	The student correctly answers: 3:06 7:28 12:52

Module 8: Time, Shapes, and Fractions as Equal Parts of Shapes

A STORY OF UNITS – TEKS EDITION End-of-Module Assessment Task 2•8

Name __Samantha_____ Date _____

1. Match each description to the correct shape name by drawing a line. Draw an example for each shape to the right.

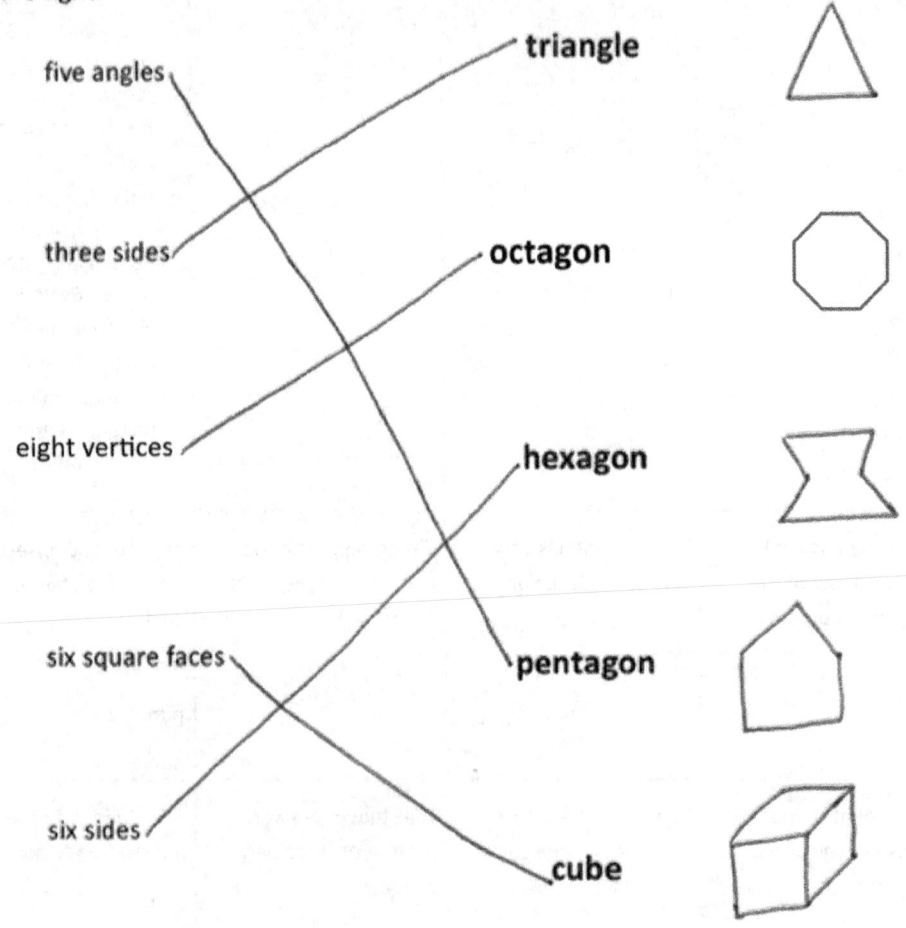

   five angles —————— triangle

   three sides —————— octagon

   eight vertices —————— hexagon

   six square faces —————— pentagon

   six sides —————— cube

2. Partition each whole circle into equal shares of 2 halves, 3 thirds, and 4 fourths.

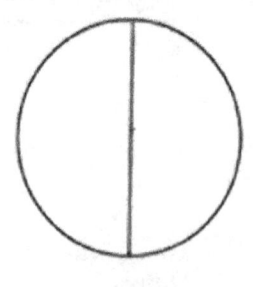

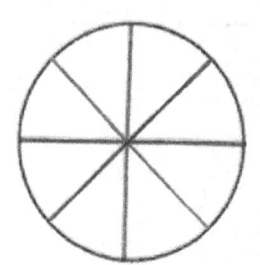

   2 halves   4 fourths   8 eighths

250 Module 8: Time, Shapes, and Fractions as Equal Parts of Shapes

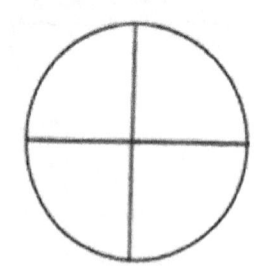

3. Solve.
   a. 1 whole = __2__ halves   1 whole = __4__ fourths   1 whole = __8__ eighths

   b. Use vertical lines to partition rectangle:

      A into halves.

      B into fourths.

      C into eighths.

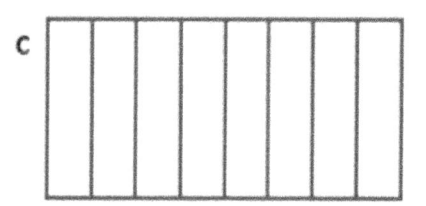

   c. Use horizontal lines to partition rectangle:

      D into halves.

      E into fourths.

      F into eighths.

d. Circle all of the rectangles that are partitioned into fourths, and cross out any rectangle that is not partitioned into fourths.

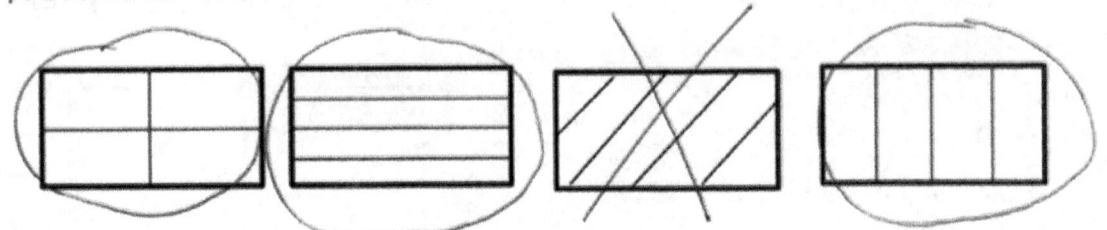

4. Draw the hands on the analog clock to match the time shown on the digital clock. Then, circle a.m. or p.m. based on the description given.

   a. Time to go to school.

      8:10   (a.m.) or p.m.

   b. Time for lunch.

      12:25   a.m. or (p.m.)

   c. Time for dinner.

      5:45   a.m. or (p.m.)

A STORY OF UNITS – TEKS EDITION End-of-Module Assessment Task 2•8

5. Write the time shown on each analog clock.

a.

    3:06

b.

    7:28

c.

    12:52

Answer Key

Eureka Math® Grade 2 Module 8

TEKS EDITION

Special thanks go to the Gordon A. Cain Center and to the Department of Mathematics at Louisiana State University for their support in the development of *Eureka Math*.

Answer Key
GRADE 2 • MODULE 8

Time, Shapes, and Fractions as Equal Parts of Shapes

Lesson 1

Sprint

Side A

1. 9
2. 19
3. 29
4. 59
5. 9
6. 19
7. 29
8. 59
9. 9
10. 39
11. 9
12. 49
13. 39
14. 11
15. 41
16. 58
17. 12
18. 62
19. 70
20. 74
21. 90
22. 96
23. 80
24. 88
25. 12
26. 120
27. 127
28. 12
29. 120
30. 123
31. 87
32. 13
33. 130
34. 134
35. 79
36. 79
37. 65
38. 81
39. 70
40. 90
41. 150
42. 74
43. 73
44. 157

Side B

1. 8
2. 18
3. 28
4. 48
5. 8
6. 18
7. 28
8. 48
9. 8
10. 78
11. 9
12. 79
13. 49
14. 11
15. 51
16. 68
17. 12
18. 72
19. 70
20. 76
21. 90
22. 94
23. 80
24. 87
25. 11
26. 110
27. 117
28. 13
29. 130
30. 133
31. 97
32. 14
33. 140
34. 144
35. 89
36. 89
37. 75
38. 91
39. 50
40. 90
41. 160
42. 76
43. 77
44. 164

A STORY OF UNITS – TEKS EDITION

Lesson 1 Answer Key 2•8

Problem Set

1. a. Answer provided
   b. 4 sides, 4 angles, 4 vertices
   c. 5 sides, 5 angles, 5 vertices
   d. 4 sides, 4 angles, 4 vertices
   e. 6 sides, 6 angles, 6 vertices
   f. 6 sides, 6 angles, 6 vertices
   g. 8 sides, 8 angles, 8 vertices
   h. 12 sides, 12 angles, 12 vertices
   i. 7 sides, 7 angles, 7 vertices

2. a. E
   b. F
   c. D
   d. 4
   e. All
   f. B and C

3. Answers will vary.

Exit Ticket

1. C
2. D
3. A
4. All
5. A and D

Homework

1. a. 3 sides, 3 angles, 3 vertices
   b. 4 sides, 4 angles, 4 vertices
   c. 5 sides, 5 angles, 5 vertices
   d. 8 sides, 8 angles, 8 vertices
   e. 6 sides, 6 angles, 6 vertices
   f. 4 sides, 4 angles, 4 vertices
   g. 7 sides, 7 angles, 7 vertices
   h. 11 sides, 11 angles, 11 vertices
   i. 6 sides, 6 angles, 6 vertices

2. a. A
   b. D
   c. E
   d. 6
   e. All

3. Both shapes on the right of the board shaded; shape on the left circled; explanations will vary.

Lesson 2

Sprint

Side A

1. 101
2. 102
3. 103
4. 106
5. 104
6. 107
7. 105
8. 101
9. 102
10. 103
11. 108
12. 105
13. 107
14. 104
15. 106
16. 111
17. 122
18. 133
19. 144
20. 155
21. 166
22. 177
23. 111
24. 122
25. 133
26. 144
27. 155
28. 166
29. 177
30. 134
31. 143
32. 145
33. 154
34. 166
35. 175
36. 167
37. 176
38. 194
39. 192
40. 194
41. 193
42. 194
43. 192
44. 186

Side B

1. 101
2. 102
3. 103
4. 107
5. 105
6. 108
7. 104
8. 106
9. 101
10. 102
11. 103
12. 107
13. 105
14. 106
15. 104
16. 111
17. 122
18. 133
19. 144
20. 155
21. 166
22. 177
23. 111
24. 122
25. 133
26. 144
27. 155
28. 166
29. 177
30. 124
31. 133
32. 135
33. 144
34. 156
35. 165
36. 177
37. 186
38. 192
39. 194
40. 196
41. 191
42. 192
43. 194
44. 184

A STORY OF UNITS – TEKS EDITION

Lesson 2 Answer Key 2•8

Problem Set

1. a. Octagon
    b. Triangle
    c. Pentagon
    d. Hexagon
    e. Triangle
    f. Quadrilateral
    g. Heptagon
    h. Hexagon
    i. Pentagon
    j. Quadrilateral
    k. Nonagon
    l. Decagon

2. a. 1; 3
       1 line drawn to complete each triangle
    b. 4; 6
       4 lines drawn to complete each hexagon
    c. 2; 4
       2 lines drawn to complete each quadrilateral
    d. 3; 5
       3 lines drawn to complete each pentagon

3. a. Answers will vary.
    b. Hexagons will vary.

4. Explanations will vary.

Exit Ticket

1. Pentagon
2. Hexagon
3. Quadrilateral
4. Triangle
5. Quadrilateral
6. Pentagon

Homework

1. a. Nonagon
    b. Triangle
    c. Octagon
    d. Pentagon
    e. Pentagon
    f. Hexagon
    g. Decagon
    h. Quadrilateral
    i. Hexagon
    j. Quadrilateral
    k. Pentagon
    l. Heptagon

2. a. 2; 4
       2 lines drawn to complete each quadrilateral
    b. 3; 5
       3 lines drawn to complete each pentagon
    c. 1; 3
       1 line drawn to complete each triangle
    d. 4; 6
       4 lines drawn to complete each hexagon

3. Explanations will vary.

4. Explanations will vary.

Module 8: Time, Shapes, and Fractions as Equal Parts of Shapes

Lesson 3

Fluency Practice Sets

Set A

1. 19
2. 11
3. 13
4. 19
5. 20
6. 17
7. 18
8. 16
9. 18
10. 19
11. 18
12. 17
13. 19
14. 13
15. 11
16. 18
17. 15
18. 17
19. 15
20. 16
21. 12
22. 12
23. 14
24. 16
25. 12
26. 13
27. 11
28. 14
29. 10
30. 13
31. 11
32. 16
33. 14
34. 14
35. 15
36. 13
37. 11
38. 12
39. 14
40. 13

Set B

1. 18
2. 14
3. 19
4. 16
5. 16
6. 16
7. 19
8. 4
9. 2
10. 18
11. 20
12. 18
13. 20
14. 12
15. 16
16. 7
17. 7
18. 7
19. 6
20. 6
21. 13
22. 13
23. 8
24. 6
25. 8
26. 8
27. 17
28. 12
29. 12
30. 12
31. 13
32. 5
33. 16
34. 12
35. 12
36. 12
37. 7
38. 9
39. 9
40. 11

A STORY OF UNITS – TEKS EDITION
Lesson 3 Answer Key 2•8

Set C

1. 10
2. 8
3. 7
4. 10
5. 3
6. 8
7. 12
8. 11
9. 10
10. 3
11. 9
12. 9
13. 12
14. 9
15. 8
16. 8
17. 11
18. 9
19. 7
20. 7
21. 8
22. 9
23. 8
24. 9
25. 9
26. 8
27. 7
28. 5
29. 7
30. 11
31. 8
32. 9
33. 6
34. 6
35. 6
36. 4
37. 7
38. 5
39. 5
40. 2

Set D

1. 9
2. 8
3. 9
4. 7
5. 9
6. 11
7. 7
8. 6
9. 8
10. 7
11. 2
12. 5
13. 5
14. 5
15. 4
16. 6
17. 4
18. 9
19. 7
20. 4
21. 6
22. 6
23. 11
24. 7
25. 8
26. 3
27. 7
28. 8
29. 8
30. 6
31. 4
32. 9
33. 5
34. 8
35. 7
36. 9
37. 9
38. 8
39. 14
40. 3

A STORY OF UNITS – TEKS EDITION

Lesson 3 Answer Key 2•8

Set E

1.	9	11.	8	21.	12	31.	17
2.	7	12.	9	22.	13	32.	20
3.	14	13.	14	23.	18	33.	9
4.	4	14.	13	24.	6	34.	9
5.	15	15.	13	25.	9	35.	7
6.	15	16.	12	26.	8	36.	3
7.	11	17.	4	27.	3	37.	11
8.	19	18.	6	28.	16	38.	18
9.	4	19.	7	29.	12	39.	16
10.	8	20.	6	30.	15	40.	19

Problem Set

1. Drawings will vary on all answers.
   - a. 3; triangle
   - b. 5; pentagon
   - c. 4; quadrilateral
   - d. 6; hexagon
   - e. 8; octagon
   - f. 10; decagon
   - g. 9; nonagon
   - h. 7; heptagon
2. Answers will vary.

Exit Ticket

Drawings will vary; 5; pentagon

Homework

1. Drawings will vary on all answers.
   - a. 4; quadrilateral
   - b. 6; hexagon
   - c. 3; triangle
   - d. 5; pentagon
   - e. 10; decagon
   - f. 9; nonagon
   - g. 7; heptagon
   - h. 8; octagon
2. Answers will vary.

Lesson 4

Problem Set

1. 2 parallel lines of different lengths drawn
2. 2 parallel lines of the same length drawn
3. a. Both pairs of sides highlighted
   b. 1 pair of sides highlighted
   c. Both pairs of sides highlighted
   d. Both pairs of sides highlighted and boxes drawn around all 4 angles
   e. 1 pair of sides highlighted
   f. Both pairs of sides highlighted and boxes drawn around all 4 angles
   g. Both pairs of sides highlighted
   h. 1 pair of sides highlighted
4. Drawings will vary.
5. Drawings will vary.
6. Answers will vary.
7. Answers will vary.

Exit Ticket

1. 1 pair of sides highlighted
2. Both pairs of sides highlighted and boxes drawn around all 4 angles
3. Both pairs of sides highlighted
4. Both pairs of sides highlighted

Homework

1. 2 parallel lines of different lengths drawn
2. 2 parallel lines of the same length drawn
3. Parallelogram drawn and named
4. Rectangle drawn and named
5. Answers will vary.
6. Total colored red quadrilaterals: 2
   Total colored blue quadrilaterals: 2
   Total circled green quadrilaterals: 5

Lesson 5

Sprint

Side A

1. 7	12. 19	23. 21	34. 32
2. 17	13. 59	24. 26	35. 52
3. 6	14. 58	25. 2	36. 48
4. 16	15. 56	26. 20	37. 46
5. 3	16. 5	27. 21	38. 30
6. 13	17. 15	28. 28	39. 20
7. 23	18. 25	29. 40	40. 20
8. 53	19. 65	30. 44	41. 56
9. 51	20. 67	31. 30	42. 23
10. 8	21. 2	32. 37	43. 49
11. 9	22. 20	33. 30	44. 67

Side B

1. 6	12. 16	23. 31	34. 42
2. 16	13. 56	24. 36	35. 72
3. 5	14. 57	25. 3	36. 68
4. 15	15. 59	26. 30	37. 66
5. 2	16. 8	27. 31	38. 40
6. 12	17. 18	28. 37	39. 30
7. 22	18. 28	29. 30	40. 20
8. 52	19. 68	30. 34	41. 53
9. 51	20. 69	31. 20	42. 27
10. 5	21. 3	32. 25	43. 48
11. 6	22. 30	33. 40	44. 47

Lesson 5

Problem Set

1.

Solid Figure	Number of Faces	Shape of Faces	Number of Edges	Number of Vertices
Cube	6	square	12	8
Rectangular Prism	6	rectangle	12	8
Triangular Prism	5	rectangle, triangle	9	6
Cone	1	circle	0	1
Cylinder	2	circle	0	0
Sphere	0	n/a	0	0

2. Student responses will vary. Check to ensure proper use of vocabulary. Sample answer:

Solids with Vertices	Solids with Circular Faces	Solids with No Edges
cube	cone	cylinder
rectangular prism	cylinder	cone
triangular prism		sphere
cone		

3. A cone does not have an edge. An edge is where 2 faces meet. A cone has only 1 face.

Exit Ticket

1. a. face   b. vertex   c. edge
2. A cylinder is not a prism because it doesn't have any faces that are quadrilaterals.

Homework

1. cylinder
2. sphere
3. triangular prism
4. cube
5. cone
6. Hal is incorrect because although a cylinder does have opposite, congruent bases, it does not have any faces that are quadrilaterals.

Lesson 6

Sprint

Side A

1. 11	12. 9	23. 16	34. 9
2. 8	13. 12	24. 8	35. 13
3. 11	14. 5	25. 15	36. 13
4. 9	15. 12	26. 6	37. 11
5. 11	16. 6	27. 18	38. 4
6. 5	17. 14	28. 9	39. 13
7. 11	18. 6	29. 14	40. 6
8. 4	19. 13	30. 7	41. 12
9. 12	20. 4	31. 17	42. 11
10. 8	21. 15	32. 9	43. 13
11. 12	22. 7	33. 16	44. 13

Side B

1. 11	12. 8	23. 15	34. 8
2. 9	13. 12	24. 6	35. 12
3. 11	14. 7	25. 16	36. 13
4. 8	15. 12	26. 8	37. 13
5. 11	16. 6	27. 14	38. 5
6. 4	17. 13	28. 7	39. 13
7. 11	18. 9	29. 18	40. 7
8. 5	19. 14	30. 9	41. 13
9. 12	20. 6	31. 16	42. 12
10. 9	21. 15	32. 7	43. 15
11. 12	22. 8	33. 17	44. 12

Problem Set

1. a. Triangle
   b. Parallelogram
   c. Square
2. a. Drawing of a trapezoid
   b. Drawing of a parallelogram
   c. Drawing of a rectangle
   d. Drawing of a right triangle
3. a. Drawing of a trapezoid
   b. Drawing of a parallelogram
   c. Drawing of a rectangle
   d. Drawing of a right triangle
4. Drawings will vary.
5. Drawings will vary.

Exit Ticket

1. Drawings will vary.
2. Drawings will vary.

Homework

1. a. Parallelogram
   b. Triangle
   c. Square
2. a. Drawing of a right triangle
   b. Drawing of a rectangle
   c. Drawing of a parallelogram
   d. Drawing of a trapezoid
3. Drawings will vary.
4. Drawings will vary.

Lesson 7

Problem Set

1.
   a. Larger triangle drawn
   b. Parallelogram drawn
   c. Square drawn
   d. Square drawn
   e. 2
   f. 2
2. Oval, parallelogram, and hexagon circled
3. Trapezoid drawn
   a. 3
   b. 3
4. Rectangle and hexagon circled
5. Trapezoid drawn with triangle added to form parallelogram
   a. 4
   b. 4
6. Hexagon and rectangle circled

Exit Ticket

1. Parallelogram and triangle circled
2. Rectangle and circle circled

Homework

1.
   a. Square drawn
   b. Square drawn
   c. Parallelogram drawn
   d. Triangle drawn
   e. 2
   f. 2
2. Triangle, parallelogram, and hexagon circled
3.
   a. 3
   b. 3
4. Rectangle and hexagon circled
5.
   a. 4
   b. 4
6. Hexagon and rectangle circled

Lesson 8

Problem Set

1. a. Triangle
   b. Parallelogram made of 2 triangles drawn
2. a. Trapezoid
   b. Hexagon made of 2 trapezoids drawn
3. a. Rhombus
   b. Hexagon made of 3 rhombuses drawn
4. a. Triangle
   b. Trapezoid made of 3 triangles drawn

5. a. Square made of 4 squares drawn
   b. Fourth
   c. Fourths
   d. Half
   e. 4
6. a. Triangle
   b. Hexagon made of 6 triangles drawn

Exit Ticket

Square; 2 squares drawn within rectangle

Homework

1. Triangle
   2 triangles drawn within the rhombus
2. Trapezoid
   2 trapezoids drawn within the hexagon
3. Parallelogram
   3 parallelograms drawn within the hexagon
4. Triangle
   3 triangles drawn within the trapezoid

5. Square; 4 squares drawn within the square
   a. Fourth
   b. Fourths
   c. Half
   d. 4
6. Triangle; 6 triangles drawn within the hexagon

Lesson 9

Sprint

Side A

1.	4	12.	23	23.	8	34.	57
2.	14	13.	22	24.	9	35.	47
3.	24	14.	20	25.	19	36.	57
4.	74	15.	10	26.	29	37.	67
5.	3	16.	60	27.	49	38.	17
6.	13	17.	50	28.	39	39.	1
7.	23	18.	10	29.	5	40.	2
8.	73	19.	70	30.	6	41.	42
9.	3	20.	60	31.	7	42.	41
10.	30	21.	30	32.	17	43.	32
11.	33	22.	80	33.	27	44.	19

Side B

1.	3	12.	12	23.	5	34.	53
2.	13	13.	11	24.	6	35.	43
3.	23	14.	10	25.	16	36.	53
4.	73	15.	10	26.	26	37.	63
5.	2	16.	60	27.	46	38.	13
6.	12	17.	50	28.	36	39.	8
7.	22	18.	10	29.	1	40.	9
8.	72	19.	70	30.	2	41.	49
9.	2	20.	60	31.	3	42.	41
10.	20	21.	40	32.	13	43.	39
11.	22	22.	70	33.	23	44.	19

A STORY OF UNITS – TEKS EDITION
Lesson 9 Answer Key 2•8

Problem Set

1. First and third shape circled
2. Shapes (b), (e), (f), (g), (i), (j), and (k) shaded
3. Partitions and shadings will vary.

Exit Ticket

Shapes (a), (b), (e), and (g) shaded

Homework

1. First, third, and fourth shapes circled
2. Shapes (e), (f), (g), and (h) shaded
3. Partitions and shadings will vary.

Lesson 10

Sprint

Side A

1.	10	12.	31	23.	24	34.	35
2.	20	13.	22	24.	34	35.	21
3.	40	14.	32	25.	24	36.	22
4.	10	15.	22	26.	34	37.	23
5.	20	16.	32	27.	25	38.	31
6.	40	17.	23	28.	26	39.	32
7.	11	18.	33	29.	35	40.	22
8.	21	19.	23	30.	36	41.	31
9.	31	20.	33	31.	24	42.	23
10.	11	21.	21	32.	25	43.	27
11.	21	22.	21	33.	34	44.	37

Side B

1.	10	12.	31	23.	24	34.	36
2.	20	13.	22	24.	34	35.	21
3.	40	14.	32	25.	24	36.	22
4.	10	15.	22	26.	34	37.	23
5.	20	16.	32	27.	25	38.	34
6.	40	17.	23	28.	26	39.	34
7.	11	18.	33	29.	35	40.	32
8.	21	19.	23	30.	36	41.	21
9.	31	20.	33	31.	25	42.	33
10.	11	21.	21	32.	26	43.	37
11.	21	22.	31	33.	35	44.	27

A STORY OF UNITS – TEKS EDITION

Lesson 10 Answer Key 2•8

Problem Set

1. a. Halves
   b. 1 line drawn in each shape to partition into fourths
2. shape partitioned into eighths, shape shaded to show the appropriate fraction
3. Circles partitioned by 2 perpendicular lines, appropriate number of segments shaded
4. a. Horizontal and/or vertical lines drawn to partition into fourths, 3 parts shaded
   b. Partitions drawn to make eighths, 1 part shaded
   c. 1 line drawn to make halves, 1 part shaded
   d. Perpendicular lines drawn to partition into fourths, 2 parts shaded
   e. lines drawn to partition into eighths, 5 parts shaded
   f. 4 lines drawn to make eighths, all parts shaded
   g. 2 perpendicular lines drawn to make fourths, 1 part shaded
   h. lines drawn to make eighths, 2 parts shaded
   i. 2 lines drawn to make fourths, all parts shaded
5. 2 perpendicular lines drawn to partition into fourths, drawing labeled with four names
   a. 1 fourth
   b. 3 fourths

Exit Ticket

1. 1 line drawn to make halves, both parts shaded
2. lines drawn to partition into eighths, 1 part shaded
3. 4 lines drawn to partition into eighths, 3 parts shaded
4. 1 line drawn to make halves, 1 part shaded
5. Horizontal and/or vertical lines drawn to partition into fourths, 2 parts shaded
6. Horizontal and/or vertical lines drawn to partition into fourths, 1 part shaded

Homework

1. a. Halves
   b. 1 line drawn in each shape to partition into fourths
2. lines drawn to partition rectangles into eighths, shape shaded to show the appropriate fraction
3. Circles partitioned by 2 perpendicular lines, appropriate number of segments shaded
4. a. 1 line drawn to make halves, 1 part shaded
   b. Horizontal and/or vertical lines drawn to partition into fourths, 1 part shaded
   c. lines drawn to partition into eighths, 2 parts shaded
   d. Perpendicular lines drawn to partition into fourths, 2 parts shaded
   e. 1 line drawn to make halves, both parts shaded
   f. lines drawn to partition into eighths, 6 parts shaded
   g. lines drawn to partition into eighths, 1 part shaded
   h. Perpendicular lines drawn to partition into fourths, 3 parts shaded
   i. 2 lines drawn to make fourths, all parts shaded
5. Circle partitioned into fourths, labeled with the four boys' names; 4 fourths

Lesson 11

Problem Set

1. a. 1; 2; 3; 4
    b. Second circle circled
    c. 1; 4; 5; 7
    d. Second rectangle circled

2. a. 7 eighths
    b. 1 half
    c. 2 fourths
    d. 2 eighths
    e. 1 half
    f. 1 fourth

3. a. 1 half drawn to complete the shape
    b. 7 eighths drawn to complete the shape
    c. 3 fourths drawn to complete the shape

Exit Ticket

1. 1 fourth
2. 1 half
3. 3 fourths
4. 9 eighths or 1 and 1 eighth

Homework

1. a. 1; 2; 3; 4
    b. Second square circled
    c. 1; 4; 6; 7
    d. Second rectangle circled

2. a. 1 half
    b. 5 eighths
    c. 3 fourths
    d. 2 fourths
    e. 2 fourths
    f. 1 half

3. a. 1 half drawn to complete the shape
    b. 7 eighths drawn to complete the shape
    c. 3 fourths drawn to complete the shape

Lesson 12

Problem Set

1. 1 quarter; 2 quarters or 1 half; 3 quarters; 4 quarters or 2 halves
2. a. 6:00
   b. 6:15
   c. 3:30
   d. 9:30
3. Line drawn from time to corresponding clock
4. Minute hand drawn pointing to 9 (3:45), 6 (11:30), and 3 (6:15), respectively

Exit Ticket

Minute hand drawn pointing to 6 (7:30), 3 (12:15), and 9 (2:45), respectively

Homework

1. 1 quarter; 2 quarters or 1 half; 3 quarters; 4 quarters or 2 halves
2. a. 6:45
   b. 12:30
   c. 10:45
   d. 9:15
3. Line drawn from time to corresponding clock
4. Minute hand drawn pointing to 6 (3:30), 9 (11:45), and 3 (6:15), respectively

Lesson 13

Sprint

Side A

1.	5	12.	40	23.	15	34.	60
2.	10	13.	35	24.	20	35.	55
3.	15	14.	30	25.	25	36.	50
4.	20	15.	25	26.	30	37.	65
5.	25	16.	20	27.	35	38.	70
6.	30	17.	15	28.	40	39.	65
7.	35	18.	10	29.	45	40.	60
8.	40	19.	5	30.	50	41.	150
9.	45	20.	0	31.	50	42.	200
10.	50	21.	5	32.	100	43.	150
11.	45	22.	10	33.	55	44.	100

Side B

1.	5	12.	40	23.	15	34.	60
2.	10	13.	35	24.	20	35.	55
3.	15	14.	30	25.	25	36.	50
4.	20	15.	25	26.	30	37.	65
5.	25	16.	20	27.	35	38.	70
6.	30	17.	15	28.	40	39.	65
7.	35	18.	10	29.	45	40.	60
8.	40	19.	5	30.	50	41.	150
9.	45	20.	0	31.	50	42.	200
10.	50	21.	5	32.	100	43.	150
11.	45	22.	10	33.	55	44.	100

A STORY OF UNITS – TEKS EDITION

Lesson 13 Answer Key 2•8

Problem Set

1. 45; 35, 30, 25; 15, 10, 5, 0
2. 0 or 60, 5, 10, 15, 20, 25, 30, 35, 40, 45, 50, 55
3. Hands drawn to show 3:05, 3:35, 4:10, 4:40, 6:25, and 6:55, respectively
4. 7:25; 12:55

Exit Ticket

Hands drawn to show 12:55 and 5:25, respectively

Homework

1. 15, 20, 25, 30; 40, 45, 50, 55, 60
   60, 55, 50; 35, 30, 25; 10, 5, 0
2. First two answers provided, 10, 15, 20, 25, 30, 35, 40, 45, 50, 55, 60
3. Minute hand drawn to show 3:25, 7:15, and 9:55, respectively
4. Hour hand drawn to show 12:30, 10:10, and 3:45, respectively
5. Hands drawn to show 6:55, 1:50, 8:25, 4:40, 7:45, and 2:05, respectively
6. 1:35; 10:05

Lesson 14

Problem Set

1. a. a.m.
    b. p.m.
    c. p.m.
    d. a.m.
    e. p.m.
    f. p.m.
    g. p.m.
    h. a.m. or p.m.

2. a. Hands drawn to show 7:10; a.m. circled
    b. Hands drawn to show 5:55; p.m. circled
3. Answers will vary.
4. 3:55

Exit Ticket

1. Hands drawn to show 6:10; a.m. circled
2. Hands drawn to show 3:40; p.m. circled

Homework

1. a. a.m.
    b. p.m.
    c. p.m.
    d. a.m.
    e. p.m.
    f. a.m. or p.m.
    g. p.m.
    h. p.m.

2. a. 7 a.m.
    b. 8:25 p.m.
3. a. Hands drawn to show 8:15; p.m. circled
    b. Hands drawn to show 12:30; p.m. circled
4. Answers will vary.

Lesson 15

Problem Set

1. a. First and last tick marks labeled as 7:00 a.m. and 8:00 a.m.
    b. Each interval labeled by fives below the number line up to 8:00 a.m.
    c. Point D plotted and labeled above 7:10 a.m.
    d. Point E plotted and labeled above 7:35 a.m.
    e. Point T plotted and labeled above 7:40 a.m.
    f. Point L plotted and labeled above 7:45 a.m.
    g. Point W plotted and labeled above 7:55 a.m.

2. Every 5 minutes labeled below the number line
    First clock not matched to the number line
    Second clock—5:50 p.m.
    Third clock—5:15 p.m.
    Fourth clock not matched to the number line
    Fifth clock—5:40 p.m.
    Last clock—5:25 p.m.

3. First and last tick marks labeled as 5:00 p.m. and 6:00 p.m.; each interval labeled by fives below the number line up to 6:00 p.m.; 5:45 p.m. located and plotted on the number line

4. Answers will vary.

Exit Ticket

a. 10:10 a.m.
b. 10:20 a.m.
c. 10:50 a.m.
d. 1 hour

Homework

a. First and last tick marks labeled as 4:00 p.m. and 5:00 p.m.
b. Each interval labeled by fives below the number line up to 5:00 p.m.
c. Point W plotted and labeled above 4:05 p.m.
d. Point F plotted and labeled above 4:15 p.m.
e. Point G plotted and labeled above 4:25 p.m.
f. Point B plotted and labeled above 4:50 p.m.
g. Point P plotted and labeled above 4:55 p.m.

Lesson 16

Problem Set

1. The times shown on the clocks are plotted correctly on the number line.

    First clock—7:17 p.m.

    Second clock—7:03 p.m.

    Third clock—7:55 p.m.

    Fourth clock—7:41 p.m.

    Fifth clock—answer provided

2. Hands on the clock drawn to show 6:48 a.m.
3. Hands on the clock drawn to show 8:23 a.m.
4. 5:27
5. a. 3:56
   b. 3:45

Exit Ticket

a. 8:04

b. Hands on the clock drawn to show 8:23 a.m.

c. The first and last tick marks labeled as 8:00 a.m. and 9:00 a.m.; Point A plotted and labeled above 8:04 a.m.; Point B plotted and labeled above 8:23 a.m.

Homework

1. The times shown on the clocks are plotted correctly on the number line.

    First clock—4:34 p.m.

    Second clock—4:01 p.m.

    Third clock—4:16 p.m.

    Fourth clock—4:53 p.m.

    Fifth clock—answer provided

2. Hands on the clock drawn to show 6:07 p.m.
3. Hands on the clock drawn to show 1:32 p.m.
4. a. 2:32
   b. 2:55
   c. Hands on the clock drawn to show 2:55.
   d. First and last tick marks labeled 2:00 p.m. and 3:00 p.m.; Point B plotted and labeled above 2:32 p.m.; Point F plotted and labeled above 2:55 p.m.